CONTROL IN THE SKY

CONTROL IN THE SKY

THE EVOLUTION AND HISTORY OF THE AIRCRAFT COCKPIT

L F E Coombs

Pen & Sword
AVIATION

This edition published in Great Britain by
Pen and Sword Aviation 2005

British Library Cataloguing-in-Publication Data
A catalogue record for this book
is available from the British Library

ISBN 1 84415 148 4

Printed and bound in Singapore by Kyodo Printing Co. (Singapore) Pte Ltd

Pen & Sword Books Ltd incorporates the imprints of
Pen & Sword Aviation, Pen & Sword Maritime, Pen & Sword Military,
Wharncliffe Local History, Pen & Sword Select,
Pen & Sword Military Classics and Leo Cooper.

For a complete list of Pen & Sword titles please contact
Pen & Sword Books Limited
47 Church Street, Barnsley, South Yorkshire, S70 2AS, England
E-mail: sales@pen-and-sword.co.uk
Website: www.pen-and-sword.co.uk

Contents

Acknowledgements

During the preparation of this book valuable help and advice was given by individuals and companies such as Airbus, Boeing, Lockheed Martin, Smiths Group and Thales. Four people in particular deserve special mention. They are named in order of appearing in my years of researching and writing about the cockpit and ergonomics in general.

Bill Gunston, the doyen of aviation writers, as technical editor of *Flight* magazine took a chance on publishing my opinions on the cockpit. That was the start that led to many articles, papers and lectures and eventually to books.

Professor John Rolfe, at the time he was with the RAF Institute of Aviation Medicine, encouraged my research into human laterality. In particular, for this book he has provided valuable reference material and advice relating to flight simulators.

Mike Hirst, at one time with Smiths Group and British Aerospace, and now at the University of Loughborough, has always been there to comment and advise on avionic systems and operational practices. His summary of PC simulation is just one of many of his papers used as reference material.

Philip Jarrett has provided valuable comments and advice from his extensive aeronautical knowledge base, in particular relating to Chapter One. He has also collected and advised on illustrations.

An aviation book relies on illustrations, and I am grateful to Mike Oakey, the editor of *Aeroplane Monthly*, and Wallace Clarke for their help. Also to Russell Plumley, Richard Bayliss, Duncan McGaw, Jennifer Villarreal and Nikitia Porter. Captain E.M. Brown RN kindly scrutinized my references to aircraft-carrier operations. I must also mention names from the 1950s, because they inspired me to research cockpit ergonomics at a time when civil aviation safety needed greater attention to the dials, switches and knobs. They are Captains Peter Bressey, Mike Broom, C.C. Jackson, Ron Gillman and Tony Spooner.

Finally, but not least, I must thank Peter Coles of Pen & Sword for his encouragement and advice, and above all his patience. In the end he is the one who brings the words and pictures together. But, of course, the opinions expressed and the errors are mine.

Introduction

Why write a book about aircraft cockpits? There could be a number of reasons, including the fact that there are few books on the subject compared with the thousands of other aviation books; that the cockpit is where the human pilot interfaces with the inhuman machine, or that among all the control positions on land and sea and in the air, it is the one requiring possibly the greatest application of skill on the part of the operator.

The cockpit is also the principal setting for drama in the air, both real and fictional. The ship's bridge, the locomotive cab, the control room of a submarine or the cockpit of a racing car provide dramatic locations in which a man or woman has to exercise skill and judgement. However, compared with an aircraft none provides such an extreme example of a machine that is so unforgiving of error, lack of attention, carelessness or inadequate training on the part of the human element.

The two pioneers of controllable heavier-than-air flight, Pilcher and Lilienthal, made themselves an integral part of their glider. The Wright brothers' Flyer of 1903 incorporated a position for the pilot at which were located the few instruments and controls.

Anyone researching the early history of the cockpit is faced with a bewildering array of different types and ideas for the pilot's position and equipment. Not until about 1910 were pilots given some protection from the slipstream and elements by covering the aircraft's skeletal frame with fabric and leaving an opening on top for the pilot's head and shoulders. Between 1914 and 1918 the demands of war forced the rapid development of new aircraft and their equipment. The regulating authorities were hard pressed to provide specifications relating to structures and engines, let alone cockpit design. Obviously by 1914 it was not necessary to pontificate over how the aileron, rudder and elevator controls should move or in which direction their associated levers should move, because the control stereotypes, which are still with us, were by then well established; whereas, although the number and type of instruments might be part of a government specification, their position was left to the aircraft manufacturer.

It is important to emphasize that until about 1915 a pilot was not very dependent on instruments. The most important 'instrument' was the sound of the engine. If it did not sound healthy then greater attention would be paid to the rpm and oil pressure instruments. This meant that it did not matter very much where the instruments were placed because they were not being constantly 'scanned'. It was not until pilots became dependent on frequently scanning both flight and engine instruments that their relative positions to each other and to the pilot became important.

By 1914 the word 'cockpit' was being used increasingly in contemporary writing. However, finding the cockpit being written about as the centre of interest before about 1930 is rare. When describing a 'new machine' writers tended to dismiss the cockpit and its equipment with a few words. A few lines about the word 'cockpit' itself are necessary. Today in the English-speaking world 'cockpit' is the most commonly used word when describing where the pilot or pilots sit. However, when there are two pilots seated side-by-side in a large transport aircraft we find 'flight deck' is sometimes preferred. There appears to be no accepted rule on the subject. Within the general meaning of the position from which an aircraft is controlled, there are single-seat, side-by-side two-seat, tandem and separated cockpits, some open and some enclosed. There are also jettisonable cockpits and prone-pilot cockpits, and pressurized and unpressurized. And we must not forget the microlight pilots whose 'cockpits' are as rudimentary as those of the first decade of powered heavier-than-air aircraft.

As for the origin of 'cockpit' as an aviation word, we might assume that as those in aircraft of the first decade were often low sided then they were similar to the shallow opening in the deck of a small sailing vessel occupied by the helmsman and tiller. In the eighteenth century one of the lower compartments of a British warship was called the cockpit.

This book addresses a number of interconnected themes which make up the history of the aircraft cockpit. They are:

The emergence from a number of early ideas of an internationally accepted arrangement of hand and foot controls.

The continuing efforts to provide controls and instruments that kept the human pilot in full control of the machine. In other words, keeping in step with the machine and not 'losing the plot'.

The technical steps taken to provide the pilot with a comfortable working environment and at the same time avoid excessive workload and fatigue. Paradoxically, a too comfortable environment along with an uneventful flight might induce sleep, or at least a loss of a safe level of situation awareness.

The provision of an ever increasing sophistication of systems, mostly electronic, which answered the pilot's questions of where am I and what do I have to do to get to the next waypoint or destination.

These key themes are discussed against the background of the continuing advance made in aircraft performance. From 1903 onwards each successive generation of aircraft went faster and higher, and many were very much larger. This being so, they entered operating environments that placed ever increasing demands on a pilot's abilities. Keeping the pilot in control, both physically and mentally, required the development of increasingly sophisticated controls and instruments, as well as life support and safety systems.

One theme runs as a thread through the history of the aircraft cockpit. This is the influence of human laterality. Laterality is a slightly pretentious word, but it is a useful one because it embraces such human characteristics as hand and side preference as well the influences of the right-hand world in which we all live. It can also influence a pilot's reaction to events within and outside the cockpit. Left hand on throttle and right hand on stick in the single-seat cockpit may not have come about by chance, and neither did the once ubiquitous left-hand circuit.

As will be described, the pilot's place was not always given adequate consideration by design offices. On too many occasions 'that will do' or 'that looks about right' (TLAR) ruled in the drawing office. In the first half of the twentieth century many pilots were of the opinion that designers rarely considered the pilot's needs. If we were able to study all the incident and accident reports published since 1903 we would find that there are many examples of inadequate or non-existent ergonomics in the chain of events and circumstances.

No attempt is made to describe and comment in detail on every type of cockpit. The number of aircraft types put into service since 1903 runs into thousands. Instead, a selection is made among the many, particularly if they are typical of their generation or include unusual or important technical features. The inevitable result is that some readers may be disappointed because the aircraft type they have either loved or hated has had to be left out. The cockpits of rotary-wing aircraft are only mentioned in passing because they deserve a book to themselves, written by someone familiar with the subject. Unfortunately there is not room enough in the book for comments on the cockpits of sport, light, and private aircraft and gliders.

Many of the chapters are concerned with developments that occurred before about 1970. Modern cockpits are 'much of a muchness'. Over the past few decades the proliferation of electronic displays has introduced a virtually standard airliner cockpit. Five, sometimes more, large-screen electronic displays now take up most of the panel space in front of the two pilots of a transport aircraft. The fighter/attack cockpit is also dominated by electronic displays. The reason why more words have been given to the pre-1970 cockpits is because their shortcomings and the solutions to their problems paved the way towards today's safer and better man-machine interface in the air.

A caveat: the reader may find that a description of the cockpit of an aircraft with which he or she is very familiar does not agree with their recollection. This could be because there have often been variations in equipment among the different marks or versions of a particular aircraft. In order to limit the size of the book it has not been possible to cover those cockpits occupied by navigators, engineers, radio operators and gunners. I attempted to do that in my *Fighting Cockpits* (Airlife 1999).

This book has its origins in an article written for *Flight* in 1956. The title 'Pilot's Place' was selected by the then technical editor, Bill Gunston, as a more appealing one than my 'History of the Aircraft Cockpit and its Equipment'.

Overpage: Curtiss type control with wheel and column for rudder and pitch control and with roll control through a brace across the pilot's back. Foot control pedals operated the throttle and the 'claw' brake. *Philip Jarrett*

CHAPTER ONE

How did it all start?

The human animal has devised ever increasingly complex machines with which to perform tasks outside its limits of ability. Some of the tasks, particularly those of prehistory, have been directed at food production; this also includes irrigation and manipulation of the earth's surface materials. Some tasks became concerned with transport, including both pacific and belligerent activities. Others were part of exploration and some just part of natural human curiosity.

Whatever our activity, control and information interfaces are all around us. Whenever we need to travel, to communicate, to make war or to help others there has to be a control and information interface to enable us to interact with the machine world. Each type of machine or mechanical artefact, be it primitive plough or moon-landing vehicle, has had to have some form of control and information interface. The interface can be conveniently thought of as having three contiguous elements or surfaces: (i) the machine, (ii) the controls and instruments and (iii) the human operator.

Although we may not associate instruments with ploughing using animal power, nevertheless throughout history ploughmen have received information through their hands as to the way in which the plough was performing. Their eyes provided an 'instrumental' view based on the view ahead. At the end of each furrow the horse or ox had to be turned on the headland. This required a set of controls, namely the reins. Therefore the control and information interface of the plough was just as important to the human operator as the interface is to the modern aircraft pilot, except that the pilot is in control of a machine capable of moving at 1,000 feet per second (300 metres per second) and having to make critical control decisions within a second.

Of all the interfaces, that of the aircraft has presented and continues to present challenges to designers and pilots. In the first decade of powered heavier-than-air flight the pioneer designer/aviators had no reference books from which they could obtain information on how to arrange the controls or on what type of instruments were needed. They were very much on their own. They were venturing not only into the unknown aspects of flight, but into uncharted ways of arranging controls and providing instruments to improve both the efficiency and safety of flight.

A control stereoptype

In recent years the control of aircraft has changed to some extent from what used to be an international standard. For ninety years the pilot's hands have directly effected pitch and roll control through a central joystick or wheel-and-column, and the feet have been used for yaw control. The advent of power-operated control surfaces, analogue and digital computers and then fly-by-wire flight systems reduced the muscular effort needed to effect control. Today the side-stick control has revolutionized the look of some fighter cockpits and transport aircraft flight decks. However, the basic allocation of fingers for roll and pitch and feet for yaw has not changed, nor have the directions of hand movements for roll and pitch changed or varied.

Man and machine

In the last decade of the nineteenth and for a time during the twentieth century, two opposing schools of thought emerged concerning the relationship between mankind and machine. One argued that the pilot need not be an integral part of the machine. On the 'bridge' there would be levers for 'go up' and 'go down', 'turn left' and 'turn right' and so on. In other words they envisaged controlling an aerial vehicle rather than a winged horse. The renowned aviation historian Charles Gibbs-Smith referred to those who understood how to control a flying machine, such as Pilcher, Lilienthal and the Wright brothers, as 'airmen'. Others, such as Langley and Maxim, he termed 'chauffeurs' who envisaged commanding an aerial ship that also happened to be able to go up or down. The 'airmen' school argued successfully that the pilot had to be able to feel what the aircraft was doing and be 'hands on' all the time.

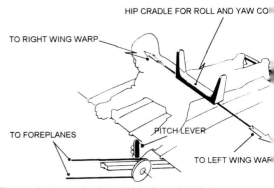

The very basic controls of the Wright Flyer of 1903. The wing warping (roll) control was combined with the rudder (yaw) control.

The Wrights soon appreciated that the control of a bicycle and an aircraft was related. The rider of a bicycle had to keep continuous control at all times in order to remain upright. They realized that a flying machine would also require a method of continuous control, and this led to the concept of the forward elevator (canard) for pitch and wing warping for bank. Even before 1903 they had discovered the need to practise keeping control of the gliders from which the powered Flyer was developed. As with a bicycle, practice was essential. They made stability and control a central feature of their approach to the design of their craft.

Diorama of the historic first powered heavier-than-air controllable flight by the Wright Flyer. *Science Museum*

They realized that a complex servo-mechanism system was needed to solve this problem, and the cheapest available version was a human.

In the first decade of powered flying machines, each innovator usually had personal ideas about the way in which the controls should be operated and in which direction they should be moved to effect a particular control surface action. There were also many different ideas about how the 'tail feathers', i.e. the empennage, should be arranged.

It is important to note that contemporary records from the first decade of heavier-than-air flying are unreliable when describing the different methods of control. To some extent this was because the early aviation journalists were trying to grasp the principles of flight and aircraft mechanisms and were often out of their depth. They had to try to understand and explain to their readers the many variations of lifting and control surfaces among the early aircraft. In addition an agreed common terminology was needed.

A significant control arrangement, because it was the first successful system, was that of the Wright Flyer of 1903. However, the controls of the Flyer did not necessarily become the ancestor of the control systems of the majority of machines that followed. Although pitch was controlled by the foreplane operating lever moving in the expected direction, and can claim to be the progenitor of the joystick, roll (banking) control was effected by movement of the pilot's hips in a cradle. Rudder or yaw control was connected to the wing warping system.

The Wright Flyer

The pilot's position in the Flyer was to the left of the engine, and this arrangement continued with subsequent Wright machines; although there were later versions with the pilot to the right of the engine. With

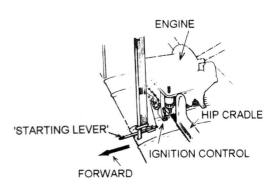

Engine controls of Wright 1903 Flyer.

the engine to the right the pilot's right ear was uncomfortably close to the exhaust. In Orville Wright's 1904 diary there is reference to the need for a silencer (muffler). Why the original arrangement was chosen cannot be determined with certainty from the Wright documents. A possible explanation is to be found from the design of the engine, which lay on its side. In that position the primary engine controls were closer to the pilot's right hand than if the engine had been on his left side. One of the controls has been referred to as the 'starting lever'. It was on a vertical pivot and moved through a horizontal arc. When moved into alignment with the machine's fore-and-aft axis the fuel cock opened. On being satisfied that the engine was performing correctly, the pilot moved the lever towards himself, and this initiated the following sequence of operations: a weak cotton loop tethering the machine to its starting rail was ruptured; the anemometer started to revolve as the machine moved forward; and the stop-watch and the revolutions counter were started. Once the machine came to rest after landing, the lever was pushed over to the 'off' position. This shut off the fuel supply and stopped the instruments. The other control was the advance-and-retard spark-control lever on the forward left corner of the engine.

The problems encountered in perfecting a safe and satisfactory system of control about all three axes are emphasized by the fact that it was not until 20 September 1904 that they achieved a 180° turn. Significantly, in relation to the future of cockpit design and airfield control rules, this was a left turn. However, this may have been chance, because the position of the hangar from which the flying machine was extracted, the shape of the field and the direction of the wind more than likely dictated a left-hand circuit.

In 1906 Santos Dumont stood at the controls of his flying machine but none followed his example. *Science Museum*

With the first Wright series, in which the pilot lay prone, his feet took no part in the control action. With the Flyer III of 1905 the rudder control was made independent of the warping control. During the pioneering long flights made in 1905 the prone piloting position was found to be uncomfortable. Writing in 1927, Orville Wright referred to the impracticability of the prone position for the pilot that had been a feature of their 1903, 1904 and 1905 Flyers. The majority of the aviator/designers of the first decade adopted a sitting position. The only precedent for a sitting position was the automobile and its ancestor the carriage. Santos-Dumont achieved no better degree of

control by standing up as if he were at the wheel of a ship.

The prone-pilot position of the early Wright machines helped to reduce drag, as it would forty years later with the advent of some experimental high-performance aircraft. We might speculate that the prone position could have become the stereotype for all subsequent flying machines. That is, of course, if the neck ache problem had been overcome. However, it was not to be. The seated, facing-forward, pilot's place became the accepted international arrangement, particularly when engines became more powerful and the drag of a seated pilot could be tolerated

Control coordination

In 1908 the Wrights adopted a seated position for the pilot. But it was not until 1912 that they equipped their machines with a rudder bar. They tried a number of different methods of control. With one system there were two levers: one to the left for pitch control and another for roll control to the right. Today no one would think of arranging the two levers that operate the roll and the pitch control in that way. The coordinating task of pushing and pulling on two similar levers, each operating control surfaces whose actions act in different planes, is one which could easily lead to fatal mistakes. Eventually Wilbur Wright recognized the danger. In a letter to Orville in September 1908 he comments on the dangerous ergonomic situation.

Complete turn not attempted until 1904 (20th Sept.). I think the error ('digging-in' in turns) is caused by the fact that the lever adjusting the tail moves fore and aft like that adjusting the front rudder [sic] (elevator) and that as I shove the left hand forward to maintain speed I instinctively tend to do the same with the other. I have noticed myself make this movement of the right hand in straight flight when a gust compels quick movement of the left hand . . I am about to discard all fore and aft movement of the right hand as dangerous.

Wilbur Wright's comment on the dangers of this type of control was echoed by one of his pupils, who remarked on the 'unnatural method' of using the warping levers, and another pupil, who, despite practice on a rudimentary flight simulator, failed to grasp the correct relationship between the way in which the lever had to be moved to effect a desired direction of turning. Eventually in desperation he 'borrowed' a machine and went off solo. His inability to master the warping lever resulted in a crash and his death.

Although the Wrights' first method of control was not taken up by others, nevertheless they continued to experiment with variations. Among them was the 'three-lever' system. At the pilot's left hand there was a fore-and-aft-moving lever to control pitch in the natural sense. For the right hand two levers were combined in one. The lower or main part operated roll control. For example, pushing the main lever forward applied left bank, pulling back gave right-bank. Today's ergonomists would consider it a most unnatural movement. The third lever at the top of the main lever could be moved from side to side to control the rudder. The Wrights devised this system to simplify making a coordinated turn. That is a turn in which the yaw and roll control surface displacements commanded are matched to avoid the aircraft either skidding inward or outward during the turn. In a left turn, for example, in a Wright machine and others with similar control surfaces, the downward projecting aileron or warped surface on the starboard side caused more drag than that on the other wing. With the result that the machine rolled to the left but at the same

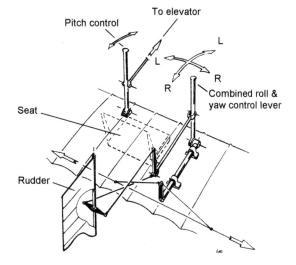

Wright two-lever control system with rudder and roll combined at one 'joystick' for the pilot's right hand. *Author*

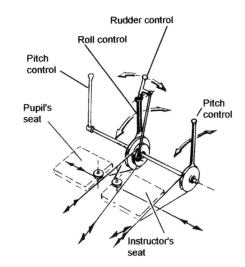

Wright side-by-side, dual control, three-lever system. The pupil used the preferred hand, the right, on the control requiring the greater manipulative and coordinating skills. Some instructors, unless left hand preferring, found it difficult to effect coordinated control of roll and yaw. *Author*

Antoinette monoplane c 1910. Roll control arranged to operate in a non-intuitive manner. Rudder bar with control wires crossed to give a bicycle handlebar action. *Author*

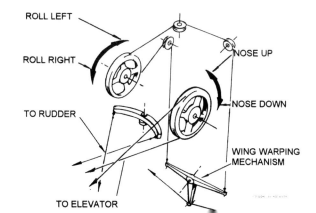

Wright biplane with a Bentley rotary engine and dual controls. Pitch and roll control by wheel and yaw rudder bar for both pilot positions. *Philip Jarrett*

time tried to turn to the right. It interesting to note that the control requiring the greater degree of coordination was for the right-hand. This was to be expected in a right-hand dominant world.

A 1909 version of the Wright-type machine had a combined roll and yaw control set at the pilot's right hand. The vertical lever could be moved fore and aft to control the rudder, forward to turn left, back to turn right. At the same time the pilot moved the lever from side to side to control wing warping. A contemporary description mentions that 'By this simple system, which is largely responsible for the "handiness" of the Wright machines, the pilot is enabled to make the decks (wings) assist the rudder, or the rudder assist the decks.'

The pioneer aviators not only devised different methods of control, they also tried different combinations of roll, yaw and pitch control. The pilot of a Bristol Boxkite used his right hand on a control column mounted by his right knee. The rudder was controlled by a foot-operated bar. Illustrations of the Boxkite when on the ground show that the control wires attached to the top of the joystick were very slack. Once flying speed built up, the control surfaces floated up, thereby taking up the slack in the wires.

Control variations

In the Antoinette of 1909 the pilot had a control wheel to each side. Their axes were at a right angle to the direction of flight. The one on the left provided roll control. For no apparent reason the designer arranged its movement so that if it was turned clockwise the aircraft banked to the left, and to the right when turned anti-clockwise. The wheel on the starboard side provided pitch control.

To raise the nose, for example, then the pilot had to turn the wheel clockwise. The rudder bar movement was the same as the handlebars of a bicycle and therefore contrary to what came to be the international standard. A contemporary comment was that '. . . this is one of the hardest machines to drive'.

Handley Page with his Type D monoplane of 1911 tried something different. Fore-and-aft movement of the wheel and column operated the elevator, side-to-side movement of the column operated the wing warping, for roll control, and rotation of the wheel operated the rudder. The Blackburn monoplane of 1912 provided yet another control variation. Roll control was effected through a wheel on the end of a control shaft and in appearance was similar to that of an automobile steering

Cockpit of Blériot Monoplane. In this version the 'instrumentation' is limited to an oil pressure gauge, an aneroid barometer and a roller map.   *Philip Jarrett.*

Cockpit of Blériot XI. The dome of the 'cloche' for roll and pitch can clearly be seen at the base of the control column with its wheel-shaped handgrip.   *Philip Jarrett.*

wheel. The control shaft was hinged at its forward end so that when the pilot moved the wheel up or down the elevator was moved.

An example of what eventually became the international hand-and-foot stereotype control was used in the Esnault-Pelterie REP and the Blériot Type XI monoplanes of 1909. These had a 'modern' joystick and rudder bar. The joystick of Blériot's 'Cloche' control for wing warping and elevator combined the two functions and was moved in the directions we have come to expect. A small wheel was mounted on the top of the control column, but this was only a hand grip and did not turn. The rudder bar movement in the Blériot machines is described in some records as being similar to the tiller of a small boat, and in others moving as a bicycle handlebar. The change from one method to the other was simply a matter of crossing or not crossing the 'tiller' cables. The Blériot monoplane was used at a number of flying schools prior to the First World War and its system of control was copied by other flying machine designers. At the start of the First World War the joystick movement, as we now know it, and the 'foot forward on the side to which we

want to turn' stereotypes were well established An interesting detail in the Blériot machines was the mounting of the throttle lever on the control column wheel.

For controlling wing warping in his Demoiselle monoplane, Santos Dumont had a pocket sewn to the back of his jacket. Once seated in his tiny and frail

The precarious position of the pilot of a 1910 Demoiselle. *Philip Jarrett*

machine, the lever that operated wing warping was pushed into the pocket so that control was effected by leaning to one side or the other. The throttle lever in the Hanroit monoplane of 1910 was on the left side of the pilot's seat. The rudder bar moved in accord with modern practice. Pitch was controlled by a lever at the pilot's right hand, and warping control was by a lever on the left that moved from side to side.

Among the ideas that were not perpetuated was the Curtiss system. The canard biplane designed by Glenn Curtiss had a brace for roll control that fitted round the pilot's back and arms. The rudder was

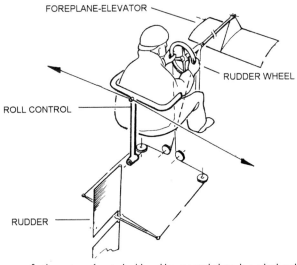

Curtiss system of control with rudder operated through a wheel and not by the feet as would eventually become the international standard. *Author*

operated through a wheel mounted on the top of the control column, which also served for pitch control. Curtiss also used foot control pedals, but these were for applying the claw brake (that dug into the ground), the wheel brakes and the throttle. Another 'first-decade' system is that of Etrich. This was described at the time as 'quite complicated, but it is really very instinctive and works well in practice'. Warping for roll control was effected with a wheel-on-column arrangement. The column also operated the empennage for pitch control. Foot pedals were used to operate the empennage in yaw and at the same time the steerable nosewheels. Another arrangement that failed to gain acceptance was that of Penaud. His patented aircraft design incorporated aft-set elevators and a vertical rudder. Their control of both was combined at a single control column (joystick).

The Farman system was similar to that of Blériot except that a contemporary report was positive in the use of the word 'usual' to describe the movement of the rudder bar in accord with our present stereotype. Wheel control, for wing warping or ailerons, was a feature of the Breguet system in the first decade. Breguet also combined roll and yaw controls in the one wheel at the top of the pitch-control lever. This was an early example of coordinated control. With the Nieuport and Avis systems of 1910 the pilot's feet operated the roll control. In the Short No. 2 built for Lord Brabazon, the

Farman III showing the control surfaces which would move up to their neutral position once the aircraft attained sufficient speed. *Philip Jarrett*

ailerons were operated by a pivoted foot rest, the foreplane by a vertical lever on the right and the rudder by a lever at the pilot's left hand. The Voisin had a single control column at the pilot's right hand for combined elevator and rudder control, but there was no separate control for roll.

It is clear from contemporary writings that the many different systems were causing confusion and that there was a need to standardize. Pilots tended to keep to one particular type of machine and not attempt to 'try' a strange method of control. Among the questions asked were whether control should be direct or indirect and whether the motion of a control should be in the direction in which the machine was to react or opposite it. Today we do not hesitate to agree that a control must move in the direction we want the machine to move. Except, of course, the rudder bar!

Instruments

The Wright Flyer had no cockpit. As noted, the place for the prone pilot alongside the engine was equipped with a stop-watch, an anemometer and an engine revolutions counter. By combining the three readings the Wrights derived distance flown, speed and horsepower at the propellers. However, these were test instruments and therefore not strictly flight instruments. In their aircraft of 1909 a piece of cloth or string was attached to a crossbar in front of the pilot to give an indication of side slip during a turn. Philip Jarrett, an authority on early flying machines, points out that Pilcher used a piece of string on his 1896 hang gliders, and so that may have been the first aviation instrument.

Contemporary accounts of flying in the ten years before the First World War emphasized

Blackburn monoplane of 1912 whose 'array' of instruments includes just two: a directly driven RPM indicator and two pulsometers as an indicator of engine 'health' in front of which is the engine control lever. The 'blip' ignition button is mounted on the wheel.
Smiths Group

Deperdussin of 1910 with no discernable instrumentation.
Philip Jarrett

that an rpm indicator was most essential because it provided a means of monitoring the health of the engine before take-off. It was not a flight instrument because the early engines had to be operated at near maximum rpm in order to overcome the built-in drag of the maze of struts and wires. In flight the pilot usually avoided making adjustments to engine speed.

Many aircraft crashed, either from structural failure or from stalling. Some pilots were killed, but others, such as Geoffrey de Havilland, were able to extricate themselves from the tangle of broken wood, torn fabric and tangled wires. In their rudimentary cockpits they stood a good chance of escaping from a crash with only a

few cuts and bruises.

The increasing number of accidents resulting from allowing an aircraft to stall encouraged the development of incidence and airspeed indicators. In 1907 a vane-type incidence indicator was introduced. Pilots learning to fly Wright aircraft were instructed to keep the incidence indicator pointer within two limiting red marks on the scale. This ensured that the aircraft was not flown at a dangerous attitude. One of the earliest type of airspeed indicator consisted of a flat plate normal to the direction of flight. Air pressure forced back the plate to which was attached a pointer moving across a scale to indicate speed. Other types of airspeed indicator were based on the manometric tube, whereby increasing air pressure against the open end of the horizontal extension to one leg of a U-tube

Elliot integrated instrument panel of RPM, Altitude and Airspeed.
c 1910
GEC Avionics

Mk.IV instrument panel by Casella
c 1910.
Smiths Group

Fore and aft clinometer for the RNAS.
c 1913.
Smiths Group

changed the level of the liquid in each leg so as to give an indication of speed. Inventors devised more elaborate and accurate manometric-type airspeed indicators. Eventually diaphragm-operated indicators were developed whose accuracy was unaffected by aircraft attitude.

Another instrument considered essential to maintaining control was the clinometer, particularly for indicating the fore-and-aft level of an aircraft. These were glass tubes partly filled with a liquid, which were mounted vertically on the instrument board. Once aviators started to venture away from airfields they had to exercise some form of navigation in order to arrive at a destination. They used a combination of map reading and compass headings. But the early compasses were difficult to use because the magnetic needle tended to swing from side to side and not all the error-inducing effects to which it was exposed in an aircraft, as opposed to those in a ship, were fully understood.

One instrument that did not come into extensive use during the first five years of the flying machine was the altimeter. It so happened that the early machines were rarely flown much above a few hundred feet. If a height record was attempted then the pilot took up an aneroid barometer and climbed from 'Set Fair' to 'Stormy', the needle moving anti-clockwise as air pressure decreased with increasing height. The first British altimeters designed for aviation use continued to show increasing height by the anti-clockwise rotation of the needle. Those that followed also had the same movement, and this type of indication was still in use as late as 1930.

In 1913 a commendable attempt was made to provide an integrated array of instruments on one mounting. The British War Department Mk IV cast aluminium unit incorporated an altimeter, tachometer, air speed indicator and stop-watch. This was exhibited in the cockpit of a BE 2 but did not inspire aircraft designers to specify it or

similar instrument boards. At this time 'board', or even the horse-drawn vehicle's 'dash-board', was used to name what eventually became the instrument panel.

Asymmetrical man

We are not as symmetrical as we might suppose. Sometimes one leg or one arm is slightly shorter or stronger than the other. One eye is stronger than the other, and so on. One hand is more skilful in executing precise and delicate tasks, such as writing. This aspect of human laterality is usually termed 'handedness'. Individuals declare themselves to be 'right handed' or 'left handed'. Some might consider they were ambidextrous, although this is usually limited to one or two specific hand actions.

The Handley Page 'Yellow Peril' of 1913. The cockpit equipment is representative of the limited technology available for all types of aircraft in the years prior to the First World War. *Smiths Group*

As with research in other areas of human behaviour, 'right and left handedness' is too much of a generalization because a laterality pattern might be present to some extent in people who have no overt handedness characteristics. Laterality is a convenient word when observing the differences between the left- and right-hand sides of the human body.

Throughout the many centuries of mankind's evolution its lateral characteristics have influenced the ways in which tools, weapons, animals and vehicles have been shaped and used. Human laterality has affected the physical (such as tactile) and visual senses as well as perception, conceptual processes and decision making. The boundary between a human being and things, such as vehicles, is conveniently termed the interface. Across this interface mankind and machine exchange information. Human receptors, such as the eyes and the sensations felt through the hands, enable the human element to perceive the way in which a machine is behaving within its operating environment.

Hand-held weapons, such as clubs, spears and swords were usually held in the preferred hand, and some were shaped in a particular way to suit the right-hand-preferring majority. A modern analogy is the different golf clubs for left-handed and right-handed players. Mankind interfaced with animals, particularly with the horse. Early on in the evolution of horse riding in Europe it became customary to approach and mount a horse on a particular side. Outside the Far East and the eastern provinces of Russia, horses were and still are mounted from the horse's left, or near, side. Control of the horse became the task of the left hand of the rider so as to leave the other free to hold and use a weapon or a polo stick (for reasons of safety players may not wield the polo stick in the left hand). As this book is concerned with aviation, the origins of transport side preferences are relegated to the Appendix.

Left or right?

Aviation was born into a right-handed world. Customs, habits and artefacts were developed primarily for those whose preferred hand was the right. At the beginning of the twentieth century about 80 per cent of people were right-handed, 10 per

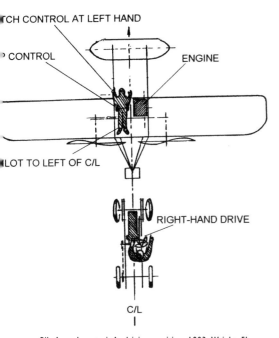

CH CONTROL AT LEFT HAND

CONTROL

ENGINE

LOT TO LEFT OF C/L

RIGHT-HAND DRIVE

C/L

Pilot's and motorist's driving position 1903. Wright Flyer with prone pilot to left of engine. Driver to right in accord with horse-drawn vehicle practice. *Author*

cent were ambidextrous to some degree and the remainder significantly preferred the left hand, particularly for writing. The pioneers of flying machines had more important things to worry about than whether or not one side of a machine was better than the other or that a lever should be positioned on the left rather than on the right. However, the records show that deliberately or possibly from habit they allowed right-hand dominance and preference to dictate the positioning of the controls.

The right-hand preference of the majority may have influenced the pioneer designer/pilots, although we cannot be too sure about this. Nevertheless, by the end of the decade it was realized that the preferred hand of the majority, the right, should be used to operate the control needing the greater sensitivity of touch and coordination. The later Wright biplanes with two side-by-side seats provide an example of right-side preference dictating the arrangement of

controls. The pilots were close to the fore-and-aft centre of lift; as was the engine, which was alongside the right-hand seat and to the right of the centre-line of the aircraft. Between the two seats was the principal control, the combined wing-warping and rudder lever. The lever controlling the forward 'canard-type' elevator was at the 'outboard' knee of each pilot. This arrangement placed the lever requiring the greater degree of skill in operation at the right hand of the person in the left-hand seat. Walter Brookins was deliberately trained as a left-hand pilot so that he could then fly in the right-hand seat and train pupil pilots who sat in the left-hand seat. This meant that the important combined wing-warping and rudder lever was operated by Brookins with his left hand. In 1909 Massac-Buist commented: 'Has it ever struck you that MM. de Lambert, Tissandier and Gerardville are learning to drive the Wright aeroplane left-handed?'

Many years later Orville Wright wrote about the training of 'left-hand' pilots so that they could instruct from the right-hand seat. Apparently, they were never able to fly using the right-handed controls of the left seat. Orville Wright tried the right-hand seat in order to see whether a right-hand pilot could operate the left-hand controls. He reported, 'That was the wildest flight of my life. I never again attempted to pilot using the left-hand controls.' In 1911 the Wrights installed a dual right-hand control arrangement in one of their machines so that a right-handed pilot could instruct pupils in the use of the right-hand controls.

The Wright brothers were consciously or subconciously influenced by the world around them; by the people and their artefacts; by customs and traditions. Those that followed on, either as designers or pilots (sometimes both), were also influenced by the world in which they lived.

The left-hand circuit

From this era we can find evidence for the establishment of the left-hand circuit as the normal direction. Of course it eventually lost its importance, except at small airfields, when traffic control procedures were introduced in the vicinity of airports. The requirement of safe separation and optimum routeing became of greater importance than tradition.

In the first ten years of aviation after 1903 the number of flying machines was so small that the chance of a mid-air collision away from airfields was remote. However, on the ground and in the circuit of aerodromes there might be a significant number of machines taxiing, taking off and landing. In *The Aeroplane* for 27 June 1912 one aviation writer at least emphasized the need for discipline when taxiing, taking off and alighting so as to avoid collisions. Under the heading 'Need for control in [sic] aerodromes' the following observation was made after a mid-air collision between two military Breguet aircraft.

At practically all aerodromes there have been a number of minor accidents that might easily have been fatal but for sheer luck, and might never have been anywhere near accidents if there had been strict rules for conduct on the aerodromes, which could be enforced by a responsible official.

One hears complaints, for example, that certain machines have a trick of swerving to the left, with the result that when they leave their sheds they run down the left side of the aerodrome, so going in the wrong direction of the course and meeting machines that are flying in the opposite direction.

The comment about the 'course' suggests that by 1912 the left-hand, anti-clockwise circuit was accepted as the normal. The origin of the left-hand circuit is, like so many things in aviation and life in general, a question of what came first. If we put on one side mechanical, aerodynamic and chance influences, there remains only the influence of the left-hand Olympic circuit. The athletes at the first Olympics ran anti-clockwise, and since then the majority of athletic and competitive events have been run in the same direction. Horse, skating and bike racing tracks, for example, are usually arranged anti-clockwise. The major exceptions are the

In no way can Anthony Fokker be said to be 'in the cockpit' of his first aircraft. *Philip Jarrett*

A Valkryie c 1910 with control column to pilot's right hand. The only instrument is an oil pulsometer to the left of the seat along with the engine control levers. There appears to be no provision for attaching a safety strap. *Philip Jarrett*

majority of Formula One tracks and about half the horse races in the UK, including Royal Ascot. In North America at the time of the Wright brothers, horse and car racing tracks were run anti-clockwise.

The photographs of the Wright Flyers of the first few years of powered flight emphasize that the left turn was preferred to the right, but that may be pure chance and therefore not of significance. However, Gibbs-Smith was inclined to the theory that the first time a turn was made by the Wrights it was to the left. Of fifteen photographs used by Gibbs-Smith in his study of the Wright brothers and the design of their Flyers in this period, twelve suggest that the left-hand circuit was the preferred direction. When Farman made his first circuit of 1 km at Issy on 12 January 1908 he went anti-clockwise. Wherever it was necessary for circling to take place as part of a competitive event or a parade the number of left-hand circuits appears to exceed the number of clockwise examples. Therefore when the organizers of aviation events in this period had to decide on which way round the aircraft would fly they may have been influenced by the predeliction for left-hand circuits in non-aviation activities.

The year 1909 was important in the development of competitive aviation and the flying of aircraft around closed circuits. It was the year of meetings at Reims, Brescia, Monte Carlo, Blackpool and Doncaster. At the beginning of that year the Commission Aérienne Mixte in France introduced a preliminary set of rules for competitive events, but these did not specify a particular circuit direction. The Commission proposed that aircraft, like ships, pass left side to left side, that is 'red' to 'red', and that aircraft keep to the right of a track between navigational points on the ground.

A map of the course at Reims published before the meeting shows the main stand with the starting and finishing line in front. The direction of flight is shown as left to right across the front of the main spectators' stand and round on a left-hand circuit. However, another map shows, as a dotted line, the alternative right-hand circuit should the wind direction not favour a take-off for a left-hand one. As it happened, the strong gusting wind and rain that handicapped the first day's flying dictated a left-hand circuit, and so all the records we have of this important meeting show the aircraft banking round the pylons anti-clockwise.

Also in 1909, de Lambert flew in a Wright biplane from Juvisy to the Eiffel Tower, around which he made a left-hand turn. The Belmont Park, New York, meeting was run anti-clockwise, but in contrast the regulations for the Blackpool meeting in England in October included Article 12, which stated that in all events, machines must travel in the same direction as the hands of the clock. The same rule applied at Doncaster.

In November 1909 the following

reference to the left-hand circuit appeared in the technical press:

> French pilots... prefer to make their circuits in an anti-clockwise direction, that is to say, they would rather turn to the left when rounding a mark than turn to the right. This is, of course, a mere prejudice, resulting from custom.

That opinion prompts the question: 'What custom?' Was the writer referring to the Olympic circuit? In the following year the Aero Club of France proposed the following rules of the air:

> Aerial traffic shall keep to a height of not less then 50 metres when passing over buildings; all passing by flyers to be done to the right; aeroplanes at all times to give way to airships.

Possibly those rules reflected the marine rule-of-the-road, and also incidentally the requirement that 'steam' give way to 'sail', because aeroplanes were more manoeuvrable than airships.

Related to these early control ideas are the subsequent left-hand circuit rule, the right hand on stick and left on throttle in single-engined aircraft and the principal-pilot-to-the-left practices that became standard. However, the last was not adopted by British aircraft designers until ten years after the First World War. The naval tradition of the starboard side being superior to the port may have influenced the decision to place the pilot of the RNAS/RAF heavy bombers in the First World War to the right of the centre-line. There is also the possible influence of the horse and horseless (automobile) carriage driving positions on the right. Right-hand drive was retained until the 1930s for the more expensive automobiles operated on keep-right highways. In Italy, at one time, the

Evocative of the first decade: a low-sided cockpit, the cabane to which the landing wires are attached and the pilot wearing a cap back to front. *Philip Jarrett*

Blériot monoplane with the distinctive cabane structure ahead of the open cockpit. *British Aerospace*

side of the road on which you drove depended on whether you were in a city or out in the country. Eventually the Rules of the Road at sea were adapted to aviation, and these are described in the Appendix.

Communicating

Powered heavier-than-air flight emerged in parallel with that of the development of wireless communication. The advancement of aerial navigation and the development of aircraft for military use would depend on the development of wireless. Away from the airfield the pilot of a reconnaissance aircraft needed instant communication with those on the ground who awaited his observations. Wireless was evaluated by the British Army for air-to-ground communication as early as 1907. In the following year a wireless-telegraphy (W/T) receiver was tried in a captive balloon. Similar experiments were conducted by both the German and French air services.

By 1912 a BE 2 was equipped with an engine-driven generator for W/T, and Commander Samson, who did so much to advance naval aviation, used a W/T set in a Short floatplane to signal destroyers over a distance of ten miles. As with the Army, the Royal Navy recognized the potential importance of W/T, and placed Lt Fitzmaurice in charge of W/T in all naval aircraft. The first decade of heavier-than-air aviation and the increasing battle for naval supremacy in Europe encouraged greater interest in electronic systems. For example, and as a precursor of future aviation developments and in particular cockpit instruments, Marconi in Italy and the UK, and Hulsmeyer in Germany, described and demonstrated systems that were the precursors of radar.

Keeping control automaticaly

At the start of this era the Wrights' design philosophy recognized that a human pilot provided the very necessary servo- mechanism system needed for control and stability. At the end of the first decade of powered heavier-than-air flying-machine evolution, Lawrence Sperry demonstrated how a system of gyroscopes could automatically provide stability and 'hands-off' flying. His demonstration flight in a Curtiss flying-boat equipped with the precursor of the automatic pilot is an important milestone in the history of control in the sky.

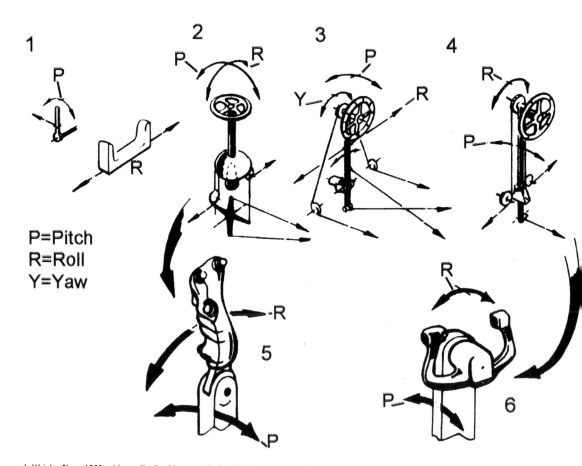

P=Pitch
R=Roll
Y=Yaw

1. Wright Flyer 1903 with cradle for hip control of roll. Not perpetuated.
2. Blériot 'cloche' control of 1909.
3. Breguet c 1910 with yaw control through wheel and roll through column. One of the few examples without a rudder bar for yaw control.
4. Simplified Breguet c 1911. Ancester of modern transport aircraft wheel and column.
5. Fighter roll and pitch control descended from Blériot.
6. Modern wheel and column descended from Breguet.   *Author*

CHAPTER TWO

1914-1918
The Start of Air Power

Both the Italian air force in Libya in 1911 and the US Navy at Vera Cruz early in 1914 had gained experience, albeit in a limited way, in the use of air power. However, August 1914 is a convenient year to start this survey of the aircraft cockpit at war, and its development, because the next four years saw an unexpected and massive increase in the number of aircraft, in the number of different types and in the cumulative experiences of thousands of pilots. In the four years of war cockpit equipment, such as instruments, was multiplied and improved.

The opening phase of the First World War saw the use of frail Blériot tractor-type and Farman pusher-type machines. Their cockpits were sparse both in controls and instruments and in protection for the pilot. In 1914 a pilot depended entirely on what he could see around him and what he could sense from the vibrations of the aircraft. In unrestricted visibility and without any distractions from an erratically running engine or poor aircraft rigging, the pilot could give his undivided attention to observation of the enemy terrain and a lookout for enemy aircraft. Eventually the two principal weapons, the bomb and the machine-gun, introduced an extension of the pilot's relationship with the aircraft. Both turned an essentially benign machine into a lethal weapon. With the bomb and the machine-gun came the need for aiming systems, and these added to the list of cockpit equipment.

Look, lean and turn to the left?

A number of habits or traditions related to left and right were established by the end of the First World War: the left-hand or anti-clockwise circuit; climbing into the cockpit on the port side; throttle lever on the left; principal or only pilot to the right in British multi-engined aircraft, but to the left in German. There were exceptions, the early version of the Bristol Fighter with its throttle on the right being one, and the Curtiss JN-4 Jenny another.

In the First World War the rotary engine,

Principal elements of the Sopwith Camel. *Author*

1. Engine
2. Guns
3. 'Hump'.
4. Fuel tank
5. Cockpit.

Lloyd CII c 1917. Unusual in having the engine controls to the right in a single-seat cockpit. The Bosche starting magneto (right), with handle, is similar to those fitted to Allied aircraft in WWI.

Smiths Group Archives

with its propeller, induced strong gyroscopic and torque reaction effects. A 1919 technical report pointed out that the Sopwith Camel was basically longitudinally unstable and was deliberately rigged tail heavy to counter this instability. A 10–14 lb forward force was needed on the stick in order to fly level. It was considered dangerous to rig it to cruise hands off because, if left to itself in a dive, it would finish up on its back. The Sopwith Camel has been the subject of many comments on the ways in which its handling characteristics were affected by gyroscopic precession and propeller torque. However, if we are looking for a definitive description of flying a Camel there is a problem because of conflict among the different authors. Some wrote, for example, that it pitched one way in a turn, others that the effect was the opposite. There are even those who could not recall any problem.

That there were handling problems with the aircraft there is no doubt because of the significant number of accidents to embryo Camel pilots. Coping with its flight characteristics became second nature.

Left-hand circuit

Did the way in which an aircraft had to be flown predispose pilots to make a left-hand circuit for a landing? In addition there was the right-hand preference of the majority of pilots. They flew left hand on throttle, right on stick. In doing so they may have found it more comfortable to lean to the left so that they were not obstructing the movement of their right arm on the control column. This combination suggests a preference for side-slipping to the left when landing out of an anti-clockwise circuit. Apart from gyroscopic and torque effects in other types of aircraft, their pilots may also have preferred to lean and side-slip to the left. Did the position of the exhaust pipes or pipes of an engine, such as on the right in the Albatross V, mean that pilots preferred to lean and look to one particular side when landing?

As mentioned, a number of reasons have been given for the emergence of the left-hand circuit as the preferred direction when approaching an airfield and when landing. It is possible that another reason was the preference for avoiding a right-hand turn in the Camel. As the Camel was one of the principal types operated by the British air services its pilots may have exerted a strong influence on what eventually became a standard.

The subject of the Camel's turning characteristics generated much comment, and from the following the reader might reach an opinion:

Camels were wonderful fliers when you had got used to them, which took about three months of hard flying. At the end of the time you were either dead, a nervous wreck, or the hell of a pilot and a terror to the Huns. . . . A Camel was a wonderful machine in a scrap. If only it had been fifty per cent faster.

In a letter to the author from C.R. Cuthill:
An ex-Camel pilot was asked to comment on

the gyroscopic effects. 'I cannot remember having any trouble with that, just flew it like any other aircraft and everything was all right.'

About the [Camel's] yaw to the left on take off (and to the left again as the tail comes up) and then as you pull it up into a climb presumably there will be a yaw to the right. The spiralling slip stream will also help to make it yaw left. I checked several articles and books on this initial take-off yaw and two said that left rudder would be needed and two agreed that right rudder would be needed. Some notes on the Snipe say do not pull back too hard on the stick in a turn to the left, but pull back as hard as you like when turning right. The gyroscopic couple due to yaw, it appears, was helping the elevator to the left and opposing it to the right. Air Publication No. 129 of 1920 says that if with a Camel an attempt is made to loop her with the engine at high revolutions it will be found that if the control column be pulled back gyroscopic effect is such that a couple is imposed, tending to turn her nose to starboard and her tail to port. This may be countered by ruddering to port.

The Sopwith Camel in the hands of an experienced pilot held its own against the best that Germany could put in the air. In the hands of an inexperienced pilot and, of course, most pupil pilots were very inexperienced, it could be lethal. Only in the last months of the First World War was a two-seat version produced. This enabled a pupil to be taught how to avoid getting into trouble and how to get out of a spin. It also enabled an instructor to demonstrate the correct way to execute a right-hand turn. As the propeller spun clockwise, when seen by the pilot, the aircraft, if unchecked, would tend to spin round its axis anti-clockwise. Examples of aircraft types which had right-hand rotary engines and tractor airscrews – that is, airscrews which rotated clockwise

when seen from the cockpit – were the Sopwith Baby, Pup, Triplane and Camel, and the Vickers ES 1. In the Airco DH.2 the airscrew was a pusher that rotated clockwise when viewed aft from the cockpit, and presumably this aircraft had opposite handling characteristics to the others.

The torque effect on the Sopwith Camel, for example, was pronounced. Even when taxiing, care had to be taken not to apply power suddenly, as a ground-loop would otherwise result. Full right rudder had to be used when starting the take-off run to stop the tendency for the aircraft to swing to the left as the torque effect 'unloaded' the right wheel. As speed increased, the built-in twist of the fin began to take effect. Turns in the air were affected by the torque of the tractor propeller to such an extent that it was sometimes easier for the pilot to make a 'combat' turn to the right by allowing the aircraft to pull itself round to the left through three-quarters of a circle. Obviously, hazards which faced pupil pilots flying aircraft with such characteristics included the sudden changes in the handling of the aircraft as engine speed was altered. Ab initio pilots were warned against these effects, but unfortunately they still became the cause of a large proportion of training accidents.

Rotary engines

Control of the rotary engines of this violent period in aviation development had to be exercised with great care. Altogether there were four items: ignition switch or switches, fuel fine adjustment, throttle and 'blip' switch. The 'blip' switch allowed the pilot to cut the engine momentarily without having to use the throttle and 'fine' control levers. It was not wise to try and control the engine with the throttle alone because for each position there was an optimum fine-adjustment-lever setting. Failure to achieve the correct combination could result in the engine stopping. This may not have been of consequence well above the ground, but when taking off or landing it could be fatal to the pilot. We have to remember that these early flying machines, with only modest engine power over a limited range of rpm, had considerable drag from the wires, struts and the many excrescences. The moment the engine stopped the aircraft immediately lost flying speed. If there was insufficient height in which to put the nose down and gain speed, the aircraft would spin in. The Gnome Monosoupape 150 hp rotary engine in some Sopwith Camels had an adjustable ignition system. This allowed the pilot to operate the engine on one, three, five, seven or nine cylinders as a means of controlling power.

Neil Williams wrote of the complications of controlling a rotary engine:

The engine control in a Sopwith Pup would defeat any modern pilot. There is no fuel cock visible, and the throttle quadrant is graced by two levers of which the larger controls the air passing through the choke while the smaller meters the fuel via a needle valve. They are known as the 'air lever' and the 'fine adjustment' respectively. Originally the air lever was used more or less as a throttle, but this was not very efficient, and one really has to balance the mixture continuously as engine conditions change. A large hand-pump in the cockpit produces 2.5 psi pressure in the fuel tank, and when this is achieved the blow-off valve hisses. . . . A single brass ignition switch and a 'blip' button on the stick completes the list of controls.

The engine has an rpm range from 800 to 1,150. It normally flies at full power but needs the 'idle' [control settings] for landing. The lever settings for take-off and approach must be memorized; these change with atmospheric pressure and temperature. Even at full power one cannot push the levers beyond half-way as the rpm

will fall. There is one place and one place only for the levers if the Pup is to get airborne.

Instruments of the First World War

Before 1914 few British aircraft had more than one or two instruments in the cockpit. During the war few aircraft had more than six. The essential set consisted of airspeed indicator, altimeter, bubble lateral level, compass, fuel pressure gauge and pulsometer. The last item was a sight glass in which the pilot could see that the engine oil pump was working correctly by observing the pulses of oil. Some cockpits might have an ammeter.

Typical WWI British airspeed indicator. Few aircraft could touch 160, even in a dive. *Smiths Group*

Formation flying

On 14 January 1916 HQ RFC ordered that a reconnaissance aircraft had to be escorted by at least three other 'fighting machines' [sic]. Thus formation flying, as it became known, became a part of aviation practice and history. The effect of formation flying on the design and equipment of the cockpit was

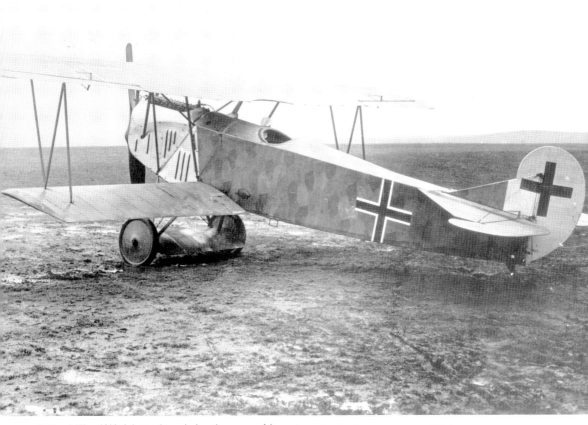

Fokker D VII c 1918. A better forward view than many of its contemporary types.

Philip Jarrett

indirect but nevertheless deserves mentioning. For example, it influenced the retention of the open cockpit because of the need for hand and arm signals by the leader of a formation. Until the advent of reliable and effective radio-telephony (R/T), 'zogging', as the arm signals came to be known, had to suffice. One hand signal that did not appear until the latter part of the First World War was 'Chocks away', for the simple reason that chocks were either not always available or not considered.

Variations of the principal elements

Designers tried different arrangements of the principal elements that together made a single-engined aircraft. These were the gun(s), pilot, propeller, engine and observer/gunner. Providing unusual locations for the pilot's cockpit was indulged by many designers during the First World War. The Booth design of an anti-airship fighter armed with a Davis recoilless QF gun positioned the pilot's place on top of the centre section.

In many aircraft types the fuel tank was positioned adjacent to the engine. In the event of a crash, or even a carburettor fire in the air, the crew was unlikely to survive the ensuing inferno. Not until the end of the First World War did design offices consider providing a fire-retarding bulkhead between engine and fuel tank. The 'Farman' pusher arrangement gave the pilot in front a good view ahead, but at the risk of being crushed by the engine in the event of a crash.

BE2c night fighter c.1917 with twin Lewis gun armament. The guns are shown in the 'reload' position. The long lever outside the cockpit was used to position the guns at the inclined firing angle for attacking airships from below. *British Aerospace*

AIRCRAFT AND COCKPITS OF THE FIRST WORLD WAR

BRITISH AIRCRAFT

When the Royal Flying Corps (RFC) moved to France in August 1914 it had two basic types of aircraft: the tractor, engine-in-front, biplane and the pusher biplane. The tractor types were represented by the BE (Blériot Experimental). The pushers included the FE (Farman Experimental). The French air force also used both pusher and tractor aircraft. There were few monoplanes because the RFC had decided they were structurally unsound. However, the German air service was less concerned about any structural shortcomings of the monoplane. The Fokker Eindecker (i.e. monoplane) performed well and for a time in 1915 became the scourge of the RFC. Not until the last year of the First World War did the US air service join in the air war to a significant degree; and mostly using European designed aircraft.

BE 2

The BE 2, a two-seater, had two very open low-sided cockpits. In the improved BE, the 2C, the cockpit sides were higher; thereby

Vickers Gunbus c 1915 in an unusual setting. The pilot had a forward view unobscured by engine, struts and wires. *Vickers*

reducing the drag caused by the crew's bodies. The BE 2C introduced the question as to which of the two seats should be for the pilot. In the BE 2C the pilot sat aft. When it became necessary to carry defensive armament the observer/gunner in the front seat was hemmed in by struts and wires. It was some time before it became more usual to position the pilot in front of the observer in tractor-propeller machines. The Sopwith 'One and a half' Strutter went into production with the observer/gunner aft of the pilot.

At 14,000 feet over northern France one realized how very exposed were the seats of a BE. I was thoroughly chilled myself and I had a windscreen, whereas the observer's had been removed to make way for the forward

BE 2C with Lewis gun on a mounting that allowed it to be used by either the pilot or the observer. *Philip Jarrett*

gun mounting. With the engine running slowly it was possible to make oneself heard. I shouted to ask how he felt, but his face was stiff: he could barely move his jaw enough to shout something back at me. I got the one word, 'Awful'.

DH 1

The DH 1 followed the BE 2C to France. This had the 'Farman' pusher arrangement of engine and crew. The pilot sat behind the observer, who occupied the front of what was nothing more than the engine nacelle extended forward. The crew out in front was remote from the noise of the engine and had an exceptional view on all sides. The FE 2B was similar.

DH 2

The fixed forward-facing Lewis gun in front of the pilot of the DH 2 proved a popular arrangement for combating German fighters and ensuring that the RFC always took the war to the enemy. The DH 2 was one of the first types to present the pilot with the problem and the dangers of the gyroscopic couple effect from the spinning rotary engine. For example, when making a right-hand turn the pilot had to use left rudder. Should he instinctively use right rudder then

he could be in serious trouble: at the least he would lose speed; at the worst a spin would result. The DH 2 earned the appellation 'spinning incinerator' following numerous spins. Experienced pilots only became 'experienced' once they learnt to centralize the rudder quickly at the onset of a skidding turn. An RFC pilot's comment on the gyroscopic effect was, 'There was the same quick lurch of the wings as engine came on and off . . . .'

Farman MF-7 Longhorn

Another 'pusher' was the two-seater Farman Longhorn. The following description by Grinnell-Milne serves well to set the 1915 cockpit scene:

One of the instructors and a senior pupil picked their way through the wire entanglements, stepped over the wooden horns where they curved to the ground to become skids, mounted upon the wheels and clambered with a good deal of difficulty into the 'nacelle'. No, it was not a body, nor a fuselage, nor yet a cockpit; it was a nacelle. The same name used for the things that hang beneath balloons, but this nacelle was not of wicker. It was smooth and fairly solid looking. It recalled the bath in which Marat was murdered.

FE 4

The forward part of the fuselage of the FE 4

FE 2B pusher with observer/gunner in front of pilot. When climbing up into the cockpit the pilot had to find his way amid numerous rigging and control wires. *Philip Jarrett*

FE 2B single-seat night fighter version with one Lewis gun on a fixed mounting and another which could be aimed upward. Both guns had illuminated pillar sights. *Philip Jarrett*

resembled a shoe with the heel leading in the direction of flight. There was a small transparent section in the 'back' of the shoe and two large nosewheels of the undercarriage at the front.

FE 8

XE ìFE 8îThe FE 8 of 1915 had, for its time, a carefully streamlined nacelle to accommodate gun, pilot, fuel-tank and engine, in that order. At the time it was suggested in the lay press that the aluminium cladding of the nacelle provided the pilot with some protection against enemy fire. The thin aluminium scantlings were not riveted to the structure of the airframe but laced on, as with conventional fabric covering. The single Lewis gun in the FE 8 was initially mounted low down in the nose of the nacelle, with the spade-grip just ahead of the control column and the pilot's shins. The gun was allowed a limited degree of traverse. In line with the pilot's eye point was a sighting bar. The sighting bar was linked to the gun and had a downward-projecting portion whereby the pilot could move the gun. This arrangement may have been decided upon in order to simplify changing ammunition drums, an important requirement in 1915 because at that time a drum held only forty-seven rounds (a three-second burst of fire).

Fixed gun

The conclusions of those on the staff, who may not have had any practical air fighting experience, were in conflict with the FE 8

Instrument panel cut away on left to accommodate the Vickers/Maxim gun. The ammunition tank is mounted at the pilot's feet. The RPM indicator, in contrast to the other instruments, has black numerals and pointer. This may not have been a standard type. The handle at lower right is for hand pumping up the air pressure in the fuel tanks, the tank selector control for which is at the top centre of the panel.
Philip Jarrett

pilots at the 'sharp end'. The pilots wanted to use the gun with the fixing clamp in place so that they only had to aim the aircraft and not try and fly and move the gun at the same time. Staff officers did not always appreciate the complication of having to fly with the one hand so as to leave the other free to operate the gun and not having a third hand to operate other controls. Both the French and the Germans, on the other hand, lost little time in adopting the fixed forward-firing gun and perfecting methods for firing through the propeller disk of tractor-type aircraft.

A contemporary report on the FE 8 cockpit and its equipment remarks that the hand pump for pressurizing the fuel tank and associated change-over cock were awkwardly positioned. The pilot's seat was reported as 'comfortable'. However, the author of the report did not like the resulting backward inclination of the pilot's body. A more upright position was recommended. Another suggestion was that the gun be raised. An important comment related to visibility and the effectiveness of the windscreen, and the fact that the pilot did not necessarily have to wear goggles. Nevertheless the gun mounting and its position engendered much adverse comment once the FE8 entered squadron service.

SPAD VII of 1916. Prominent is a roller map. Just visible to the right of the seat is the magnetic compass. The wicker-work seat is provided with a safety harness. Philip Jarrett

FE 10

The Royal Aircraft Factory at Farnborough persisted with the cockpit ahead of the propeller idea, as tried for the gunner's position in the BE 9. The FE 10 was to be a single-engined fighter with the engine between the wings and the propeller revolving just clear of the leading edges of the wings. The pilot and a Lewis gun would have been in a cockpit carried on struts out in front. Would the pilot have appreciated such a wonderful view all round when attempting a difficult landing?

Short 166

The RNAS's Short 166 torpedo-bomber of 1915, a single-engined floatplane, provides an early example of the pilot's forward view being of secondary consideration. The heat exchanger (radiator) for the engine cooling system was mounted on top of the fuselage above the engine and directly in the pilot's forward line of sight. Perhaps the long-established naval practice, handed down from the days of sail, of not necessarily providing the officer conning a ship with an unwooded view applied also to aircraft.

Sopwith Pup

Although not the only RFC/RNAS fighter in which the designer concentrated the principal weights close to the centre of gravity (CG), the Sopwith Pup of 1916, in side elevation, emphasized the close proximity of engine, pilot, gun and fuel tank. One of the disadvantages of positioning the pilot close to the aircraft's CG, and therefore close to the centre of lift, was the lack of view forward and up. The pilot's head was close to the trailing edge of the upper wing. In the Pup and in many other types, the centre-section trailing edge was cut back. Sopwith also used transparent Cellon in place of fabric on the centre section.

Pilot's view ahead shared with the two large upward projecting exhaust pipes. *Philip Jarrett*

SE 5A. The arming (cocking) lever for the single Vickers/Maxim 7.7mm gun is top left in the cockpit. There are two triggers on the control column: one for the Vickers gun and the other for a Lewis gun on a Foster mounting. An Aldis collimated sight is mounted in front of the windscreen. *British Aerospace*

AW FK 8. Aldis sight in front of small glass screen. Fire extinguisher behind the pilot's head. *Philip Jarrett*

SE 5

The SE 5A had a cockpit whose equipment exemplified the advances that had been made in aircraft performance and lethality. It was one of the first RFC types to be equipped with an Aldis collimating gunsight in addition to the conventional ring-and-bead system. The tube of the Aldis became a familiar item of cockpit 'furniture', although it was mounted on top of the engine nacelle and forward of the windscreen and did not necessarily project into the cockpit. It is sometimes incorrectly referred to as a 'telescopic' sight. In its usual form the Aldis sight did not magnify. It contained a system of lenses that projected an aiming dot and circle focused at infinity. The pilot did not have to close one eye and keep his head in one precise position when using the sight. An SE 5 was also used to test an armament of three Lewis guns inclined up at 45° for attacking airships.

AFB 1

In 1917 RFC ace Albert Ball was involved with the design of the AFB 1 (Austin Fighting Biplane). The designer interpreted Ball's ideas as best he could. He located the pilot's eye-point nearly level with the upper wing so as to give maximum forward view. To give some downward view there were large cut-outs in the lower wing on each side. The arcs of view from the cockpit were compared with those from the cockpit of the Sopwith Camel. As the pilot's view from the cockpit of the Camel was one of the most restrictive in some directions, the designer of the AFB 1 had little difficulty in doing better and being able to report that 'The general opinion is that the view from the Austin Fighter is considerably superior to that from the Camel.' Interestingly, this is one of the earliest examples of using pinhole camera photographs taken from the pilot's eye-point to establish the arcs of view.

Ball wanted the AFB 1 to have a Vickers gun mounted at the pilot's knees, just forward of the control column, and firing through the hollow propeller shaft of the geared engine. However, there was not enough room, and so a Lewis had to be specified. This is where the problem of changing ammunition drums when flying above 15,000 feet had to be considered. Above that altitude the lack of oxygen made any physical effort, other than flying the aircraft, extremely difficult. The pilot also had to change the drum of the upper Lewis gun on its Foster mounting. However, these problems did not have to be faced because the AFB 1 did not go into production.

Avro 504K

In 1916 Smith-Barry was appointed commander of No. 1 Reserve Squadron RFC Gosport, with a free hand to use his training methods. He selected the Avro 504K as the

Avro 504K of WWI. The few instruments include a clinometer for flying wings level and a pulsometer (bottom of panel). The pump is for pressurizing the fuel tank.

British Aerospace

basic training machine. He also insisted that the instructor occupied the front cockpit and not the safer (in the event of a crash) rear seat. The front cockpit had a control column and rudder bar, fuel tank pressurizing pump handle, electrical master switch, 'running' switch, 'blip' and two engine control levers switch, but no instruments other than a fuel contents sight glass.

The pupil's cockpit in the 504K had an array of instruments similar to that of the first-line aircraft to which he hoped to graduate: compass, cross-level inclinometer, rpm indicator, altimeter, airspeed , fuel tank air pressure, and oil pulsometer. The controls were a duplicate set of those in the front cockpit. Not until 1917 was there a reasonable method of communication between instructor and pupil. Smith-Barry's Gosport speaking-tube solved the problem and obviated much of the need for arm and hand signals. It remained in use in RAF trainers until the end of the Second World War. The front cockpit of the Avro 504K had the usual control column and rudder bar, but no instruments other than a fuel contents indicator in the form of a sight glass.

Dolphin

At the end of 1917 Sopwith produced the Dolphin as a successor to the Camel. Again the design office adhered to the principle of concentrating large items close to the CG and maximizing the pilot's arcs of view. The pilot sat with his feet against the back of the engine and his head partly protruding above the cabane. He was surrounded by the structure and in front by the twin Vickers guns. There was also provision for two Lewis guns mounted at eye-level on the cross-member of the cabane. In the event of the aircraft crashing on its back the pilot had little chance of escaping.

F 2B

The Bristol two-seater fighter F 2B of 1917 was designed to 'mix it' in a dogfight with

Sopwith Snipe c 1918 illustrating the concentration of engine, pilot and guns close to the C of G. The pilot's eye reference point is only just below the trailing edge of the upper wing. *Philip Jarrett*

DH 9A of 1918. This illustrates the increase in the number of instruments compared with the cockpits of 1914. Should the pilot's head be slammed forward the minimal padding would not have prevented him being injured by the array of instruments and other equipment. Interesting details are: the provision of electric lighting for some of the instruments; the main fuel pipe and cock; and the 11 instruments. On the left side of the cockpit is the cocking (arming) lever of the Vickers gun, the firing trigger lever of which is on the control column. *Philip Jarrett*

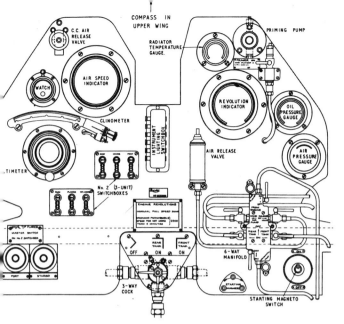

enemy fighters as if it were an SE 5 or a Camel. An interesting feature of the cockpit controls was the adjustable treads on the rudder bar and the reserve control column on the right-hand side of the observer /gunner's cockpit. The F 2B had, for its time, an impressive array of instruments and controls in the front cockpit. The instruments were altimeter, clinometer, clock, airspeed indicator, radiator coolant-temperature, rpm indicator and oil pressure indicator. The controls consisted of an arming lever for the Vickers gun (top centre of instrument panel), fuel tank pressure release valve, fuel tank pressurizing hand pump, fuel system controls, starter magneto hand crank, radiator shutter control, tailplane incidence control, throttle and mixture control levers, rudder pedals and control column with gun trigger. Of course, there were also three other

Bristol Fighter. Although this shows some post war equipment it serves to illustrate a WWI cockpit. Points of interest: The cut out part at the top of the instrument panel for the single Vickers gun. The compass was housed in the trailing edge of the upper wing. Instrument lighting was fitted. The two rows of three switches (middle left) are for the electrically heated clothing circuits, the gun circuit and for the flares and navigation lights. Lower left are the wing-tip landing flare selector buttons. The complicated plumbing and six-way manifold controls the air supply to the fuel tanks. Other than the clinometer there are no purpose designed 'blind' flying instruments. *J M Rolfe*

Bristol Fighter F2 B. The single Vickers gun is mounted top centre on the curved cross tube. The trigger lever for the Bowden cable to the gun is on the control column. The engine controls are to the left and not on the right as in some F2 Bs. *Philip Jarrett*

RE 8 c 1918. RAF Mk II compass in prominent position with instrument lighting switches below. The instruments have black markings and pointers on a white dial. The only 'flight' instrument is the cross level clinometer. The forward-firing Vickers gun is outside the cockpit on the port side. By leaning out the pilot could clear a stoppage. *Philip Jarrett*

Pfalz D III. With the exhaust pipe on the right. Did German pilots prefer to approach a landing by banking and side slipping to the left? *Philip Jarrett*

'instruments' – the Aldis sight, the ring-and-bead sight and the compass, the last item being inset at the trailing edge of the centre section.

GERMAN FIGHTERS

The Albatros D V of the German air service arrived over the French battlefield in the spring of 1917. It was a streamlined biplane fighter. The cockpit positioned the pilot with his eyes just below the centre section. The control column had two hand grips at the top with the two gun triggers between. The gap between the centre section and the fuselage was largely taken up by the twin Maxim machine-guns. The Fokker Triplane and D VII also had twin guns in front of the pilot. Along with the Junkers D 1, the engine and gun controls were concentrated at the top of the joystick, which had two hand-grips. These were arranged so that

the pilot's right hand held the fixed grip and the other hand operated the throttle control. Between the hand-grips were the gun triggers, In the Fokker Triplane the triggers were supplemented by a third trigger for operating both guns together. Between them was the engine 'blip' button.

Fokker D VII c 1918. Cockpit dominated by the cross tube and mounting brackets for the two Maxim guns. At the back of each breech is the arming lever. The RPM indicator is driven directly off the engine cam shaft. The control column top has two levers: on the left the throttle; on the right the hand grip. Between the two are the gun triggers arranged for the fingers of the pilot's right-hand. *Philip Jarrett*

Engine control levers

Gun triggers

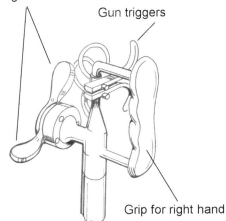

Grip for right hand

Junkers DI control column illustrating influence of the right-hand world. *Author*

Missing the prop

Not until May 1915 did synchronizing or interrupter systems come into use that enabled a gun or guns to fire through the propeller disk of tractor-type aircraft. Until then pilots had to make do with guns mounted at a considerable angle to the line of flight. Any schemes for mounting guns away from the cockpit in more favourable positions were unacceptable because of the need to attend to the frequent stoppages to which guns were prone at that time.

In 1913 an interrupter gear was patented by Schneider, the Swiss-born designer employed by LVG Werke in Germany. However, it was turned down by the British as an unnecessary complication. In the same year Saulnier developed a gun/engine synchronizing system. The idea was sound but the ammunition had an unpredictable delay between the firing pin striking a round and the bullet leaving the muzzle, so that some rounds were striking the propeller. The system was abandoned in 1914. In its place came the Garros deflector plate arrangement that diverted any bullets whose path happened to coincide with a passing blade. The Germans captured a Morane-Saulnier parasol monoplane fitted with deflector plates on the propeller blades. On realizing the reason for recent French successes, particularly by Lt Roland Garros, Fokker

Sopwith Snipe c 1918. The two Vickers gun with their prominent cocking (arming) levers dominate the cockpit. Between them is the magnetic compass. The other instruments are an altimeter, rpm indicator and a cross level clinometer. The spade grip control column, with its two gun triggers, would remain a distinguishing feature of British aircraft for the next 20 years. *Philip Jarrett*

installed an interrupter gear, possibly based on the Schneider system, in a Fokker monoplane. From May 1915 onwards most German fighter aircraft were equipped with synchronized forward-firing guns.

The British adopted the hydraulic interrupter system developed by Constantinesco and Colley, hence CC gear. This required additional equipment in the cockpit in the shape of a hand-pump for pressurizing the hydraulic reservoir. The advent of gun-interrupter or synchronizing gears made many pusher and multi-engined designs unnecessary. This meant that unusual gun, engine and cockpit arrangements were abandoned either at the drawing board or at the prototype stages.

Weights

Throughout the First World War, designers had to make careful judgements over how much weight could be allocated to a particular item such as guns, bombs, fuel and crew. For example, the Sopwith Tabloid weighed less than 1,200 lb all-up. The structure took up 30 per cent, the engine 38 per cent and the fuel 15 per cent. The remaining 17 per cent (304 lb) had to allow for pilot and armament. Therefore the cockpit and its equipment had to be simple and light. Because the pilot had to wear many layers of clothing, including a heavy leather flying coat, to keep out the cold, this was a further debit in the weight and balance sheet.

Cameras and Bomb sights

Some Renault-powered BE 2Cs of the RFC were fitted with a conical box-camera mounted vertically to starboard outside the pilot's cockpit. The choice of the starboard side for the camera is interesting in the light of subsequent side and hand preference considerations. The location allowed the pilot to use his right hand when changing the

glass plates. A similar mounting on the starboard side was used for the bombsight when BE 2Cs were equipped with release racks for two 112 lb bombs. It was not until the middle of 1915 that a proper, scientifically designed bombsight, as opposed to two nails in a piece of wood, was developed. This was the CFS (Central Flying School) type used with a stop-watch to time the apparent movement of the target between the fixed sight and the moveable foresight. It remained in use up to the end of 1916.

Grinnell-Milne emphasized the difficulties of using the new bomb sight:

No sooner had I tried the bombsight in the air than I realized that it would be utterly impossible for me to learn to use it in under two days' time. A rather complicated apparatus, it required some skill and experience in the using. Above all it required two flights over the target: the first one to get the wind's speed and direction and to make sundry calculations with a stop-watch and notebook, the second flight to drop the bombs. Since observers had to be dispensed with owing to the added weight of bombs, all the calculations had to be done by the pilot. I did not fancy myself sitting above an angry Archie (flak) battery and scratching my head over a complicated sum in arithmetic, especially if the result was to be the totally inaccurate placing of my bombs. The more I thought of it the less the prospect pleased me.

In 1916 the Royal Aircraft Factory at Farnborough developed a periscopic bombsight. This was tested in a Martinsyde Elephant. As with the previously described method of aiming bombs, the sight required all the pilot's attention. After setting height and ground speed on the sight and checking that he was flying directly into or down wind, the pilot had to keep his left eye on the fore-and-aft bubble inclinometer, to ensure level flight, and at the same time, with his right eye on the eyepiece of the sight, keep

BE 2C c 1916. Observer's cockpit in front. Bomb release controls outside the pilot's cockpit. *Philip Jarrett*

the target against the crosswires – altogether a lot of things to be done and fly the aircraft, particularly if the enemy was contesting the operation.

Enclosed cockpits

In 1913 Igor Sikorsky's Bolshoi (Grand) four-engined biplane had a completely enclosed cabin with positions for the two pilots at the forward end. A door between the pilots led to an open cockpit in the bow. The rpm indicators for each engine were mounted outside the cabin windows. Sikorsky's success with the Grand led to the Il'ya Muromets series of military types with enclosed pilots' place used in the First World War. The larger the aircraft became, the larger their control surfaces, and in spite of aerodynamic or mass balancing, the heavier became the loads on the pilots' hands and feet.

In December 1915 the prototype of Handley Page's 0/100 twin-engined biplane bomber flew from Hendon airfield on the outskirts of London. It also had a completely enclosed pilot's cabin. The pilot sat on the centre-line behind a vertical wedge-shaped windscreen. Unfortunately the window structure was not strong enough, and during one flight it collapsed. RNAS pilots disliked it because of misting and reflections. Harald Penrose opined that though what they really felt was claustrophobia because they were conditioned to open cockpits, an attitude that would persist for another fifteen years. Therefore, subsequent versions and its descendants, the 0/400 and V/1500, had an open pilot's cockpit. It should be noted that in the majority of British multi-engined aircraft only one set of controls was provided.

The control surfaces of the HP 0/100 were larger than many pilots had met before, and the length of the control wires from the cockpit introduced an entirely new 'feel'. In consequence the aileron control wheel was large to give the pilot some purchase and to allow for the inevitable slack in the cables. There was only one throttle lever. This operated both engines together, but if the large knob on top was rotated engine power could be differentially applied. Turning the knob clockwise increased the thrust of the port engine and anti-clockwise for the starboard engine. This system was also used in the Vickers Vimy and later in the Virginia, but positioned to the left of the pilot seated on the right.

The 0/100 was eagerly awaited by the RNAS crews. However they had to wait until serious tail vibration had been eliminated.

Even after the structure had been redesigned the tail still vibrated once the speed reached 75 knots. The Handling Notes for the HP 0/100 referred to the unusual position of the pilot, which had a tendency to exaggerate all movements of the aircraft. The pilot was seated about 12 ft ahead of the aircraft's CG. In most aircraft of the time the pilot sat close to the CG.

HP V/1500

The HP V/1500, a four-engined bomber derived from the 0/400, had an open cockpit with the pilot's position on the right. The

Handley Page four-engine V1500 bomber of 1918. 'Right-hand drive'. With four V 12 engines and two magnetos for each bank of six cylinders there are 16 magneto switches on the instrument panel. The large aileron/elevator wheel was needed to overcome the heavy control loads. The aperiodic compass is an improvement on those fitted to other aircraft. In the bow is a Scarff ring mounting for a defensive gun. *Handley Page*

German air services Staaken four-engine bomber with enclosed cockpit. The noise level was so high that the crew could only communicate via an electrical visual signalling system. *Imrie*

control wheel was two feet in diameter and operated the ailerons via a 2:1 system of pulleys. There were sixteen ignition switches as well as eight petrol cocks and eight carburettor jet levers. There were two throttle levers, one for the forward tractor and another for the aft pusher engines. Each throttle, as with the earlier HP machines and with the Vickers Vimy, could be rotated so as to control the engines differentially. The instruments were few in number. In front of the pilot were a magnetic compass with an airspeed indicator and an altimeter mounted above. A panel of four engine instruments was mounted on the inboard side of each forward engine. These rpm and temperature dials could be illuminated by individual electric lamps.

AD 1000

Another early example of an enclosed pilot's position is what was, for its time, the 'giant' AD 1000 twin-fuselage, three-engined seaplane bomber for the RNAS. It had a 'bullet-proof greenhouse' in the nose. An assessment of its flying qualities included Harald Penrose's comment: 'It took 15 miles to unstick and get airborne, but could not attain more than 70 knots, which was not far above the stall . . . [there would have been an] immense reduction of resistance and weight if the bullet-proof glass greenhouse were replaced with an open Maurice Farman type nacelle.' The reference to speed is a reminder that modern aviation also uses knots as the standard for speed. In the First World War the RFC used mph, and only the RNAS/RAF

Looking aft at the pilot of a four-engine Staaken bomber c 1918. *Imrie*

aircraft speeds, few engine instruments and the knowledge that if something went wrong there was little that could be done but hope, the pilot was sometimes far more concerned with what was going on in the sky around him than what was happening or available in the cockpit.

Few of the German aces, when recounting their flying experiences commented on the instruments and controls. Perhaps, like most pilots of those years, they were far more concerned with staying alive than making erudite observations on the ergonomics of their cockpits.

The 1918 Cockpit

By the end of the war cockpits had acquired far more instruments and controls than those of only four years earlier The cockpit of a typical RAF fighter of late 1918 would have had all or most of the following equipment:

maritime patrol aircraft crews used knots. French and German aircraft had airspeed indicators calibrated in km/h and altimeters in metres.

Harald Penrose's comments on the handling of the First World War aircraft are important.

Few of the thousands of war pilots ever analytically studied control behaviour. Whether flying bomber, fighter, or seaplane, there seemed no more to it than that the machine either responded to their instinctive senses, making smooth sweet turns, or felt as though it had a will of its own and skidded and swung with ugly intent.

At the same time few pilots seemed to have analysed the type and position of the controls and instruments in the cockpit. Detailed comments on the subject of what we now know as ergonomics are hard to find among the air war literature of 1914–18. With a very limited range of engine and

Ring and bead sight
Aldis sight
Signal pistol
Foster mounting for Lewis gun
Foster mounting unlocking pull ring
Triggers on control column for Vickers and Lewis guns
Ignition switches
Tail trimmer control
Engine controls
Sutton harness
Wickerwork seat
Oxygen supply mask
Oxygen supply control valve
Airspeed indicator (ASI)
Altimeter
Inclinometer
Fuel pressure gauge
CC pump handle for the Constantinesco-Colley (CC) interrupter gear
Fuel pressure release cock
Fuel tank pressure pump handle
Compass.

Parachutes

In 1797 AJ Ganerin descended 3,000 feet by parachute from a balloon. He demonstrated his parachute in October 1802 by jumping from a balloon tethered over West London. However, despite the fact that many had proved the concept of the canopy as a means of falling to earth at a safe speed, none of the pilots of the air forces that went to war in 1914 was given a parachute. There were difficulties in leaving an aircraft compared with jumping over the side of a balloon's basket. Parachutes were supplied for the safety of observation balloon crews early on in the First World War. They were hung on the side of the basket and were opened by a static line attached to the basket. However, they were not considered for aircraft crews until near the end of the war. The crews of German naval airships also used the attached type. However, there is no record of airshipmen saving their lives by parachuting. The Heinicke, an attached-type parachute, was introduced into the German air service in 1918. This was worn with an integral harness. Among those pilots who survived the destruction of their machine by enemy fire by taking to their parachute was Ernst Udet. The principle of the rip-cord was not perfected until the 1920s.

A 'parachute' debate occupied both pilots and air staff of the RFC/RNAS/RAF during the closing months of the First World War.

Among the arguments against adopting the Calthrop 'Guardian Angel' parachute, as provided for observers in balloons, was its weight. With its canister and static line it weighed 70 lb. As mentioned, in a Sopwith Tabloid, for example, only about 200 lb of the all-up weight of 1,200 lb was available for a pilot and armament. It was a question of a gun or a parachute. Those who directed the RFC and RNAS, but did not have to fly, were of the opinion that a pilot with a parachute would be tempted to abandon his aircraft rather than face the enemy.

Keeping in touch

V.M.Yeates, who wrote *Winged Victory*, describes how after a dogfight over the Western Front in cloudy conditions his compass was spinning so much that he could not tell in which direction he had to fly to return to his aerodrome. He spotted another RFC aircraft, but without any means of communication he did not know whether it was flying towards or away from enemy territory.

In the First World War the primary and sometimes only information source was the human eyeball. A patrol of single-seater fighters would take off and head in the direction provided by the pre-flight briefing. Once airborne there was no way, since there was no R/T, in which a change in the tactical situation could be conveyed from those on

Sopwith Hippo. The pilot's cockpit is in front of the back staggered upper wing. *Philip Jarrett*

the ground to the formation leader. The formation depended for both its survival and carrying out the sortie on visual clues from the ground, and, of course, keeping a constant all-round lookout for the enemy. Objects on the ground might be discerned easily or they might be confused by poor visibility and the 'fog' of war. Similarly, anti-airship and anti-bomber patrols over England were only as effective as the visual information link. Signals on the ground, Archie (flak) bursts and cooperating searchlights were usually only effective in reasonable visibility.

In two-seater aircraft W/T provided a means, albeit slow and uncertain, of keeping aircraft crews aware of what was happening to the troops on the ground. The latter sometimes advanced wearing polished metal identification plates on their backs to indicate how far they had advanced and to avoid being attacked by their own aircraft. These and ground signal panels provided information that could be communicated to headquarters using W/T. However, this was a slow process. By the time the coded signal had been passed along the chain of communication and command the tactical situation could have changed dramatically. A direct R/T link of the type developed in the next few years would have revolutionized artillery spotting and tactical reporting from the air in the First World War. The Royal Flying Corps, for example, tried out radio-telephony from 1916 onwards.

Radio communication provided the essential link that could eliminate the virtual isolation of a pilot once he was unsure of his position or of the tactical situation. At the end of the First World War a form of R/T control was instituted for the London defence area, and from then on the night-fighter pilots were no longer on their own: that is, presuming the radio set was not affected by moisture and vibration, and that the sometimes weak signal could be heard over the noise of the engine.

SPAD XIII c 1918. This emphasizes the 'forest' of struts and wires that competed with the pilot's view from the cockpit. *Philip Jarrett*

Hypoxia

At the end of the First World War fighting aircraft were being flown as high as 30,000 feet, and greater attention had to be paid to the adverse effects of high altitude on human physical performance. However, the considerable reduction of engine power above 20,000 feet precluded regular operations at extreme altitudes. Initial attempts to study the problem and devise solutions were confused by the variation among pilots and others of the subjective effects of oxygen starvation, or hypoxia. Some flyers reported that they experienced no ill effects. Some suffered only after several flights above 12,000 feet. Although most pilots and others could overcome the effects of hypoxia for a short time above, say, 15,000 feet, routine flying in those conditions imposed a severe strain on the heart, and induced tinnitus and deafness along with the immediately observable symptoms of fatigue and nausea.

In 1917 some German pilots had the benefit of an oxygen supply for use above 15,000 feet. Although oxygen face-masks were tried, these tended to ice up and therefore they preferred to use a pipe-stem mouthpiece. Gaseous oxygen was used at first, but was soon replaced by cylinders of liquid oxygen. This was the Ahrendt u. Heylandt system that weighed only 15 lb when full and supplied 1,800 litres of gaseous oxygen. In the last year of the war the RFC/RAF improved the methods of supplying oxygen for aircrews. Those responsible for considering the technologies that would be needed, were the war to continue for another year or more, realized that the air force whose aircraft could attain the greatest heights would have the advantage.

Clothing

Just as the pilot is part of the cockpit as a subject, so is clothing and special life support and comfort equipment. In early 1915 Wing

F2 C 'Felixstowe' Porte flying boat of the RAF c 1918. Points of interest are: two sets of controls with principal pilot's position on the right and access forward to front cockpit in which can be seen the anchor windlass. *Crown copyright*

German bomber pilot c 1918. On the left can be seen the oxygen apparatus with tube leading to the pilot's mouthpiece. Unlike British multi-engine aircraft the principal or only pilot's position was on the left. *Imrie*

Commander Samson, RNAS Dardanelles, ordered that his pilots must always be armed with a revolver or pistol, and carry binoculars, a life-saving waistcoat or an empty petrol can. Fur- and sheepskin-lined leather coats were typical garments for combating the cold of the open cockpit. A leather or fur helmet plus scarf protected the head and neck. Field boots, worn by both German and British pilots, were elegant on the ground but did not prevent frozen legs and feet. In the RFC and particularly in the RNAS, pilots sometimes wore 'fug' boots. These were sheepskin-lined, cloth, thigh-high boots similar to a fisherman's waders. Pilots learnt the hard way by experience that many layers of close-fitting clothing did not necessarily keep out the cold. Sidney Cotton of the RFC designed a one-piece flying overall that combined comfort, flexibility and warmth. This became the Sidcot suit, copied by air forces in all parts of the world, and it was still being supplied to RAF aircrews in the Second World War.

Electrically heated garments

Electrically heated garments were available in 1918 to the crews of the RAF's long-range night-bombers. When the special garments worked they helped to mitigate the adverse effects of flying in air temperatures as low as -20° C. However, frequent failures of the insulation resulted in burns. Nevertheless the principle was established that electrically heated clothing was essential for flight in open cockpits above 20,000 feet in summer and above 10,000 feet in winter. Together the provision of electrically heated clothing and oxygen emphasize how the frontier of aviation in 1918 had been pushed far ahead of the limits of human ability and the aspirations of the Wright brothers.

Safety harness

Until about 1917 pilots were usually kept in their seat during violent manoeuvres or a sudden downdraught by a lap strap. Sutton of the RFC devised a four-strap harness that had a simple quick-release fastening. The Sutton harness became the standard for RFC, RNAS and RAF pilots. However, at the end of the First World War the admirable Sutton harness was forgotten by the RAF and was only revived ten years later. The reason for this backward safety step lay possibly with the original object of the harness, which was to keep a pilot firmly in his seat during a dogfight; the original intention was not

Neuport XVII. As with most single-engine fighters, the pilot, gun, fuel tank and engine were close together. *Philip Jarrett*

concerned with protecting the pilot in the event of a crash. A similar four-strap harness was used in some French fighters.

Meteorology

Initially the RFC, the French air force and the German air services in France were without weather information other than that issued by the different army headquarters. The RFC depended on the meteorologists of the Royal Engineers. The service most reliant on meteorological data was the artillery. The shells of big long-range guns described trajectories whose zenith could be above 10,000 feet. The path of a shell could pass through layers of air, each exhibiting differences in temperature, density and wind strength and direction. Meanwhile the airmen relied to a large extent on 'sniffing the air' and studying the clouds: if the hills in the distance could be seen then it would rain; if they could not be seen then it was raining. Low cloud and rain usually prevented contact flying in support of the ground forces and spotting for the guns.

The airships of the RNAS and those of the Imperial German Navy required comprehensive meteorological information and forecasting. Airships were very dependent on acceptable flight conditions. Of those lost on both sides during the First World War a significant proportion were casualties of storms. The RNAS established a number of meteorological stations whose data were collected and coordinated by radio. From the analysis of the data, pilots could be given weather reports and forecasts.

In 1918 the RFC/RAF had a 'Meteor' flight whose aircraft went up to 15,000 feet for gathering data for the artillery and as an aid to weather forecasting. The observations included air temperature and humidity, visibility and the observation and photographing of cloud forms. The records make little mention of instruments for cloud-flying. One comment relating to the subject was 'A pilot who specializes in the work can fly up through any thickness of cloud, while a pilot without experience of cloud-flying is liable to get into difficulties if he attempts to do so.'

Inventors

In English-language histories of the First World War there are a number of items of cockpit equipment named after their inventors, e.g. Foster for the upper wing mounting for a Lewis gun; Hutton and Neame for electrically illuminated gunsights; Sutton for a restraining harness; Calthrop, Heinicke and Irvin for parachutes; Sidney Cotton for the Sidcot suit; and Maxim for versions of his machine-guns made by Vickers in the UK and by the Spandau works in Germany.

Roland two-seat scout. The pilot's head protrudes above the upper wing which meant that the view forward and downward was restricted. *Philip Jarrett*

CHAPTER THREE

Civil Cockpits 1919-1939

The time span of this era in aviation is chosen because it sits between the two world wars. During the first, aviation had come of age under the forcing demands of war. In the Second World War aviation technology would be advanced at an even greater pace. At the beginning of this era civil aviation was born out of wood, wire and fabric: by the end it had matured into stressed-skin metal structures and completely enclosed cockpits. Also, instruments were developed for 'blind' flying and radio links with the ground along with electronic aids to navigation were established.

Serious civil air transport had three origins or sparks that would eventually ignite an expanding flame of passenger airways. The first were the airships of Count Zeppelin, which provided a passenger service in 1909, even though it was one plagued by accidents. The second, the US government's postal service, started in 1917, and its pilots flew the 2,600-mile route in stages between New York and San Francisco via Chicago. The Airco DH 4Ms used had open cockpits and no instruments for 'blind' flight. Except when flying straight and level the magnetic compass could not be relied upon because it was subject to errors, such as the 'northerly turning error'. The third was when the RAF flew senior officers and politicians between London and Paris. These RAF flights were no different from those used to ferry aircraft across the English Channel. Other than being provided with many layers of warm clothing, the VIPs flew in the same Spartan conditions imposed

Farman F 60 Goliath used on the Paris-London service in 1919. The solo pilot sat in a cockpit set within the port side of the passenger cabin and well back from the nose of the aircraft. *John Stroud*

Cabin of a Farman Goliath of 1919 with the pilot's position on a pedestal bringing his head and shoulders up into the open cockpit. *John Stroud*

DH 9 with enclosed cockpit for passengers behind the pilot. *Philip Jarrett*

The captain of the AW Argosy of 1928 occupied the right-hand seat in the open cockpit. *John Stroud*

on an observer or gunner.

In the ten years following the First World War passenger air transport slowly developed. At first the aircraft used to inaugurate city-to-city services were adaptations of military types, such as the Farman Goliath. The nascent civil operators had no difficulty in obtaining aircraft because there were hundreds being disposed of at bargain prices. Their cockpits and equipment were 'as sold'. It took a few more years in which to develop instruments and radios suitable for civil operations in which timekeeping and reliability were important incentives.

International rules of the air were agreed in 1919. One required aircraft to be flown so as to keep to the right of any track designated as an air route. In an open, single-pilot cockpit the view on each bow was about the same, although the forward view might be compromised by the engine and cabane struts. In 1922 a French and a British passenger aircraft collided head on as both pilots followed the line of a river. The cockpits of the British multi-engined airliners, such as the HP 0/10, HP W8bg, Vimy Commercial and the AW Argosy, were 'right-hand drive'. Not until the HP 42s and other 'big' Imperial Airways airliners arrived was the left-hand seat in the cockpit designated as that of the captain, or in today's terminology, P1.

The Pilot's Lot

During this period in civil aviation, airlines and air services proliferated. However, some consisted of only one aircraft and one pilot. Many became insolvent overnight. The lot of the pilots, particularly with the small operators, was not a happy one. Their salary, or rather pay, because of uncertain finances, was nowhere near that of a professional in other jobs. The insecurity of their position as pilots was such that in times of high unemployment they were reluctant to 'rock the boat' in order to improve their status and working conditions, and, above all, to argue for the better design and equipment of the cockpit.

The image they presented on the tarmac was very different from that of a captain with one of the major airlines. In place of a smart navy blue uniform they often wore oil-stained trousers, a sports jacket, whose sleeves were patched with leather, and a battered floppy felt hat. They were also expected to help with maintenance, refuelling and loading the cargo. Some of the 'big' operators, such as Imperial Airways in the UK, could be parsimonious. For example, the steward was not allowed to give the flight crew a meal. They had to bring their own sandwiches.

Even when an airline was reasonably prosperous and had a number of aircraft, the pilots were often considered to be no more important than the clerk in the office. Edward Hillman, a bus and coach operator in East Anglia who went into the airline business, had no romantic ideas on the skill, experience and initiative needed to be an airline pilot. To him they were just another lot of 'bus' drivers. The commercial pilot was

Breguet 280T single-engine transport of 1927 showing the external cables to the elevator and unusually for its time an enclosed cockpit. *John Stroud*

expected to keep to the published schedules despite the absence of proper flight instruments, adequate radio equipment and for many years radio aids to navigation. This situation applied up to around 1930. From that year on there were significant advances in civil aviation aimed at improving safety and schedule keeping. Within ten years many of the small operators were either absorbed into the big companies or went out of business. Apart from those who flew their own aircraft there were the numerous pilots who were not involved in passenger flying. They included 'bush' flying, as well as aerial advertising, by towing a banner or with the message spelt out in lights spaced along the aircraft. There were also stunt pilots at air shows or with film production units. Most had to fly whatever was presented to them, and they could not always pick and choose, even when the airworthy condition of the aircraft was uncertain.

More instruments

In general, transport aircraft cockpits of the 1920s were not very different from those of the First World War bombers. There were few instruments and these were usually dedicated to engine-performance parameters. A book on instrument design written in

Blériot SPAD 33 with the open cockpit behind the passenger cabin. *John Stroud*

1929 includes the observation that 'few skilled pilots, for example, would care to venture over difficult country without good engine speed indicators and oil pressure gauges. Although they would do so without altimeters, air speed indicators or cross levels.'

The development of better instruments in the 1920s was hampered by the vast quantity of the First World War equipment available at low cost. After 1930, when the research and development of 'blind' flying instruments and the inclusion of more electrical systems began to take effect in production aircraft, the cockpit became more crowded with instruments and controls. This reflected the increases in aircraft performance and versatility compared with those of the First World War. Notable instrument developments were the aperiodic magnetic compass, Sperry's artificial horizon, the Pioneer Company's earth inductor compass and turn and slip indicators. The last included the Reid control indicator and the Schilovsky-Cooke turning indicator. The development of one instrument in particular was slowed by a lack of demand. This was the vertical speed indicator (statoscope), or as it was usually called, the 'rate of climb'. It was used during test flights when evaluating the performance of a new aircraft type but was not suitable for ordinary flying. Eventually indicators became available that were both sensitive and responsive to vertical speed.

Although from about 1929 onwards a greater range of better instruments became available, there was no comparable advance in cockpit design related to improving the pilot's 'work-station', as some might call it. What we now term human factors and ergonomics were virtually unknown disciplines in civil aviation. Scientists concerned with people at work tended to concentrate on their overall performance, particularly fatigue, with little or no attention given to the way they reacted to the tools, such as instruments and controls, of their work-station. Their health was usually the province of a separate group of researchers.

One particular aviation hazard present in some aircraft, particularly single-engined types, was carbon monoxide in the exhaust. Aircraft were lost because the pilot or pilots were overcome by exhaust fumes being sucked into the cockpit. Those who survived were sometimes assumed to be drunk.

Ergonomics

Today the word 'ergonomic' is frequently used to enhance the sales of a product. Chairs, automobile controls and domestic appliances, and even toothbrushes, are advertised as having been 'ergonomically designed'. In 1919 the controls of industrial and agricultural machinery, vehicles (including aircraft) and ships were shaped and arranged according to one or more of the following factors:

Tradition: 'We have always done it this way, don't ask me why.'

Human hand and side preferences, such as equestrian and road vehicle customs.

The most convenient and lowest cost, shape and arrangements, with little or no consideration given to the needs of the operator.

'That looks about right' (TLAR)

Among the scientific papers in the UK of the 1920s there were few related to the pilot and the cockpit. After 1930 there were a few more.

Throughout the history of the aircraft cockpit the interface between man and machine has seldom been ideal. Both sides have been deficient in one or more aspects. The human element has well-known physical limitations, particularly when removed from the normal 1013 mb at 15° C atmosphere, or

when exposed to excessive G forces. The machine element also has limitations of which the most significant is a tendency to embrace the laws of Sod and Murphy with enthusiasm. The combination of these two 'machines' has varied widely between happy and unhappy.

Night, cloud and fog

More instruments and more night flying highlighted the problem of reflections on the windscreen from instrument lighting interfering with the pilot's view ahead. The reversed-rake windscreen was one solution and was applied to the Stinson Model A c 1931 and Boeing 247 of 1933, and to other aircraft types, including the first version of the Lockheed 10A.

In the 1920s and 1930s the aviation certificating bodies specified the provision of an openable window to give the pilot a view forward when attempting a landing in low-visibility conditions exacerbated by rain or snow. In those years some experienced pilots could 'feel' their way down through the overcast and then pick out landmarks leading to the landing field. Descending through cloud when uncertain of position was risky, even for the most experienced pilot. Even when the pilot assumed that he was close to an airfield there were rarely any aids to approach and landing. Both W/T and R/T, if fitted, could be used to obtain an indication of position relative to the airfield. Such information from the ground as 'Engines [noise] to the south' or 'Overhead' was often the only help available in getting down safely. Unfortunately even the experienced pilots came to grief when the visibility closed in after take-off.

Radio Range

Radio aids to navigation and landing were advanced in the 1920s. These were aimed at improving the safety and regularity of civil

Ford Trimotor with enclosed pilots' position. *Philip Jarrett*

airline operations. Following on from experiments with R/T during the war, the 'wireless telephone' became an essential part of passenger aircraft operation. In 1920 two British airline companies each equipped an aircraft with R/T. A year later a call was made to an airliner in flight from a public telephone. In the next ten years radio would make significant changes and additions to cockpit equipment.

The establishment of the Transcontinental Air Transport (TAT) Company in 1928 to operate an air-rail passenger service between Columbus Ohio and Los Angeles, using Ford trimotors, was another encouragement of better instruments and radio aids. It also furthered the development of airfield lighting and navigational light beacons. Although the TAT schedules embraced only flying by day, storms and poor visibility might be met at any time when flying over the plains of the mid-West.

Attempting to complete a landing when the visibility was 300 ft (100 metres) or less was a frequent cause of accidents. In the UK some airline pilots were expected to make an

approach without sight of the ground using QDMs (magnetic course to steer) and QFG (you are overhead) of the Q Code passed to them over the R/T. However, as an example, the instruments and controls in the cockpit of the DH 86 four-engined airliner were not arranged so as to help the pilot to make a low-visibility approach safely.

The major advance in navigation, which in turn improved safety and regularity of operations, came with the radio range system of the United States and similar systems developed in Germany. In 1927 Dunmore & Engel patented the four-course radio range, and radio navigational beacons were being introduced for airways in USA. The radio range enabled a pilot to navigate to a range station or to an airfield. It has a significant place in the history of the cockpit because from that time on a pilot could navigate by listening to the Morse 'A's and 'N's or continuous signals in his headphones.(A if to the left of the beam, N if to the right and a continuous note when on the beam) This system made the pilot independent of another crew member, such as a radio operator. Year by year the USA became dotted with more and more range stations. Each of the four 'legs' or beams intersected at some point the legs of another station. Although 'flying the range' was not always 'as the crow flies', providing the aircraft was kept to the right of the beam it was a safer and surer way of operating passenger aircraft.

In parallel with radio communication developments was the introduction of the German Lorenz beam approach system for use when landing in poor visibility. In the late 1930s this was further improved in the UK and became the Standard Beam Approach (SBA). In 1937 the Radio Compass became available for civil operations. The importance of R/T, radio navigational beams, SBA and the Radio Compass to this history is that they were pilot-operated systems and therefore independent of another crew member. In particular, the navigational techniques employed by pilots within the USA in the 1930s would have a significant influence on the design of future airliner cockpits throughout the world.

Flying to the limit

One group of pilots was involved in pioneering flights. These attempts to fly further than before, or higher, or even to destinations that had never seen a flying machine, were sometimes undertaken in specially designed or adapted aircraft, but many used whatever type was available. Their cockpits were often spartan. They demanded great stamina on the part of their crews and were not always equipped with adequate flight and navigation instruments. In 1927 Lindbergh flew the Atlantic solo in his Ryan monoplane equipped with an earth

inductor compass as the only reliable navigational aid. And (Sir) Francis Chichester made an epic solo flight from New Zealand to Australia via Lord Howe Island using a marine sextant and the sun line navigational technique to avoid missing the tiny island. Amy Johnson flew to Australia in 1930 without any radio and without much experience as a navigator. This was in her open-cockpit DH Moth, *Jason*.

Intrepid French pilots, such as Mermoz and St Exupery, pioneered commercial air routes to Africa and South America. The persistently strong winds of the southern tip of Argentina often exceeded the top speed of St Exupery's Latécoère aircraft. At

Couzinet 71 'Arc-en-Ciel' flown by Mermoz. An interesting detail is the four Venturi tubes on the side, below the cockpit window, for powering the flight instruments. *John Stroud*

Commodoro Rivadavia, Exupery had to touch down between two lines of soldiers armed with hooked bamboo poles and a trolley. With the aircraft virtually flying stationary against the wind, a trolley was pushed under the tailwheel The aircraft, steadied by the bamboo poles, was then taxied into the shelter of a hangar.

The cockpit of Lindbergh's Ryan monoplane, 'Spirit of St Louis', was as

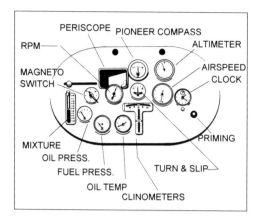

The instrument panel of Lindbergh's Spirit of St Louis. There was no forward view because the fuel tanks occupied the space between the cockpit and the engine, hence the periscope that projected from the left side of the fuselage. *Author*

remarkable as the navigation technique used and his 28-hour feat of endurance. His aircraft was equipped with the best instruments available but the complete control and information interface was, by our present standards, crude. Perhaps the lack of comfort, the aircraft's instability and no autopilot helped to prevent him falling asleep for too long at a time.

Altogether the cockpit of 'Spirit of St Louis' was equipped with eleven instruments plus a periscope for seeing ahead. The periscope was necessary because the two fuel tanks (208 and 86 gallons) took up all the space between the engine and the cockpit. A turn-and-slip indicator was the only gyroscopic instrument. This and the fore-and-aft and lateral bubble-in-glass tube clinometers, used in conjunction with the airspeed indicator and rpm indicator, were Lindbergh's only help when maintaining straight and level flight in cloud or at night. The primary navigational instrument, apart from the stars, was the Pioneer Earth Inductor Compass. Below the bottom edge of the instrument panel was the distribution manifold for the fuel system, along with a test cock and tundish at the top of a drain

pipe. Had the instruments and controls in the cockpit been arranged in accord with our present standards we might assume that he might have nodded off far more frequently. As it was, he was kept very busy for most of the time. In his book *The Spirit of St Louis* Lindbergh describes how he had at times to decide between flying by reference to the stars and concentrating on the instruments.

. . . the monotony of flying with eyes always on the instrument board, the strain of flying by intellect alone, forcing the unruly senses of the body to follow doubted orders of the mind, the endless bringing of one needle after another back to its proper position, and then finding that all except the one my eyes hold tight have strayed off again. [The aircraft] is too unstable to fly well on instruments. It's fast, and it has greater range than any plane that flies; but it's high strung, and balanced on a pin point. If I relax pressure on stick or rudder bar for an instant, the nose will veer off course.

'Blind' flight

Given good visibility, navigating the embryonic air routes by reference to features on the ground, in other words 'contact' flying, provided reasonable safety and regularity. In other conditions, when sight of the ground was lost, a pilot depended on a combination of airmanship and experience. But these did not always prevent a pilot losing complete control on a black night or in thick cloud when there was no visible horizon. But why do we lose control? To paraphrase the Bard, 'The fault, dear Brutus, is not in our stars but in our ears.' The vestibular apparatus in our ears can be fooled when there is no visual reference and when subjected to abnormal accelerations. The human body was designed in the first place to experience a constant 1G vertical force exerted by gravity. Apart from being on fairground swings and roundabouts or when

DH Hummingbird of 1925. The only 'flight' instrument as such is the clinometer at the top of the panel. Note the altimeter pointer moves anti-clockwise for increasing height. *British Aerospace*

DH Cirrus Moth c 1925 up-graded with a turn and slip indicator for 'cloud' flying. Note the twin altimeters. *British Aerospace*

at sea, the body is not usually subjected to the three-dimensional forces that can be applied to it when flying. These forces can completely confuse the human senses. Each of the three semicircular canals of the vestibular apparatus in our ears is disposed at 90° to each of the others. Together they detect angular movement in the same way that an autopilot detects changes in roll, pitch and yaw. There is also the otolithic organ in each ear that senses the apparent direction of gravity by acting as a pendulum. Among the 'false' sensations experienced in flight are the illusion that the nose of the aircraft is pitching up when speed is suddenly increased in level flight; conversely, there is the illusion that the nose is pitching down when speed is reduced. The illusion of pitching down is often experienced by airline passengers after take-off, when thrust is reduced in order to comply with noise-abatement regulations.

Vision is a very powerful and most essential sense; particularly when flying. Therefore, when deprived of a view of the horizon at night or in cloud, the pilot has to rely on the vestibular senses and the apparent direction in which gravity is acting on the body. These can produce sensations that deprive the pilot of knowing where up or down, or left or right, are. They can give the illusion that the aircraft is turning when it is not; or even turning to the left when the pilot assumes it is turning to the right. As mentioned, the pilot can sense that the nose of the aircraft is pitching up when thrust is increased.

In the 1920s there were hundreds of patent applications relating to devices that would enable a pilot to retain control of the aircraft when the natural horizon was obscured. The Sperry artificial horizon deserves more than a few words because it represents one of the most important advances, if not the most important, in instrumentation. In one step it replaced the bubble clinometers on which a pilot depended for maintaining control when the horizon was no longer visible. Entering cloud, for example, and determined to hold a straight and level attitude, constant altitude and rpm, along with keeping the bubbles at the zero mark, more often than not resulted in failure.

The Sperry artificial horizon was a gyro-based instrument. At the centre of the dial was a representation of a monoplane as seen from behind. This was fixed in position. The line representing the horizon moved up and down to indicate aircraft pitch and tilted to

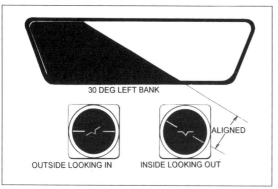

Two versions of the artificial horizon. In the 'outside looking in' version the horizon line is fixed. In the 'inside looking out' type the horizon line moves relative to the fixed aircraft symbol. The latter is the more usual presentation. *Author*

the left or right to show bank. When the Sperry horizon was introduced there were arguments over the way in which it displayed aircraft attitude relative to the horizon. There were two ways: the outside looking in or the inside looking out. With the former the horizon was fixed and the small aircraft symbol moved. With the latter the model aircraft was fixed and the horizon moved,

and this became a world-wide standard, although when Russia started developing its own flight instruments the outside-looking-in arrangement was preferred. Until the 1980s this did not matter, but when the Soviet regime collapsed and interchanges of aircraft and pilots with the West started there was sometimes dangerous confusion. Incidentally the aircraft on the dial of the Sperry artificial horizon resembled Lindbergh's *Spirit of St Louis*. It is important to note that although the Sperry instrument was a milestone in cockpit instrument technology progress it did not tell the pilot directly what to do to achieve a desired aircraft attitude. The degree and direction in which the controls needed to be moved required interpretation and judgement on the part of the pilot. They could only be acquired from practice.

Breaking the visibility barrier

On 26 September 1929 James Doolittle undoubtedly gained his place in the Pantheon of aviators when he took off in a Consolidated NY-2 biplane, completed a circuit of the airfield and landed back without reference to the ground. The rear cockpit was completely enclosed by a hood so that he was entirely dependent on the instruments. Ben Kelsey sat in the front cockpit as safety pilot, but did not touch the controls.

The NY-2's rear cockpit was equipped with advanced flight instruments. These had been developed by Kollsman, Pioneer and Sperry in the USA, with the sponsorship of the Guggenheim Foundation. Not only was Doolittle a notable competition pilot, he was determined to overcome the problems of flight when the horizon was obscured and the resulting disorientation experienced by pilots attempting to maintain control. He worked with Sperry on the development of the gyro-based artificial horizon, and after

These are the instruments that Doolittle concentrated on when flying 'under the hood' on 26 September 1929. The three specially developed instruments for this milestone 'blind' flight are the Kollsman sensitive altimeter (top right), the Sperry artificial horizon (bottom left on panel) and below it the radio beacon direction finder developed by the Radio Frequency Laboratory. *Sperry*

An early version of the Sperry artificial horizon. This, along with the directional gyro and the turn and bank indicator, enabled pilots to stay the right way up and fly in cloud without losing control.
Sperry Gyroscope Co.

Hawker Tom Tit two-seat biplane c 1933. The important aid to 'blind' flight, the Reid & Sigrist turn and slip indicator, occupies a prominent position alongside the fore-and-aft clinometer. *Smiths Group*

more than one hundred proving flights declared that he was ready to attempt a 'blind' take-off, circuit and landing. In addition to the usual instruments, the NY-2's rear cockpit was equipped with the gyro artificial horizon and directional indicator developed by Sperry, as well as a special sensitive Kolsmann 0-20,000 ft altimeter. Throughout the flight around Mitchell Field Doolittle followed the indications of the special radio guidance system and the new flight instruments to hold the correct attitude and to descend at a steady and precise rate toward a landing back at the field. It took great courage just to rely on the instruments.

During this 'milestone' flight in the history of aviation, Doolittle paid most attention to the new Kollsman altimeter, the directional gyro (heading indicator), the artificial horizon and the vibrating reeds of the radio beam indicator. The directional gyro was positioned at the top of the instrument panel. The artificial horizon was located away from it at bottom left. The beam indicator was a 'lash-up' below the panel. Ideally those four instruments should have been closer together. The Kollsman sensitive altimeter developed for this historic flight became the progenitor of more accurate altimeters used throughout the world. The Sperry artificial horizon became an essential part of instrument flying, along with the heading indicator, turn-and-slip indicator, airspeed indicator and vertical speed indicator.

There was a plethora of patents granted in the early 1930s for instruments intended to assist a pilot to maintain control of an aircraft without reference to the horizon. Among the patents granted in 1930 was one that described an elaborate gyroscopically operated, all-purpose, instrument. A model aircraft behind the glass face of the instrument rolled, pitched and yawed in concert with aircraft movements. In addition an optical system projected airspeed, altitude and magnetic heading. In 1933 Nistri described an elaborate optical system whereby the individual indications of four instruments were combined and projected onto the face of a dial. Nigri, as did others, anticipated the format of the electronic attitude directors of the 1980s, in which attitude, heading, airspeed and vertical speed and other parameters are presented close together on one display. The lists of patents included a number concerned with giving the pilot a warning of the onset of a stall.

In the absence of radio beam systems accurate enough to guide an aircraft to a smooth touch-down, there were many schemes, as there had been since the early days, to indicate to the pilot when the aircraft had descended to a predetermined height above the ground. Most were based on a trailing arm or cable, which when it contacted the ground triggered an alarm in the cockpit.

In the 1920s and 1930s hundreds of patents were filed for cockpit instruments and equipment. For example, Fiat introduced (c 1931) an elaborate four-lever engine control unit whereby the principal lever could be used to control all engines, differentially if necessary, and secondary levers for individual engines. Boeing may have considered the Fiat idea, but preferred its own, far simpler four-engine 'bar' throttle levers, as used in the B-17. Many of the ideas

were extremely complicated and did not incorporate features that would ensure reliability and, if they failed, warn the pilot. Some of the inventors had no perception of how an aircraft was controlled. This is not surprising when we consider that among the great body of inventors some were still obsessed with the ornithopter; including using human muscles as the power source.

Control position of the 12-engine Dornier Do X. The majority of the engine instruments and controls were in a separate flight engineer's station. *John Stroud*

One-engine, one-pilot airliners

If the operator of passenger aircraft did not want a converted twin-engined bomber then there were a number of single-engined biplanes on the market. A common feature of many was the 'Hansom Cab' position of the pilot, who was seated well aft of the passenger cabin. In this position the pilot had a well-wooded view forward, thereby making both watching out for other traffic and taxiing difficult. Examples were the SPAD 33, DH 61 Giant, the DH 18, the Breguet 14T and the Potez 9. The pilot of the Boeing 40A mailplane of 1927 was seated

Boeing 40B Mailplane c 1928 with pilot seated more than half way back from the engine. *Philip Jarrett*

Lockheed Vega c 1931 with cockpit close up under the leading edge of the wing. The view each side was limited.
Philip Jarrett

Lockheed Orion with the cockpit well forward so that the pilot's feet were against the firewall. Compared with the Vega the view ahead and to the sides was much better. *Philip Jarrett*

15 ft back from the engine. The Boeing Monomail monoplane of 1930 also had the pilot's position well aft of the cabin. It also had a retractable undercarriage and, in consequence, another lever in the cockpit.

In the early 1930s Lockheed produced a number of single-engined passenger transports to be flown by a solo pilot. One of these, the Orion, had cockpit equipment typical of the time. The instrument panel had a crackled finish to reduce reflections and was dominated by the Sperry autopilot control panel with its gyro heading indicator and artificial horizon. Of particular interest was the positioning of the autopilot hydraulic actuator cylinders and associated rods and cables immediately below the instrument panel, a reassuring position for the pilot, who could easily check that the 'works' were working. At this time flaps were not very common. In the Orion, despite its importance, the flap setting could only be verified on a very small indicator. There were

also twin-engined airliners flown by one pilot. In the L et O 213 of 1932 the pilot sat on a pedestal on the port side of the passenger cabin, with his head and shoulders in the open cockpit.

Two pilots and three engines

As airliner all-up weights increased, and as the demand for air travel expanded, two engines became insufficient, and so we enter the era of the tri-motor transports. In 1926 Imperial Airways introduced the AW Argosy three-engine, seven passengers, on its London-Paris service. The captain was positioned on the starboard side of the open cockpit. Not until the advent of the HP 42 and the large British flying-boats would the captain's position be on the left. The two pilots in the Argosy sat before an array of instruments and controls positioned and inserted at locations convenient to the designer. Typical of its time was the directly driven recording tachometer for the middle engine; the outer engine instruments were on the side of the nacelles. The top centre of the instrument panel was dominated by the Reid Control Indicator. This combined an ASI with lights to indicate rate of turn and angle of bank. It incorporated an air-driven gyro to detect the rate of a turn that was indicated by a row of lights. The indicator also included a mercury-in-glass clinometer that operated an arc of lights to indicate the angle of bank. Below the indicator and mounted on a projecting bracket was the magnetic compass.

The Achilles' heel of many air-driven instruments, such as the Reid Control Indicator, was the venturi tube that provided the suction to operate the gyro. This could be blocked by ice, thereby depriving the pilot of essential information; particularly as ice might be associated with turbulence and with no visible horizon on which to maintain straight and level flight. Another feature of the Argosy instrumentation was the altimeter. At that time many altimeters still indicated increasing height by the anti-clockwise movement of the needle.

Boeing, Fokker and Ford were among the tri-motor builders. The Boeing 80 was put into service with the company's own airline (Boeing Air Transport) having a completely enclosed cockpit. This assumed concession to the well-being of the pilots was not greeted by them with enthusiasm. The next version of the 80 had an open cockpit. Without reliable windscreen wipers and heated glass, pilots were averse to being completely enclosed. The frames of the cockpit enclosure and

A famous cockpit. The Junkers 52 3m. In this version the principal engine instruments for the three engines are on the main panel and the second pilot's position is equipped with the radio controls along with the trailing aerial winch. *John Stroud*

An unusual arrangement of the primary controls on one yoke. This is the cockpit of a three-engine Bloch 220 of 1938. *John Stroud*

Fokker XII of DDL. One of the first three-engine airliners to have all the engine instruments on the main panel. The flight instruments include a Sperry artificial horizon and gyro heading indicator as well as a turn and bank indicator. A British P type magnetic compass is mounted on the central controls pedestal. *Philip Jarrett* unwanted light reflected off the glazing made it difficult to 'eyeball' the landmarks used for navigation in the days when it depended on light beacons spaced along the airways. The open-cockpit version of the 80 was set higher than the enclosed type so that the pilots could see astern. Eventually all the Boeing 80s were given an enclosed pilots' position. Presumably the pilots had decided that despite its disadvantages they preferred to be protected from the sometimes fierce elements of the

Wibault trimotor of Air France c 1933. Three flight instruments in front of the captain and 12 engines, instruments neatly arranged on an engine-turned metal panel. *John Stroud*

mid-West and its freezing 'Blue Northerners' on the run from Chicago to San Francisco. With an operating ceiling not much above 15,000 ft they could not climb above the weather.

The Fokker VII's cockpit of 1930 had a typical array of instruments. The 'flight' instruments were concentrated on the centre of the main panel, and included ASI, turn-and-bank and altimeter, along with clinometers for fore-and-aft and cross levels.

The enclosed cockpit version of the Boeing 80. *Philip Jarrett*

The captain only had an altimeter and turn-and-bank in front of him. Only the instruments for rpm and oil temperature for the centre engine were in the cockpit. The outer engine instruments were mounted on the inboard side of each nacelle. However, the most important instrument for monitoring the health of each engine was its oil pressure. Therefore the three oil-pressure gauges were in a prominent position on the main instrument panel.

Fokker F VII. C 1931.The instruments for the centre engine are on the middle of the instrument panel. The indicators for the other two engines are on the inboard side of each nacelle. There are two clinometers: one for pitch, the other for lateral level. These plus an altimeter and airspeed indicator are the only flight instruments.
Philip Jarrett

Bloch 220 of 1938 with stepped nose derived from the example of American transports such as the DC-3. *John Stroud*

French airlines also continued to favour three engines in the 1930s. An illustration of the cockpit of a Wibault 283, for example, suggests that there were only three flight instruments. These were in front of the captain, and apparently they were all that he had to control the aircraft in adverse conditions and no visible horizon. The greater part of the instrument panel was taken up by the indicators, of which there were twelve, for the three engines. All were mounted on an aluminium panel with an engine-turned finish. There were two sets of three throttles on a small central pedestal, along with the elevator-trim wheels. As was customary in French aircraft, the throttles were pulled back for increased power. The absence of effective windscreen wipers and de-icing systems at the time is emphasized in the cockpit of the Bloch 220, because the glass in front of each pilot could be slid sideways to improve the view ahead in rain, sleet and snow! Of course, the pilots were also used to driving fast cars with the windscreen lowered in similar conditions.

HP 42

From personal experience, the cockpit of the HP 42 of Imperial Airways was the first introduction to the cockpit of an airliner. The many controls and instruments were fascinating; although the stately but wallowing progress among the hot summer thermals were not good for the stomach. The most outstanding feature was the two very large aileron wheels needed to multiply the pilot's muscle power when moving the control surfaces. There was no central controls pedestal as in other aircraft. Instead, a large bracket extended out from the instrument panel so as to bring the throttles and mixture controls back past the rims of the two big wheels. At the mock-up stage Imperial Airways specified that the bottom edge of the windscreen should be straight and not curved, and that the profile of the nose should fall away steeply so as not to be visible from the cockpit and thereby not reflect the sun into the pilots' eyes. The cockpit was certainly a room with a view, having large windows forward and to the sides. Unfortunately any ideas about the

HP 42 c 1930. The poor quality of the radio telephone required the pilots to wear close-fitting leather helmets to keep out the noise of the four engines and the rush of air through the many wires and struts. The flat-fronted fenestration and the rough finish to the cockpit structure were in keeping with the 80 knot cruising speed. The large aileron/elevator wheels were needed to overcome the heavy control loads. *Handley Page*

magnificence of the HP 42 were dispelled on visiting the cockpit of a DC-3. The HP 42, as seen in 1938, was very much a child of the 1920s, whereas the DC-3 was the precursor of the future.

HP 42 c. 1930. Engine instruments in front of second pilot. Airspeed indicator between forward windows and engine controls on a bracket extending back between the two pilots. Ignition switches for the four-engines on the overhead panel. Very few instruments on the captain's panel. Excellent fields-of-view through the large windows. At the outboard knee of each pilot is a P-type magnetic compass. *Handley Page*

Cockpit comments

In this era the cockpit and its equipment tended to be taken for granted or even ignored by writers. There are few comments even in the technical press on the position or suitability of instruments and controls. Of course, at the same time there were few, if any, publications to which they could refer for guidance. One example comes from a description of the ungainly AW Atlanta four-engined airliner put into service among the rival sleek, retractable-undercarriage machines:

Right across the front of the pilots' cabin . . . is a large instrument board with a wonderful array of instruments. Those which require constant observation are placed at the port end . . . under the eyes of the chief pilot, while those which need less frequent reading are in front . . . of the second pilot.

The obvious comment is: Why did the reporter not explain what was meant by 'wonderful'? Possibly they were so wonderful that words failed the writer, or he was being sarcastic.

Record-breaking cockpits

From 1913 to 1931 the races for the Schneider Trophy provided a focus for the efforts of designers to extract the maximum speed out of the available technology. By winning the 1931 event the RAF High Speed Flight's Supermarine S 6b secured the trophy outright for Britain at 340 mph. The cockpits of the S 6b seaplane and of its rival Macchi machines, as with those of the 1927 and 1929 events, closely confined the pilot. The top of the windscreen was only slightly above the top line of the fuselage. Forward visibility was limited, and the pilot was always at risk from hot oil and exhaust fumes. When taking off from the water the throttle had to be opened gradually to full power, otherwise the torque reaction from the fixed, coarse-pitch propeller could roll the aircraft right over. Some of the Trophy aircraft carried more fuel in the starboard float than in the other in order to counteract the torque effect. Banking to the left was easier than to the right. Starting with the first in 1913, all the events were run anti-clockwise. The Italians persisted with record breaking after 1931. In 1934 Agello in the twin tandem-engine Macchi MC 72 achieved 440 mph, thereby setting a record for seaplanes that has yet to be bettered. Eleven Italian test pilots were killed flying high-speed seaplanes. Many of the accidents were attributed to the cramped cockpits, aircraft control problems and poor forward view. The poor forward view with tail down in most single-engined aircraft was made worse in some cases because of the minimal windscreen. Notable examples were the Travel Air 'Mystery Ship' and the Granville GB racer. The restricted forward view, even after the tail came up, and poor longitudinal control made every take-off a hazardous adventure. Because they were designed primarily for circuit racing, such as the National Air Races, the instrumentation was minimal, with the engine parameters being the most important displays.

Lockheed Vega

As with the previous decade, the 1930s were a time of distance and altitude record attempts. Some succeeded, some failed. The Lockheed Vega was a typical shoulder-wing monoplane of the era. The cockpit was partly inside the leading edge of the wing so that the side windows were very small. In 1933 Wiley Post made his solo round-the-world flight in a Vega. A Sperry A2 autopilot was an essential item. From this year on more and more autopilot systems came into use, particularly in large transport aircraft.

Boeing 247

In 1932 Boeing used the technologies of both its B-9 bomber and Monomail to develop the 247; a low-wing, twin-engined monoplane. The instruments and controls of the 247D were typical of the era. However, compared with some of its contemporaries there was no flap lever to confuse with the undercarriage lever. The 247D was flapless and therefore its approach path was at an angle of about 3 degrees instead of the

Boeing 247 showing the forward raked vee shaped windscreen used to eliminate reflections onto the instruments. *Philip Jarrett*

Boeing 247 of 1933. Trademark Boeing wheels. The majority of the flight instruments are concentrated in the centre below the autopilot control panel. The controls pedestal includes a landing gear lever but no flap lever because the 247 was 'flapless'. *Philip Jarrett*

more usual 5-6 degrees of a fully flapped aircraft. This characteristic would eventually be of particular benefit when it was used for automatic landing system experiments in the late 1940s.

DH Comet

In 1934 a DH 88 twin-engined monoplane won the UK-Australia Race. The two pilots sat in a tandem glazed cockpit. The front pilot was given a full set of instruments and controls, including a large wheel for manually raising and lowering the undercarriage. The instruments were disposed in no particular order – but then, this was 1934. Both pilots had a an aperiodic magnetic compass. The centre of the front instrument panel was occupied by the very important artificial horizon and gyro heading indicator. The importance of these two instruments is emphasized in A.E. Clouston's report on a flight crossing the Alps in a DH 88. He mentions that no de-icers were fitted and that both the Sperry gyro artificial horizon and the gyro heading indicator depended on a pump driven by the port engine. With the pitot head iced up the ASI was useless, and the only way to maintain straight and level flight at 19,000 feet when flying over the jagged peaks was to concentrate on the Sperry instruments.

Curtiss Condor

Although Curtiss did not take the plunge and produce a monoplane, as had Boeing and Douglas, its twin-engined biplane Condor of 1933 had a fully enclosed cockpit of the stepped-nose type. A Sperry A1 electro-–hydraulic autopilot eased both the mental

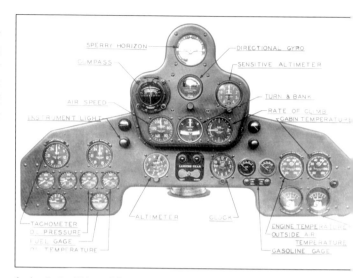

Curtiss Condor biplane airliner of 1933. The essential flight instruments are grouped for use by either pilot on the centre line of the cockpit. For its time the Condor had a comprehensive array of instruments as well as an autopilot. An interesting detail in a biplane transport is the landing gear indicator panel, bottom centre. *Curtiss Wright*

and physical strain of flying the routes of Eastern Air Transport (later Eastern Airlines) in turbulent winter weather.

DC-3

The DC-3 epitomized the all-metal, monoplane, twin-engined passenger aircraft of the mid-1930s. The DC-3 from the Douglas company set a design standard that would be emulated by other aircraft manufacturers. The side-by-side, two-pilot cockpit as part of the steeped nose style was equipped both for instrument flight (IFR) and for navigating the radio ranges that delineated the airways of the USA. A flap lever and undercarriage selector, along with engine and propeller controls, were concentrated on a pedestal between the pilots. The instruments were arranged in no particular order, and to our eyes they now appear crude. The Sperry autopilot control and instrument panel occupied the upper centre of the main panel; a position favoured for most American aircraft cockpits. Assan

The cockpit of a DC 3. There were many different arrangements of controls and instruments among the 11,000 DC 3s built between 1936 and 1946. This is a KLM aircraft.

Lockheed 10 Electra. One distinguishing feature is the unusually small engine control levers on the central pedestal below the Sperry autopilot control panel. Flight and other instruments are arranged in no apparent order related either to function or frequency of use. *Philip Jarrett*

Jordenoff's book *Through the Overcast*, which described in detail the instrumentation and navigation of an airliner, was written around the DC-3 because by then it made up a large percentage of American and of some European airline fleets. By 1941 more than 800 had been produced.

A design failing applicable to many transport aircraft in the 1920s and 1930s was the leaking windscreens. Even DC-3 pilots in their 'modern' aircraft had to put up with water dripping down the instrument panel. This problem was overcome when aircraft became pressurized. The windscreen of the Boeing 247D was of the reversed rake-type used on a number of aircraft types of this period because it eliminated reflections of light from within the cockpit. The records do not indicate whether or not it was less prone to leaking.

Above the weather

In 1931 Junkers tested a Ju 49 with a pressure cabin. The next year the cabin of a Farman experimental aircraft exploded at 30,000 ft, killing the pilot. TWA was determined to 'get above the weather', and in 1934 experimented with a DC-1 and a Northrop Gamma fitted with pressurized cabins. In 1939 Farman 2234 mailplanes with pressurized cabins flew at 25,000 ft on the South Atlantic crossings.

The Boeing 307 of 1938 was the first production, as opposed to experimental, passenger aircraft to be designed from the start to have a fuselage pressurized so as to give a cabin altitude of 8,000 ft when flying at 15,000 ft. A domed pressure bulkhead sealed off the rear of the cabin. At the cockpit the designers had the more difficult task of resolving the conflict between strength and the need to provide adequate arcs of vision for the pilots. To achieve this the twelve windows of the flight deck were blended into the rounded nose of the aircraft. Although it was a pressurized aircraft, there was nothing particularly special about the types and position of the instruments and controls, other than that Boeing did not provide separate sets of throttle levers outboard of each pilot as in its 314 flying-boat. The

By the middle of the 1930s the typical stepped civil transport aircraft nose had become the standard. Lockheed 10 Electra of 1937.
Philip Jarrett

The Boeing 307 Stratoliner. The blended lines of the cockpit windows reflected the structural demands of pressurization. *Philip Jarrett*

throttle, mixture, propeller and other engine controls were on a central pedestal. The Sperry autopilot control panel was on the central instrument panel with engine rpm and manifold pressure indicators above. As was often the case in American aircraft, the readings of pairs of engines were combined in a twin-pointer indicator. Pan Am, one of the principal operators of the 307, had its own preferred arrangements of controls and instruments, with flap and undercarriage position indicators above the top edge of the windscreen. The six flight instruments in front of each pilot were grouped on the top row, left to right: ASI, gyro heading indicator and artificial horizon and with sensitive altimeter, turn-and-bank and vertical speed below. This being

Latecoere 521 showing its two-level cockpit with the navigation compartment forward of the pilots' position. *John Stroud*

1938, the two pilots were assisted on the flight deck by a radio officer, a navigator and a flight engineer.

Boeing 314

Flight deck is a better descriptive term for the cockpit of this, for its time, very big four-engined flying-boat. A spacious deck was provided for the two pilots, flight engineer, navigator and radio operator. The instruments were grouped on the main panel by function. Both pilots had a full set of flight instruments. The centre part of the panel had the engine instruments forming a top row with the Sperry autopilot panel below. Because the flight engineer had a comprehensive array of instruments and controls, only the most essential were provided for the pilots. The pilots' throttle levers were mounted outboard of the seats so that there was no need for a central controls pedestal. The 314s operated by British Overseas Airways were given a 'British' look by installing a P-type aperiodic compass alongside the outboard knee of both pilots. A feature of many flying-boat cockpits were the pendent overhead throttle levers, such as in the Sikorsky 42.

Boeing 314 Four-engine flying boat. No central controls pedestal. Engine controls outboard of each pilot. The presence of a P type aperiodic compass on the left shows that this is one of the 314s operated by British Overseas Airways Corporation.
P Jarrett

Martin M 130 'Clipper' flying boat of 1935. The engine control levers, as with other types of flying boats, are pendent from the cockpit overhead.   *Philip Jarrett*

Ju 86

This twin-engined monoplane of 1934 had only one set of controls and instruments in the cockpit. The Ju 86 was available in two versions – as a ten-seater airliner or as a bomber. To give access to the forward bomb-aiming position, all instruments and controls were over to the left, and there was no provision for a second pilot; although in the civil version a seat was provided to the right of the pilot for a radio operator.

Rules and customs

Although not part of the cockpit instrumentation, nevertheless the view of the landing area and the circuit, along with any signals displayed on the ground, constitute part of the overall aircraft control environment. On both British civil and service aerodromes there were a number of standard signals available to the airfield controller. One of the most important when displayed indicated that the customary left-

Lockheed 14 c 1937. Compared with airliners of only five years before there are far more instruments. However, their arrangement, particularly the group in front of the captain, is not particularly well ordered. The primary flight instruments are concentrated on the centre panel above the controls and instruments of the Sperry autopilot. The engine and flight instruments mixed up in front of the second pilot are typical of the era. The elevator trim indicator and control are not positioned so as to relate to the movement of the elevator, whereas the rudder trim moves in the same sense as the required trim angle. *Lockheed*

hand circuit did not apply. Also of great importance were signs and apparatus designed to give a pilot an indication of wind direction. In this era crosswind landings were avoided whenever possible, and therefore full advantage was taken of the wide expanse of turf, allowing landings to be made directly into the wind from a number of different directions. By the mid-1930s civil air traffic had expanded to such an extent that positive control had to be exercised from the ground using R/T communication with aircraft. The UK's premier airport, Croydon, was designated within a QBI zone into which private aircraft were not allowed to fly unless equipped with radio. When QBI was in force this was indicated to non-radio-fitted aircraft by a large ground panel displayed at the eight airfields and a lighthouse that marked the boundary of the control zone. A different panel would be displayed when QBI did not apply.

CHAPTER FOUR

Military Cockpits 1919-1939

The end of the Great War (the First World War) came just as military aviation was about to enter a new phase. Aircraft performance was significantly better than in 1914 and the potential of the bomber had been proved. Higher fighting altitudes encouraged the development of oxygen systems, and the parachute was about to become a standard item of equipment. In Germany civil aviation was allowed but nothing pertaining to the development and warlike use of military aircraft was permitted under the terms of the Versailles Treaty.

The end of the war meant a sudden stop to aircraft production and to many research projects. Up to then both had had virtually unlimited resources, but in peacetime other matters took priority. Air forces had to make do with existing aircraft and equipment as much as possible. Therefore many

Bristol Fighter post war fitted with both ring and bead and Aldis sights for the single forward-firing Vickers/Maxim gun. *Philip Jarrett*

Vickers Vimy. Note the brass 'domestic' switches for the four ignition systems and the few instruments, of which only one, a clinometer, provides some indication of aircraft attitude. Bottom right is the throttle lever controlling both engines simultaneously. Turning the large knob on top of the lever applied differential engine control. *Vickers*

technological advances that might have been made, say, in 1919 or 1920, were delayed for another ten years. Of course, for aviation as a whole the sudden removal of Germany as a belligerent also eliminated an important source of aviation research and development. In consequence engine development in Germany was at a low level for the next few years. However, all-metal structures were advanced, particularly by Rohrbach and Junkers. Eventually the aviation industry was gradually built up again, and German cockpit equipment, such as instruments and radio, began to contribute to the overall technology of military aviation. By 1930 radio aids to navigation and landing were developed that would match the technology of the United States.

In 1927 the number of accidents, mostly fatal, incurred by the Royal Air Force prompted questions to be raised in the House of Commons. Members pressed the Air Minister to table the number of casualties. Lord Trenchard, the RAF Chief of Staff, however, was reluctant to give the minister the figures because he believed it would adversely affect the morale of the service pilots. Trenchard argued that pilots might relate the total hours they had flown to the accident rate per hours flown and thereby assume they were about to have an accident. Although the accident figures were not disclosed, nevertheless a start was made toward a greater use of what we now term human factors research. The Air Minister arranged for the appointment of a psychologist to the staff of the RAF's medical services. He was tasked to study:

Human factors in acquiring flying sense and skill in the order of their importance

Factors that foster the retention of flying skill under service conditions

Factors that react unfavourably from the point of view of bodily performance and temperament and which may be potential causes of accident

Cases of nervous breakdown.

So at last both the pilot and the cockpit were to be investigated along more scientific lines.

In the United States an even more ambitious programme of human factors

DH 9. Pilot well aft and sharing the view with numerous struts and wires as well as the engine and the gravity fuel tank under the upper wing. *Philip Jarrett*

research was instituted. This expanded over the years to meet the ever increasing demands on the human body and its faculties imposed by higher G forces and altitudes. It also embraced research into the ergonomics of instruments and controls.

Instrument developments in North America

In the United States after the First World War the air service had to fight hard for both new aircraft and equipment. In France during the war the American squadrons had usually used French and British equipment. De Havilland aircraft were built in the USA in the last year of the war. Therefore there was a strong European influence, which included cockpit equipment. Indigenous instrument development was slow. However, by the middle of the 1920s American instruments and other cockpit items were as advanced as those in Britain and France. Pioneer, Sperry and Kollsman were among instrument companies in the USA that devoted their resources to developing better cockpit equipment.

Radial engines

The rotary engine was eventually displaced by the radial, the former having reached the upper limit of power. The radial type would have entered service earlier with the Allied powers had there not been serious development problems to be overcome. Its importance to the history of the cockpit is the improvement it afforded the pilot, who no longer had to breath fumes laden with castor oil. The new breed of engines, both radial and in-line, developed, on average, 400 hp. They were more reliable than the earlier types. The lessons of war were applied to engine installation, and the fire-retarding bulkhead became a standard feature between cockpit and engine. 'Firewalling the throttle' in the USA meant 'full throttle'.

Keeping in touch

In the last year of war, cockpits in general had acquired more instruments and controls, and wireless apparatus was no longer an experiment and confined to artillery spotting tasks. The radio-telephone was in use and was about to become the principal means of communication between ground and air and between air and ground. No longer did interceptor pilots have to depend on visual ground-based signals, such as searchlights, white panels and arrows, or patterns of lights, to indicate the position of the enemy.

In 1919 RAF pilots started training in the use of R/T for formation flying and for reconnaissance reporting. In August of that year a radio-telephone link was demonstrated for the benefit of Members of Parliament between an RAF aircraft and the Palace of Westminster. However, RAF bombers were yet to be equipped with R/T as a squadron standard. In contrast, in 1921 Instone equipped its passenger aircraft with R/T for the London–Paris service.

For both W/T and R/T, headphones had to be worn; usually as part of some form of headgear. Helmets of cloth or leather were essential in open-cockpit flying. Various methods and materials were devised for keeping out unwanted noise because both W/T and R/T signals were not always easily discernible against the noise of engine and slipstream. However, not all military pilots wore a helmet designed to protect the head against injury in the event of a crash. In 1908 Lt Selfridge died from a fractured skull after the Wright aircraft in which he was a passenger crashed. In the First World War French pilots wore a helmet made of cork, rubber and metal stiffening. This gave some protection in the event of a crash. Photographs of German, British and American pilots suggest that the soft cloth or leather helmet was the preferred head protection. At flying schools in America in the First World War both instructors and pupils often wore a football helmet. Leather helmets continued in use up to and during the Second World War. With the increasing height at which military aircraft were designed to operate, helmets had to include an oxygen mask as well as a microphone.

Radio aids to navigation and landing advanced slowly in the 1920s. Although these were intended in the first place to improve the safety and regularity of civil airline operations, they were also applicable to air force operations. Both France and the air services of the USA kept their eyes on these developments, which in the next ten years were to make significant changes to cockpit equipment. In the late 1920s the four-course, radio range and radio navigational beacons were being introduced for airways in USA. Members of the air staff in the UK were interested, but with reservations, because they did not want an air force dependent on fixed ground systems, such as radio beams. Instead they encouraged the development of radio direction finding (DF). A DF set in those years had to be attended to by a radio operator and was not directly under the control of the pilot. In 1925 the first UK autopilot patent (Meredith & Cook) was granted, but it would be another ten years before RAF bomber aircraft cockpits were equipped with autopilot controls.

Irvin parachute

A major advance in safety came in 1919 when Leslie Irvin proved the effectiveness of his back-pack-type parachute. This had the now familiar D ring, which when pulled released the canopy from the pack. He made his first jump with the new parachute on 28 April 1919. The US Army Air Service was impressed and ordered three hundred. In July of the same year the air service evaluated the Calthrop Guardian Angel attached-type parachute. It was found to be unsuitable, and

even more so when the RAF officer demonstrating the parachute was killed because the harness became entangled with the aircraft and failed under the load.

Gun aiming

The ring-and-bead and the collimated Aldis sights continued in use after 1918. Although the former was less accurate than the Aldis, it had the advantage of maintaining the pilot's awareness of what was happening over a wide field of view. During the First World War, fighter pilots attempting to intercept bombers and airships at night were provided with illuminated sights, such as the Hutton and the Neame used by the RFC and RNAS. Aiming at night would continue to be a problem, even in the Second World War.

Although the optical, collimated reflector sight was available to the German air services in 1918, it remained only a possible alternative to the Aldis. In Britain in 1924, Barr & Stroud designed their GD1 reflector sight. This was evaluated in an Avro 504, but had a number of shortcomings. However, by 1927 the Barr & Stroud GD2B successfully completed its service trials, and thereafter the RAF used reflector sights as the principal aiming system. The GD5 sight of 1934 used the windscreen as the reflecting surface.

Perhaps the most important legacy of the First World War to all the world's air forces was the fuselage, synchronized, guns. These were still being mounted so as to be within reach of the pilot so that the stoppages to which they were prone could be dealt with. Similarly the gun triggers remained part of the control column.

Open or closed

The shape and position of the military aircraft cockpit remained for fifteen years very much as it had been in 1918. The enclosed pilot's place was rare. Attitude instrument development was slow, and the bubble-in-glass clinometer remained the primary indication of attitude in most aircraft for the next ten years. Pilots generally preferred to rely on the 'wind-on-the-cheek' as an indicator of side slip in a turn. Fighter pilots have always wanted to be able to see without obstruction in all directions, but the forward view from the cockpit of most biplanes had to be shared with that of the upper wing and its struts. Obviously the monoplane conferred a good all-round view for the pilot, but designers were reluctant to change from the wire-braced structure of the biplane to cantilever monoplane wings.

Even the pilots of single-seat monoplane aircraft were sometimes reluctant to be in a fully enclosed cockpit. For these reasons, a number of new monoplane fighters had open cockpits, even though others gained a reduction in drag by having an enclosed pilot's position. The pilot tradition of the need to 'feel the wind on the cheek' died hard, and there was always the possibility that lethal engine exhaust gas might gather in a completely enclosed cockpit.

In the 1920s there were only a few experimental aircraft with a completely enclosed pilot's place. Many pilots enjoyed driving fast cars, most of which were open topped, and so it was the macho thing to do the same in an aircraft. Pilots of those air forces that operated flying boats, such as the French and US navies and the RAF, had to suffer the effects of the spray thrown up when on the water. The open cockpits gave little protection against waves breaking over the bow or spray picked up by the propellers and blown forward when taxiing downwind.

Since the 1930s, fighter pilots of the more

Bristol Bulldog. Typical biplane fighter cockpit which positioned the pilot's eyes in line with the trailing edge of the upper wing. *Philip Jarrett*

advanced air forces have been directed through R/T towards their target by a controller on the ground. But in the 1920s a fighter pilot had limited guidance from the ground and therefore needed a good all-round view when searching for the enemy. The structural members of an enclosed cockpit sometimes limited a good all-round view. Another drawback to an enclosed position was the difficulty it presented when using arm signals to other pilots in a formation. The open cockpit of the 1928 Boeing P-12 biplane of the US Navy could be used to demonstrate a 'hands-off' characteristic of the aircraft. As one P-12 pilot commented, 'Poke your left hand out. She'll do a nice turn to the left.' This characteristic may have limited the use of hand signals! The open cockpit was retained for fighter and two-seater aircraft by most air forces well into the mid-1930s.

Cockpit design in the 1920s

Cockpit designers had to solve two basic and conflicting requirements. They had been present in the previous decade but had not been so critical. Firstly, they had to position cockpit equipment in such a way as to simplify the pilot's many tasks that had increased with the increase in aircraft systems and aircraft potential. Secondly, they wanted, as they always would, to simplify the mechanical linkages that connected cockpit controls to the different aircraft systems and equipment; such as throttle and mixture levers to the engine, fuel system control cocks and levers to the actual fuel cocks, and so on. As has often happened in cockpit design, practical considerations dictated compromises. For example, the primary flight controls of stick and rudder bar obviously had to be within reach of the pilot's hands and feet. However, other

Formation of Hawker Harts whose open cockpits facilitated the exchange of 'Zogging' hand signals in the days of uncertain R/T.
Philip Jarrett

Vickers Vimy bomber c 1919. Engine instruments are mounted on the inboard side of each nacelle. This method of simplifying pipework was used for many types of aircraft in the 1920s and 1930s. *Vickers*

controls were sometimes positioned in locations that required the pilot to reach and grope. Awkward control positions and operation were the result of the designer having to avoid expensive and complex control linkages. The increasing use of electrical systems provided some improvement in overall cockpit design. Electrical wiring cables could be laid round, through and across other items in order to reach the switches. Nevertheless, there were many examples of cockpits in which, according to contemporary writers, the switches had been 'thrown in' to land where they might.

Ignition switches

An important, perhaps the most important, electrical system is the ignition. In British aircraft the stereotype switch movement is up for 'on' and down for 'off'. This is opposite to a domestic light switch. The reason for the apparent anomaly is that the ignition switch does not directly 'switch on' the circuit. When the switch is up and therefore 'on' the connection to earth (ground) is cut. In the down 'off' position the self-contained magneto system is earthed (grounded) and therefore safe. Hence the 'Switches off?' call before the propeller is pulled round preparatory to starting the engine. This 'up' for 'on' has been applied to other electrical systems in both civil and military aircraft, and in at least one well-known make of car. However, in American and German aircraft in particular the ignition switches were usually grouped in one rotary selector switch that provided 'all off', 'left magneto on',' right magneto on', or 'both on'.

Following a number of crashes at RAF air-to-ground firing ranges, attention focused on the ignition switches. As a pilot pulled the aircraft up after diving on the target the engine would cut. Those pilots who survived found it hard to believe that they had moved the ignition switches at such a critical point.

Those who were killed never knew why. Fortunately, before there were more accidents, an investigator noticed out of the corner of his eye that as he pulled the aircraft out of the attack dive he saw the ignition switches move down and 'off'. The switches were being moved by the G force of the pull out.

Inviting trouble

Fuel system selectors in British aircraft were not usually arranged to avoid mistakes. They were often positioned away from the pilot's normal reach and in a dark and awkward corner of the cockpit. Sometimes a tank

Bulldog cockpit exposed. The spade grip with the two gun thumb triggers inherited from WWI. The instruments are scattered on each side of the magnetic compass. The bilges are in full view. On each side is a mounting for a Vickers guns (not installed). The ignition switches on the left are marked 'Off' and 'Run'. On the right is the starting magento switch and to its left the Kigas priming pump. The RPM indicator, top centre, is positioned so as to bring the cruising RPM value at 12 o'clock. There is no brake lever on the spade grip because there were no wheel brakes. *Philip Jarrett*

Pilots' Cockpit of Vickers "Vixen"
Military Two Seater.

Two-seat, multi-purpose Vickers Vixen c 1930. At the top of the instrument panel is a Reid, gyro-based, turn control indicator. Lights around the periphery and in a row below the integral airspeed indicator, show bank angle and rate of turn. *Vickers*

selector lever was arranged so that when it pointed to the left it operated the cock for the tank in the starboard wing. Fuel system mismanagement was often the cause of accidents. In the 1930s fuel tank contents gauging was rudimentary. Contents indicators, except the direct-reading liquid type when flying straight and level, were not very accurate or reliable.

In the majority of cockpits of the First World War the pilot's heels touched the floor and there were few hidden corners into which tools and rubbish could lurk. In the 1920s fuselages were deeper, because engines were bigger. This meant that there was often space beneath the pilot's feet and seat. The 'bilges' were in full view and ready to trap any dropped objects. Rubbish of all kinds remained below until negative G was applied. Then a rain of dried mud, lost screwdrivers, spanners and other odds and ends fell past the pilot's head. There were numerous incidents and accidents caused by loose objects fouling control cables, rods and levers. Occasionally a loose object would completely jam the controls. As the number of electrical circuits and switches increased in cockpits, there emerged the new hazard of spilt liquids, such as tea or coffee.

Since the earliest days of flight an essential drill before take-off was to check the control surfaces both for free movement and to ensure that they were moving in the expected direction. The histories of the world's air forces includes many examples of disasters caused by incorrectly rigged controls. Many accidents were caused by pilots failing to remove the control locks before taxiing out to take off. Control locks were necessary to prevent the control surfaces, such as rudder and elevator, from being banged about by the wind when the aircraft was parked. Regrettably control locks have always been a 'time bomb' waiting to destroy the careless pilot.

Instrument flight

When the RAF meteorological flights reformed after the First World War, its pilots still flew in cloud without the benefit of any specialized instrumentation. Essentially they had only an airspeed indicator, compass and cross-level clinometer with which to avoid 'falling out' of the clouds upside down in a 'graveyard' spiral At the time a number of gyro-based 'blind' flying instruments were under development; notably by the Royal Aircraft Establishment (RAE) and Reid in the UK, by Sperry and Pioneer in the USA, by Schilovsky-Cooke in Russia and by Drexler in Germany.

Gp Capt Haslam's recollections of 'met' flying, from RAF Andover in 1920–22, provide an insight into the typical cockpit of the era and the problems faced by pilots. He describes how he had to spend at least half an hour above the maximum 10,000 ft height then permitted for flying without oxygen equipment. The cockpits were open and the only heating was what came back from the

Sopwith Snipe in post-war colours and equipped with navigation lights and landing flares for night flying. *Philip Jarrett*

engine. In the Sopwith Snipe, with its air-cooled rotary engine, it was uncomfortably cold. Even in the Bristol Fighter, with its water-cooled engine, it was also cold in the cockpit. The main problem was more to keep the engine from getting too cold when descending from high altitude. He used to bring the nose of the aircraft well up and fly nearly stalled on a quarter-throttle. This technique kept the engine warm and a rate of descent about the same as that of a normal glide. With no heated clothing provided (presumably because of a lack of electrical power), his hands became so cold that writing down meteorological observations was difficult.

Another problem recalled by Haslam and typical of the RAF of those years, was the lack of radio communication with the ground from which to obtain navigational assistance. With little time in which to spare from controlling the aircraft and recording observations and knowing only the wind speed and direction that had existed on the ground at the start of the flight, the pilot had to apply careful mental dead reckoning calculations which would ensure a safe descent down through cloud and close to the airfield.

Instrument development

In the United States after the First World War the reaction against war stifled the fledgling air services of the US Army. This meant that at first cockpit equipment and instrument development was slow. However, by the end of the 1920s American instrument technology had made significant advances.

In 1929, Kollsman, Pioneer and Sperry instruments enabled Lt Doolittle to take off, complete a circuit of the airfield and land his aircraft back at the starting point without being able to see out of the cockpit. From the special set of instruments developed for that important flight in the history of flying evolved a succession of better and better 'blind flying' instruments. Parallel work in Britain, notably by W.E.P Johnston and Reid and Sigrist, who developed the turn-and-bank indicator, led eventually to the RAF's Basic Six instrument panel, which included a Sperry artificial horizon and gyro heading indicator in addition to the altimeter, airspeed, turn-and-slip and vertical speed indicators. In the first four decades of British aviation the vertical speed indicator was usually referred to as the Rate-of-Climb. Similar developments in France and Germany added to the fund of 'instrument' knowledge.

Dive-bombing

There often appeared to be little relationship between the operational requirements of air forces and the intellectual exercises of the innovators. Throughout the 1920s and 1930s patent applications for weapon, bomb and torpedo aiming proliferated. Many of these bore little relationship to the real world of military flying. The inaccuracies associated with bombing from level flight encouraged the development of the dive-bombing technique, which in turn required a good view over the nose of single-engined aircraft and dedicated aiming sights.

Approaching the stratosphere

On 27 February 1920 Maj Schroeder of the US Air Service became the first man to exceed a height of 30,000 ft in an aircraft. The flight is also of significance to the history of the cockpit because the aircraft's engine was turbo-supercharged. From that flight onwards turbo-supercharging, using the engine exhaust, was advanced in the USA year by year, with the result that flight at altitudes above 30,000 ft became the accepted design requirement for many American military aircraft. As we have seen in the First World War, although the machine might survive at extreme altitudes, the pilot had to be protected from both the extreme cold and the rarefied air. The development of life support equipment became as important as the development of engines able to maintain their power at high altitudes.

Other influences

Although the arrangement and equipment of the average military aircraft cockpit of the 1920s exhibited numerous faults and shortcomings, including the lack of consideration given by designers to the needs of the human occupant, nevertheless it reflected the standards of the time. For example, neither the automobile nor the ship had control positions based on sound ergonomic design standards. In other forms of transport and in industry as a whole, particularly in process and manufacturing plants, control positions were little removed from the poor standards of Victorian times. At the majority of control positions at sea, on land, in mines and in production plants, drivers and operators were expected to stretch and wrestle with badly designed controls and share their view of the instruments with machinery and clouds of steam and gases. These, to us, generally unacceptable control interfaces were not deliberate actions on the part of designers and management. Few knew any better. We have to remember that our modern sciences of human factors and ergonomics were virtually unknown outside a narrow circle of academics. Pilots, therefore, did not expect anything better, and designers were often not aware of the problems or the alternatives.

1930-1939

The decade before the Second World War might be called the 'march back to war'. It was also the decade in which the all-metal monoplane came to dominate the thoughts of the different air staffs among the potential warring nations. It was also the decade when the multi-engined bomber superseded the single-engined. These were the years when increasing speed encouraged greater enclosure of crew positions and powered gun mountings. Of course, the change from the two-cockpit, single-engined, 'multi-role

combat' biplane did not happen overnight. The twin restraints of limited money and a conservative approach to new technologies, particularly in Britain, resulted in the retention of the biplane for both fighters and bombers long after its 'use-by' date. At the same time cockpit equipment changed little, and then only slowly from existing type to new type of aircraft.

What of the terms 'fighter' and 'bomber' in relation to the cockpit? The former is usually used for an aircraft whose primary function is the destruction of the enemy's aircraft in

Right: Handley Page Heyford bomber c 1933. Single pilot's position on the left and with a gangway forward to the bomb-aiming position. The butt of a Very pistol can be seen on the extreme right of the instrument panel and with a row of holes above for stowing the cartridges. *Philip Jarrett*

Below: 15 Years after the end of WWI and the two pilots of the RAF's latest bomber, the Heyford, enjoy a splendid all round view from their open cockpit. *Philip Jarrett*

the air. The latter usually applies to an aircraft used for destroying the enemy's ground-based resources. Air staff specifications and the ingenuity of designers have produced many aircraft types able to perform a number of different tasks. This is why it may be better, when discussing cockpits, to classify aircraft under the following:

Having only one, single seat cockpit

Having one or more single-seat cockpits in tandem

Having pilots' cockpits and crew positions connected by a gangway or crawlway

Having only one, two-seat, side-by-side cockpit.

The proposed classification is independent of the number of engines. The US Army Air Corps in the 1930s operated a number of bombers in which there were single-seat isolated cockpits, the twin-engined Boeing and Martin bombers, for example. In the late 1930s there were some French bombers with two separated pilots' positions. Presumably, they were set apart to improve survivability in the event of damage by enemy action.

Boeing F4B-4. Toe-operated brakes. Vertical tube on the right provides a simple fuel contents indicator. On each side of the instrument panel are the mountings for the forward-firing guns. note that the only 'blind' flight instrument as such is the turn and bank indicator in the middle of the panel. Otherwise it was 'needle, ball and airspeed' when in cloud. *Philip Jarrett*

Typical US Navy biplane fighter of the 1930s. The Boeing F4B-4. Despite the disadvantages of an open cockpit many pilots preferred them to being enclosed. *Philip Jarrett*

Martin 139 bomber of the Netherlands East Indies. The second pilot/navigator sat in tandem with the first pilot. *Philip Jarrett*

The designer's convenience

As in the previous decade, placing equipment where it was convenient to the designer rather than in the best position for the pilot continued to be a common feature, particularly in British aircraft. The fact that the pilot had to contort and stretch his limbs in order to reach and operate a particular lever or switch was of secondary consideration.

The convenience of the designer and the lack of other than a superficial understanding of what we now know as ergonomics contributed to some appalling cockpits. The RAF was particularly cursed by this failing, and had to operate a number of aircraft types with badly arranged cockpits. German aircraft of the 1930s usually had a better detailed design of instruments and controls, but the overall arrangement often sacrificed good instrument positions to the need by the pilot for wide forward and downward views. American cockpits of the era were little better. However, the greater use of electrically operated systems contributed to tidier cockpits. Electrical wiring could be arranged to go round corners more easily than pipes and rods and cables, and therefore the designer could group the various switches.

Fury

In the mid 1930s the RAF's first-line fighter technology and its cockpits in general were represented by the Hawker Fury II biplane with only two guns. The instruments and equipment of the Fury II cockpit were not much in advance of those in the cockpits of

Instrument panel of Hawker Hart c 1939 with P type magnetic compass between the pilot's legs. If a spanner or other object were dropped it could be lost underneath the heel trays to reappear during aerobatics. *Philip Jarrett*

1918. The Fury II, spanning the years from 1918 to 1936, combined the old with the new. The 'old' parts of the open cockpit with a diminutive windscreen descended directly from fighters of the First World War. It perpetuated the twin synchronized Vickers 7.7 mm gun arrangement of its predecessors, with the gun breeches accessible to the pilot so that he could deal with stoppages. At the tip of the pointed propeller spinner there was the 'dog' into which engaged the driving shaft of the Hucks starter. In 1936 electric starter motors were a luxury. The mechanics could also use hand starting-cranks at each side of the engine. The starting procedure made it difficult to achieve a 'scramble' take-off.

Specification F14/32, to which the Fury was designed, demanded both speed and a good rate of climb, and so endurance had to be sacrificed. With a range of only 300 miles from its 50 gallons of fuel the Fury had a limited radius of action. In 1936 fighter tactics were still pre-radar. The defence of London, for example, depended on visual and aural tracking of enemy bombers from the ground. The target aircraft had to be spotted visually by the pilot, and therefore he preferred an open to a closed cockpit. The Fury II took nearly ten minutes to reach 20,000 feet. In that time an attacker could advance thirty miles. With only a small speed margin over a typical bomber a stern chase was unlikely to succeed. This factor and the performance and the difficulties of controlling fighters in general during air exercises forced the development of radar. It also presaged the time when interceptor fighters would be integrated completely with the information and control net.

Avro Anson trainer and ocean reconnaissance aircraft with the typical pilot-on-left, with gangway to the right, layout used for the majority of RAF multi-engine aircraft from 1930 onward. *Smiths Group Archives*

Significant items of equipment missing on a Fury in 1936 were navigation lights and landing lamps. Night-flying was not a major part of a Fury pilot's life. When the aircraft was conceived in 1929 electrical systems were limited in capacity and few single-engined aircraft had engine-driven generators. Therefore they were not equipped for flying at night; having neither wingtip and tail lights nor cockpit instrument lighting. In 1938 some squadrons of the RAF's Fighter Command consisted of Furies. At the time of the Munich Crisis, when war seemed a strong possibility, only a few were fitted with navigation lights, and bicycle lamps were adapted to serve as cockpit lighting.

Anson

The RAF's principal maritime patrol aircraft prior to the Second World War, other than flying-boats, was the Avro Anson. It was slow (cruising at 140 knots), 'short legged' and had a limited offensive load. It was docile and could be flown solo. However, raising the wheels required 140 turns of a crank handle mounted on the side of the central controls pedestal. Therefore another pilot, crew member or a passenger was always welcome as 'undercarriage operative'. The pilot's seat up front, on the left, was not separated from the cabin. This made for a sociable arrangement. The ignition switches were mounted high up on the windscreen framing.

Blenheim

The Blenheim's cockpit equipment, and particularly the positions of the controls, provides an another example of a design office arranging the cocks, plungers and other controls to suit the mechanisms rather than positioning them in accordance with the pilot's tasks, particularly in difficult situations.

The following comments are extracted from a report by H A Taylor, a test and ferry pilot:

The Blenheim was a hot affair and quite a few pilots had been killed through lack of understanding of engine-failure handling techniques. But, once mastered, it was a beautiful aeroplane to fly in, and in the Mark I version the pilot sat on a kind of dais in a glasshouse; he could see ahead, below, and nearly all round him except where the two engines sprouted out of the wing.

When, in my turn, I had been shown round the Blenheim's complicated control cabin, the instructor airily waved me into the left-hand seat and settled himself beside me in a seat where the dual instruction arrangements were, to say the least of it, somewhat primitive. Did the instructor know that I'd never flown anything like this before? He did. 'There is nothing to it', he said, and began to go through the engine-starting drill. 'I'll do a circuit first and then you can have a try.'

Ten minutes later he had folded his arms in his lap while I went through the take-off drill with the Blenheim sitting across wind at the leeward end of one of Upavon's two small grass airfields. I had already learned the the basic mnemonics by which instructors taught their pupils to essential actions. For take-off the letters were HTMPFG – which I remembered by muttering 'hot-tempered Member of Parliament flaps his gills' – and for the final approach they were HUMPFG, or just HUMP. Hydraulics, trimmers (and throttle tighteners), mixture, pitch, flaps (and fuel cocks), and cooling gills (or shutters): these were the essential things on take-off; the 'U' in the mnemonic stood, importantly enough, for 'undercarriage'.

The Blenheim had a pretty odd control layout. On his right the pilot had three handled plungers – rather like the things used in old-fashioned lavatories – and these were pulled up or pushed down according to requirements. That at the rear was a master hydraulic control, providing pressure to the main systems or to the retractable dorsal gun turret; the other two operated the undercarriage and flaps. The mixture controls beside the throttles on the pilot's left had three positions – automatic weak, rich and, dramatically enough, take-off override. The two-pitch propellers were controlled by a couple of fore-and-aft moving plungers in a panel on the left, and behind the pilot: with them (protected by a lid) were similar plungers to operate the engine cut-outs. The cooling gills were operated mechanically by a handwheel.

Botha

The RAF's Botha torpedo-bomber of 1938, named after a onetime enemy general, had some very hostile characteristics. Not the least was zero one-engine performance. Adding to the bad reputation it gained in the RAF were the controls. One particular item in the Pilot's Notes for the Botha I sums up the general design philosophy applied to the cockpit: 'The pilot cannot reach or see the fuel cocks. . .'. If the cocks were not set to the 'on' position before strapping in then it was possible to start up, taxi and take-off. About ten minutes later, sometimes even earlier, when the small amount of fuel in the collector tank was used up, both engines would stop. An ominous item in the Notes states: 'If one engine fails immediately after take-off make no attempt to remain in the air.' The arrangement of the controls was designed for a three-handed pilot. Indicative of a designed-in hazard is the instruction: 'Take care not to raise the flaps by mistake when raising the undercarriage.' Both flaps and undercarriage were selected by a common 'gear' lever. With the right hand on the lever and the left on the elevator trim there was no hand on the control column.

Rudder and elevator trim wheels were on the left of the seat. The small rudder trim wheel rotated fore and aft and therefore did not move in the same sense as the rudder. The controls for the undercarriage, flaps and gills were on the throttle pedestal at the pilot's right hand. The layout of the instruments was about par for the course in 1938.

Hudson

The decision in 1938 to order a military version of the Lockheed 14 airliner ensured that RAF Coastal Command had a replacement for the Anson, should the expected war with Germany start within a year or two. The Hudson's cockpit was different in many respects from those of existing RAF aircraft. To start with there were far more instruments, levers and switches. Selected pilots who would become instructors were seconded to British Airways as co-pilots on Lockheed 14s, which cruised 60 knots faster than the Anson. The pilot's gun predilection for many of the RAF's multi-engined aircraft, such as the Hampden and the Anson, was carried over to the Hudson. There were two fixed 7.7 mm Browning machine-guns mounted in the nose above the navigator's compartment. The arming pull handles were located in the middle of the instrument panel coaming and the gun button was on the control column wheel.

The instrument layout on the main panel was typically American, which meant that the flight instruments were not arranged in accordance with the RAF Basic Six. Every now and then a design office came up with something unusual for the cockpit. Lockheed provided the Hudson with differential brake operation through the rudder pedals. However, toe pressure did not apply the degree of brake pressure. This was selected through a long lever that could be pulled back out of the base of the central control pedestal to give different amounts of braking. When taxiing the pilot had to operate the throttles by reaching across to the right with the left hand. The right hand was used to vary the degree of braking.

At this time pilots had to be wary of the trap set by the differences in operation and position of controls among the different types of aircraft. For example, in those squadrons converting from Ansons the elevator trim crank handle moved in the opposite sense to that in the Hudson. If a Hudson pilot inadvertently wound on 'nose up' before take-off, by reverting to the Anson drill, the aircraft would rear up after lifting off and stall. Further descriptions and comments on the Hudson are in the next chapter.

More complications

From about 1934 onwards air forces in general stared to re-equip with metal-clad monoplanes. The German Luftwaffe, only a year old, introduced a number of aircraft types that were far in advance of those of other countries. In doing so it spurred the development of better aircraft and aircraft equipment in Britain and France. The RAF had to get rid of its fabric-covered biplanes and replace them with monoplanes having controllable-pitch propellers, flaps and retractable undercarriages.

The new-generation cockpits were distinguished by the greater number of engine and systems controls. British engines at this time were being provided with automatic boost and mixture controls. These simplified the pilot's task; particularly in fighters, when the pilot did not want to be distracted in combat by the need to watch the boost (manifold pressure) gauge or have to adjust the mixture control. One of the most distinguishing differences between British and American cockpits was the former's use of levers and wheels to select or operate

systems and the latter's greater number of switches because of the American preference for electrically operated systems. It so happened that in the 1930s, and even in the 1940s, British aircraft were handicapped by the absence of a good supply of electrical power.

Spitfire

The Spitfire, which entered squadron service in 1938, represented the pinnacle of British aircraft design. Outwardly the Spitfire was a clean and graceful monoplane fighter armed with eight machine-guns. It had none of the discontinuities of line of its potential foe, the Bf 109. Had the war started in October 1938, as it might have, Spitfire pilots would

Mk I Spitfire. A shortage of reflector sights in 1938 meant that a ring and bead sight has had to be fitted. The large black lever on the right is for the hand-operated pump for raising and extending the undercarriage and flaps. This required the pilot to change hands on the controls after take-off. Subsequent versions of the Spitfire had a better arrangement. *Vickers*

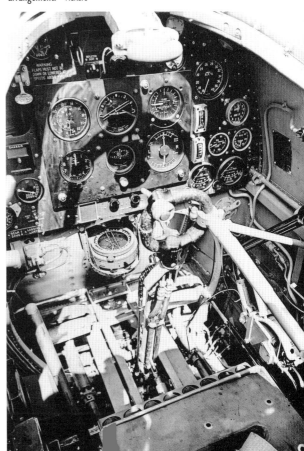

have had to make do with the old ring-and-bead sight because there were not enough reflector sights available. As with electrical power in British aircraft, sufficient hydraulic power was not available for raising the undercarriage. Therefore, on take-off the pilot had to move the left hand from the throttle to the control column and move the right hand to a long lever in order to manually pump up the undercarriage. An even more important item missing from the cockpit was a lever alongside the throttle for adjusting pitch, for the simple reason that the aircraft only had a fixed-pitch, two-bladed propeller. The result was a long take-off run and an undulating climb-out as the undercarriage pumping lever was moved to and fro. Possibly the absence of too many adverse comments about the cockpit might

be attributed to the fact that if you had been flying a Gladiator or Fury, for example, the exhilarating performance of the Spitfire made dealing with the awkward controls worthwhile.

Instruments for war

Flying military aircraft at night, in cloud or fog was avoided as much as possible by most air forces in the 1930s. It was dangerous and therefore cost lives and money. The RAF had to face up to the possibility of war in the coming ten years. Every year on from 1930 reduced the margin between preparing for war and being at war. The force had to be able to operate irrespective of the weather and the visibility. However, in 1937 only eighty-four bomber pilots had a night-flying qualification endorsement stamp in their

Bristol Blenheim Mk I (short nose). It appears neat and tidy but in practice many of the controls were difficult to reach and operate. *British Aerospace*

Gloster Gladiator biplane fighter. This is the 'Sea' version but is virtually standard with all Gladiators c 1939. Open 'bilges', aperiodic compass between the pilot's feet and an RAF Basic Six instrument panel. *Shuttleworth.*

logbooks. The annual total of flying hours for the bomber squadrons was about 140,000, of which only about 10,000 were at night. Instrument-flying training was essential for all pilots, and not just for a few. Even as late as 1939 RAF pilots were classified as either able to fly in cloud or prohibited from doing so.

A telling caveat can be found in the proceedings of a court martial following the crash of a Blenheim after the pilot lost control in cloud. 'Until modifications have been made, the Blenheim is not considered suitable for casual cloud flying.' Of course the Blenheim was intended to be flown in 'casual' cloud as well as in the clear. Therefore we might assume that a combination of lack of instrument flight training and the unsatisfactory arrangement of the controls contributed to the pilot's difficulties. Presumably the Luftwaffe planning staff at the time took careful note of this weakness.

Before about 1935 each type of aircraft in the RAF had its own unique arrangement of the instruments. Few were fitted with an artificial horizon. As mentioned, the decision was taken to standardize on a common blind-flying panel for all but the elementary trainers. This became the RAF Basic Six. The six instruments were disposed from left to right in two rows – ASI, gyro artificial horizon and vertical speed in the top row, altimeter, directional gyro heading indicator and turn-and-slip indicator in the bottom row.

An essential instrument for navigation was the magnetic compass. This had been part of the cockpit for all types of aircraft from about 1914 onwards. When a search was made through a pile of cockpit photographs, those belonging to the RAF were easily identified by the large P-type aperiodic magnetic compass. It had to be used with care because it was subject to many different errors. It could also be misused when selecting a new course, so that 'red was set on black'. This referred to North (360°), red, and South (180°), black, on the rotating grid ring of the compass. If not

One of the most distinguishing features of RAF cockpits prior to about 1945 was the P Type aperiodic magnetic compass used in conjunction with the Sperry Directional Gyro Indicator for maintaining the required heading. *Smiths Group*

detected, the aircraft would be flown on the reciprocal of the intended heading. In other words the compass was designed with a built-in error-inducing feature. Not until far too many RAF aircraft were lost in the sea or crashed into mountains, because they were being flown on a course 180 opposite to that intended, were changes made to the design of the P-type compass.

Cockpit drills

In the simple biplane-era cockpits there few controls and instruments. Cockpit checks could be verified by simple mnemonics. With the new generation of aircraft having more controls it was essential that pilots should sit blindfolded in the cockpit and practise reaching for the correct control. The general lack of attention by designers to even rudimentary ergonomic principles made such drills very necessary. Adding to the need for such drills were the differences between the cockpit ideas of one manufacturer and those of others. There was no such thing as the standard arrangement of controls and instruments for fighter, bomber, flying-boat or transport aircraft. In the RAF the only thing of importance that was common to all except elementary training aircraft was the Basic Six blind-flying panel. In some ways British cockpits may have appeared old fashioned compared with American. But in the dark, in smoke or blinded by searchlights it was often easier to feel for a lever or wheel rather than one of a number of similar switches or buttons.

Training cockpits

When specialized ab initio training aircraft were being considered a choice had to be made between tandem and side-by-side seating. The RAF preferred the tandem arrangement of the DH Tiger Moth; although one or two schools operated the Blackburn B-1 side-by-side trainers.

In 1939 the RAF received two new single-engined trainer aircraft, the NA 16 Harvard and the Miles Master. The former had

Avro Tutor with brass 'domestic' double ignition switch, starting magneto switch and the then new turn and slip indicator alongside a fore-and-aft clinometer. The mouthpiece of the Gosport tube to the rear cockpit is on the right. This is representative of British trainer cockpits c 1930. *British Aerospace*

American-type instruments and arrangement of the flight instruments, whereas the latter was equipped with the Basic Six blind-flying panel. The Master also had an unusual, for its time, but commendable concentration of throttle, mixture, propeller, undercarriage, landing lamp, rudder trim and flap controls in one neat unit. On gaining his wings on a Master an RAF pilot might move to the cockpit of a Spitfire or a Hurricane and find a far less ordered disposition of the controls. Until the Airspeed Oxford arrived at training schools in 1938, RAF pupil pilots had to learn how to handle multi-engined aircraft in two steps, from a single-engined elementary trainer via the docile Anson to such

comparatively complicated and large aircraft as the Blenheim, Wellington, Hudson or Hampden.

Take aim

The ring-and-bead and the Aldis optical sights remained in use right up to the start of the Second World War; particularly in aircraft of the US Navy. In Europe the collimated reflector sight superseded the older sights. It is said that when General Milch of the Luftwaffe made an official visit to RAF Hornchurch in 1937 attempts were made to prevent him noting that the range adjustment scale at the base of the reflector sights in the Gladiator fighters was marked

Another open cockpit biplane fighter that went on to serve in the Second World War, the Fiat CR 32. *Philip Jarrett*

He 111, Ju 88 and Do 18.

An important development in the mid-1930s was effective gaseous oxygen systems with face masks attached to the helmet. The US Army Air Corps system had a 'rebreather' bag, which conserved oxygen, inserted in the supply pipe to the face mask. In this period experiments continued with pressure cabins for flight in the stratosphere. In the USA the Air Corps flew the XC-35, a pressurized version of the Lockheed 10E, to above 30,000 ft. The crew did not have to wear oxygen masks. This and other similar experiments presaged the time when the air war would be fought at extreme altitudes.

Towards all-out war

Monoplanes with enclosed cockpits clashed with open-cockpit biplanes as Germany, Italy and Russia became involved directly or indirectly in the Spanish Civil War. The lessons learnt emphasized the need in the future for all-metal monoplanes, enclosed cockpits and radios that provided a continuous and effective link between the pilot and other pilots and with controllers on the ground.

CHAPTER FIVE

The Big Three of 1939

The three air forces, British, French and German, that fought for the skies over Europe in the first nine months of the Second World War exhibited marked differences in cockpit equipment. Together their cockpits provided an important milestone in aviation history, one that marks the decline of the First World War ideas and equipment.

Most of the equipment and operational practices, both inside and outside the cockpit, at the beginning of the Second World War would not have been strange or unfamiliar to a First World War pilot. Of course the number of instruments had increased tenfold. Most still presented their information in the shape of pointers moving over numeric scales. There were also more switches because of the greater number of electrical circuits. Nevertheless, in general and with the notable exception of radar, cockpit technology was essentially similar to that of the earlier war. In the inter-war years, especially in the USA and in the UK, cockpit design had progressed by a series of evolutionary steps as improved technologies became available. Each new generation of pilots, a generation being about five years, learnt to fly in biplanes whose design reflected the standards of ten or twenty years earlier. They then progressed to monoplanes, whose performance and abilities demanded enclosed cockpits, retractable undercarriages and variable-pitch propellers and, most importantly, instruments that permitted flight when the horizon was invisible.

The interface

Two aspects of a cockpit are important when describing its equipment and the tasks of the crew. Firstly, some instruments had to be interpreted in order to obtain the required information. This included applying

The cockpit of a Spitfire c 1940. Points of interest are: the two-position rudder pedals, the typical P4 aperiodic compass between the pilot's feet, the RAF Basic Six arrangement of the flight instruments and the knurled ring on the cross tube for mounting the reflector sight. *Vickers*

correcting factors in order to obtain a 'true' reading. The reading of the magnetic compass, for example, had to be corrected first for deviation and then for variation, and the airspeed indicator reading adjusted to take account of the aircraft's altitude. In turn the indication of the altimeter had to be corrected for outside air temperature. Secondly, engine control and monitoring was often without the benefit of automatic systems. For example, American engines, even in some fighters, were not, in general, equipped with automatic boost and mixture controls. This meant that the pilot had to watch the engine instruments carefully when making large throttle movements. In contrast, British and German engines were given more comprehensive automatic controls. These relieved the pilot of the need to constantly monitor engine indications, particularly when concentrating on a target or during an aerial battle. For example, later versions of the Spitfire even had the propeller's pitch control linked to the throttle.

Today we are used to the concept of having integrated systems, with at least some built-in intelligence, throughout an aircraft, so that they can perform their functions without frequent human intervention. They are also expected to have built-in test (BIT) and self monitoring. In 1939 such features were virtually unknown within the present meaning of those terms.

In the Second World War there were times during a sortie or patrol when a pilot might decide on, reach for and start a series of control actions, such as (according to the book) close valve A, shut valve B and open valve C. Those controls might not have been arranged in a logical and foolproof order. If the pilot was not stressed or fatigued and had plenty of time, any poor ergonomics could be overcome. But in an emergency or sudden change of circumstances, such as the enemy reacting violently, the wrong control selection might be made or an instrument reading incorrectly interpreted. The ergonomics of the cockpit had to recognize the worst scenario. However, to use the word ergonomics in a 1940s setting is of course nonsense. Neither the word nor our modern disciplines of ergonomics and human factors were widely available at the time.

A common feature of cockpit design in this period was the lack of standardization of the principal components. Important items might be on the left in one type of aircraft and on the right in another: some might be in front of the pilot, others behind his elbow. Standardization (or commonality, as it is now commonly called) was not part of the aviation vocabulary in some drawing offices. Occasionally someone, usually a pilot, argued for the maximum standardization of the type and position of controls and instruments. Given time and no distracting events, such as sudden engine failure, a pilot in an unfamiliar cockpit might have been able to make the correct control selections. The extent to which variations among different aircraft types contributed to errors on the part of pilots is not recorded. Courts of Inquiry had ready access to a 'PILOT ERROR' rubber stamp.

When cockpits for this book and earlier books were being researched, major differences of opinion came to light. This was the tendency for aviation writers, who were not necessarily pilots, to describe the instruments and controls of a particular aircraft as being arranged in 'a logical order', or similar words, whereas many of the reports by experienced pilots were critical of both instrument panel layouts and the position of controls. The primary flight instruments in the RAF of this era were often arranged as the 'Basic Six' because this improved the pilot's scanning task when flying on instruments. In the USA the primary flight and engine instruments were often mixed together. Perhaps the differences of opinion related to whether an arrangement was adopted because it conformed to the sequence in which controls and instruments were operated and scanned, or whether an attempt was made to 'tidy up' the cockpit and group controls and instruments by function or phase of flight.

Despite articles and letters in the UK technical press from pilots complaining about cockpits in general and in particular, design offices either ignored them or, under the pressure of war, could do little to effect improvements. Gordon White, an RAF pilot, proposed that all controls and instruments be arranged in logical orders and groupings. He argued that controls and their associated instruments be so disposed that for every phase of flight, particularly the take-off sequence or drill, the pilot's actions would be in the correct sequence. He further proposed that there be a greater use of colour so as to differentiate one group from another. He also advocated, as had many others, that for every class of aircraft there should be a standard arrangement of the controls and instruments irrespective of manufacturer. It would take at least another thirty years before such an ideal was achieved, and then only for the primary flight instruments. The editor of *Flight* magazine decided that the subject was of such importance that colour, rarely used at the time, was applied to highlight the text and illustrations of White's article.

Throttles

Perhaps one of the greatest variations of design in multi-engined aircraft was to be found among the throttles and other engine-control levers. There were examples of throttles to the left and to the right of the pilot. The B-17 and the B-24 had the throttles on a central pedestal, whereas each of the two pilots in a B-29 had a set of engine-control levers to his outboard side.

(The throttle-like levers on a pedestal close to the centre line of a B-29 flight deck were the brake-control levers). American flying-boat flight decks usually had pendent throttles on the overhead between the two pilots. Pendent engine controls were also applied to the Avro York four-engined transport. In German multi-engined aircraft the engine controls were more often to found to the left of the pilot. Some types of British aircraft had them to the left, and others on a central controls pedestal, as in a civil airliner.

Throttle movement

It is interesting to note the French, Italian and Polish preference for the throttle movement of pull back for increased power. The reason for this preference may lie with 'steam' engineering, in which the

A tangle of plumbing and wires in a Breguet 693. Note the throttles are fully forward in the closed position. This reverse arrangement applied to most French and Italian military aircraft until after WWII. *Aeroplane Monthly*

The right-hand side of a Breguet 693 cockpit. *Aeroplane Monthly*

internationally accepted stereotype requires a wheel or lever to move or rotate counter-clockwise for opening. This applied to the throttle when mounted on the left side of a cockpit and as seen by the pilot. However, it could have fatal consequences when pilots of other nations attempted to fly French and Italian aircraft. In 1940 a number of American aircraft, such as DB7s (Bostons) and Curtiss Hawk 75As, originally intended for the French air force, were acquired for the RAF. An important modification was the reversal of the throttle movement. Incidentally, there appear to be no references in reports by Douglas and Curtiss test pilots on these 'wrong way' throttles. Apparently some Hurricane Mk XIs intended as trainers for the USAAF had pull-to-open throttles. The reason for this is not certain. Also, as an experiment, a Hurricane I was equipped with a similar throttle movement, and this was interconnected with the propeller pitch control.

National cockpits

German cockpits had equipment, including instruments, that set them apart from those of other air forces. They were usually equipped, both in detail and overall, to a very high standard compared with those of British aircraft. Switches, selector levers, instruments and the minutiae, such as labels, were carefully designed. They reflected the generally high quality of German design and manufacture. American multi-engined aircraft cockpits, compared with British, were in general far more comfortable for the crew. In some aircraft there was extensive padded lining to isolate the crew from external noise. Ashtrays were often provided. French and Italian cockpits were distinctly different from those of the other nations. As noted, one distinguishing feature was the 'reverse' throttle action – pull back for more power; push to close.

Together or apart?

The cockpits of multi-engined aircraft exhibited significant differences among the 'air war' nations. American multi-engined aircraft cockpits often reflected the civil flight deck arrangement, with two pilots sitting side by side and with the pilot on the right responsible for managing the engines and systems. Some Japanese two-pilot cockpits had the principal pilot's position on the right; the Tachikawa Ki-92 was one example. In the 1930s and 1940s the fuselage nose containing the cockpit of multi-engined aircraft could be divided into two basic profiles: the traditional stepped nose, as with civil transports, and the unbroken, blended, nose line favoured for many German aircraft, and later in the war adopted by Boeing for the B-29.

During the Second World War there were few departures from the accepted position for the pilot or pilots. This was close to the nose in multi-engined aircraft, and behind the engine in single- and tandem-seat aircraft. German design philosophy believed in the morale-boosting effect of positioning the crew members close together, as in the Do 217 and Ju 88 and their subsequent variants. An added advantage was the ease of communication either by hand signals or shouting in the ear, and thus independent of an intercom. During the first three years of war most RAF aircraft with dispersed crew positions were handicapped by the uncertain performance of the intercom, which was not waterproof.

The majority of German multi-engined types had only one complete set of pilot's controls, and this was to the left of the centre line. A basic set of flight controls might be provided for a seating position on the right. British medium and large bombers also usually had only one pilot's position This was on the left in order to leave room for a gangway on the right leading to the navigator/bomb aimer's station in the nose. Examples included the Blenheim, Wellington, Whitley and Hudson. Although the last type was a Lockheed design, the crew positions were arranged to meet an RAF specification. British aircraft with 'two-pilot' cockpits included the Stirling and the Sunderland.

The view ahead

The size and shape of the cockpits of the Second World War fighter/attack aircraft exhibited not only national characteristics but the progressive changes needed to meet the increasing demands of the air war. The start of the Second World War was also the time when the biplane fighter made its final bow, even though some, such as the Gladiator and the Fiat CR 42, lingered on into the middle of the war. Britain clung to the biplane for carrier operations in the shape of the Swordfish and the Albacore to the end of the Second World War.

In the biplane era pilots shared the view ahead with the cabane struts and wires. With some aircraft types the view was further impaired by the mass of the engine. The return to the monoplane in the 1930s afforded better arcs of view. Throughout the era of the powerful single-engined fighters, designers were not always mindful of, or concerned about, the fact that the pilot would have a limited view directly ahead, and none at all when the tailwheel was on the ground. Only in the last two years of the Second World War were cockpits raised relative to the top line of the engine cowling so as to improve the forward/downward angle of view. To avoid colliding with other aircraft or impedimenta around the airfield pilots made frequent changes in the direction of taxiing. This was accepted as par for the course.

Most pilots criticized the poor view ahead but adapted to the problem. It was exacerbated when powerful in-line engine

fighters were adapted for aircraft-carrier operations. The naval version of the Spitfire and the enlarged version, the Seafire, are examples of the need for a proper view ahead, being set aside in order to have a British fleet fighter and not be reliant on American aircraft. USN and US Marine fighter aircraft, such as the Wildcat, Hellcat and Bearcat, with radial engines, had a high-set cockpit arranged to match the needs of the pilot when making a deck landing. However, the designers of the Corsair chose, presumably for very good reasons, to position the cockpit further aft, so that in a tail-down attitude the big radial engine and its cowling occupied much of the forward scenery.

Nearside, offside

Since the First World War the majority of single-seat cockpits have been arranged, and pilots have preferred to 'mount', on the left (port) side. This is, of course, in British terminology the 'nearside', as derived from equestrian customs via the automobile. The small flap-type door to improve access to the cockpit of a Spitfire was on the port side. Among the exceptions were the car-type door on the starboard side of the Airacobra, Tornado and Typhoon. The location of the majority of wheel and lever-type controls on the portside of the cockpit is one reason for not placing the door on the port side. The door, as with a side-hinged canopy, had to be closed when taxiing. A study of Japanese films of fighter pilots climbing into their cockpits might reveal that they preferred the starboard side because that was the traditional side on which to mount a horse in the East.

Fenestration

Each of the three principal fighters in the Battle of Britain in 1940 had a distinctive cockpit windscreen and canopy. The Spitfire started life with a windscreen and canopy

Bf 109 G. The 109 series retained the flat panel, angular framed canopy of the first version throughout WWII.
Philip Jarrett

Bf 109F with hinged canopy which had to be closed when taxiing. A part of the armour plating for the pilot's seat was fixed to the canopy. *Philip Jarrett*

FW 190 c 1944. The one-piece moulded canopy is in contrast to that of the Bf 109.
Philip Jarrett

that eventually proved unsuitable for air combat. The curved panels distorted the pilot's view and he could not adequately see astern. The experience of combat prompted major changes to the shape of the cockpit canopy. The canopy of the Spitfire was difficult to slide back when attempting to bale out. Martin Baker devised a modification whereby a series of plungers freed the canopy from its runners. To free the canopy the pilot pulled on a small red ball that hung just above his forehead. In contrast to the Spitfire, the Hurricane's canopy was made up of many small flat panels. Unlike the former, which eventually acquired a bubble canopy proud of the top line of the fuselage, the Hurricane retained its original canopy profile and structure to the end of its active life.

Avro York. RAF four-engine, high-wing, monoplane transport. As in high-wing flying boats, the engine controls hang from the overhead. The unpressurized fuselage permits extensive cockpit fenestration. *P Jarrett*

The Bf 109's canopy and windscreen had an angular shape made up of individual flat panels. The canopy was hinged on the right to allow access to the cockpit. As with other long-nosed fighters of the 1940s, taxiing required frequent changes of direction in order to see ahead. In the Bf 109 this problem was aggravated by the need to keep the canopy closed. The cockpit closely confined the pilot: its dimensions seemed to have been related to the average shoulder width and seated height of pilots, and therefore made no allowance for the large or tall pilot.

Some new aircraft types when first entering service in the early 1940s, such as P-47, Mustang and Typhoon, did not provide a good view astern, whereas from the start the Fw 190 and the Westland Whirlwind had a cockpit canopy profile giving wide arcs of view, including the important 'over-the-shoulder' view. The comment must be: Why did the specifications issued by air forces in the 1930s not emphasize the importance of giving a pilot the maximum possible arcs of view, particularly astern? However, the Typhoon, for example, was envisaged as an interceptor of bombers and not for getting into a 'dogfight', and therefore a good view astern may not have been essential.

American cockpits

What were the most distinguishing features of the cockpits of the USAAF, USN and USMC, particularly when compared with those of the other combatants? Perhaps they were soundproofing, ashtrays and twin-pointer engine instruments in the bombers; in the fighters the large canopies and tall control columns; and in all types a unique arrangement of the instruments in front of the pilot.

The two principal American heavy bombers in service before the advent of the B-29, the B-17 and B-24 had their main

Vought SB2U-3 Vindicator c 1940. This emphasizes the typical roomy American cockpits. *Philip Jarrett*

Vought-Sikorsky Chesapeakes acquired by the RAF in 1940. *Philip Jarrett*

Chesapeake cockpit, right-side. *Philip Jarrett*

Chesapeake cockpit, left side, showing the throttle and mixture levers with a mechanical indicator of left-wheel retraction above. *Philip Jarrett*

B-17 cockpit showing the distinctive Boeing 'bar' type throttle levers. *P Jarrett*

instrument panels arranged so that the second pilot could monitor the engines and systems. This meant that the captain had few instruments on his part of the panel. The flight instruments were concentrated on the centre of the main panel. Being an earlier aircraft, the cockpit of the B-17 had fewer electrical-systems switches and controls compared with the B-24. A Boeing 'trademark' was the arrangement of the four engine throttle levers. These had horizontal grips so that the pilot could, with one hand, move all four together or select either pairs of engines or individual engines.

B-24

The B-24 provided British and Commonwealth pilots with an introduction to the technology and the cockpit of an American 'heavy'. They were very different from those of the B-17, whose technology was that of the mid-1930s. The B-24 had a push-pull primary control extending back out of the instrument panel, which engendered favourable comment by 'visiting' pilots. On the controls pedestal between the pilots there were throttle, propeller and mixture control levers for each engine, along with, in later versions, a master control unit

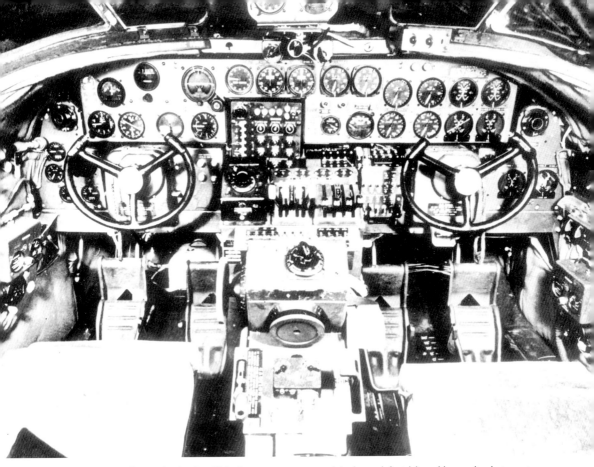

B-24 Liberator. Four-engine bomber. Flight instruments concentrated in front of Captain's position; engine instruments on second pilot's panel. Aileron/elevator wheels are on shafts which extend out of the instrument panel. On the centre panel are the Honeywell autopilot controls and to the left of the four white throttle levers is the control knob for the electronically controlled turbo-superchargers. *Smiths Group Archives*

This is an earlier mark of the B 24 as used by Coastal Command RAF. It serves to illustrate the variations in cockpit equipment between different versions of an aircraft. The autopilot control panel is before the captain's right knee. There are four supercharger control levers in place of the control box of the electronically controlled turbosuperchargers in other marks of the B 24. The aileron/elevator wheels are also different and the instrument are arranged differently. *Philip Jarrett*

for all four exhaust-turbine superchargers.

An RAF pilot recalled that:

The Liberator 3 was a complicated device by the standards of 1942 and behaved rather like an amply powered cartload of bricks. The aeroplanes to which we had become accustomed could still be 'floated', power-off, onto a runway; this B-24 had to be motored until it touched, and the rate of descent had to be controlled by carefully judged applications of power. Nor did it just fly off by itself; the Liberator had to be lifted off when the airspeed indicator showed such-and-such a figure – and not before. If lifted too soon at high weights it was inclined to 'get stuck', uncomfortably gaining neither height nor speed.

The complications of the B-24 included turbo blowers, fuel-booster pumps, a hydraulic booster pump, intercoolers for the blowers, inverters for the electric dopers for engine-starting, integral control locks and ashtrays in the pilot-seat armrests. For us, brought up on Blenheims, Hurricanes,

Wellingtons and the like, the Liberator was a phenomenal affair. For every 30 minutes in the air we seemed to spend an equivalent time going through the cockpit drill, setting up the boost for each engine separately on the turbo-blower controls, creeping along the runway to get the nosewheel straight, and unlocking and checking the control surfaces.

Side-stick

An early example of the modern side-stick controller was to be found on some B-24s. A small control column or joystick was mounted alongside the left leg of the aircraft captain. This enabled him to control the aircraft directly through the autopilot when flying in formation. It was an extension of the system whereby the bomb aimer exercised control of the aircraft in yaw when approaching a target.

B-29

The B-29 was one of the first large, successful, pressurized, high-altitude, long-range (5,000 miles) bomber. The cockpit, or

B-29 flight deck. Numerous fenestration panels provide wide arcs of view and serve for both pilots' and bomb aimer's positions. The engine control levers are outboard of each pilot. *Boeing*

B-29. The two sets of pilots' controls and instruments are separated by a gangway to the forward bomb-aiming position. In this photograph the aircraft commander has his right hand on the wheel brakes control levers. The engine controls are out of sight alongside his left arm. The instrument panel includes double pointer indicators for manifold pressure (boost) and rpm, each instrument serving two engines. *Boeing*

rather the 'flight deck', was spacious and inside the continuously curved nose section was without a stepped windscreen. Although the semi-spherical array of small windows was intended to give wide fields of view forward, upwards, below and on both bows, it exposed the crew to intense sunlight. Extending the sun blinds obviously defeated the designer's original object of providing

maximum arcs of view. At night, particularly in rain, the multiple reflections of lights on the ground, such as when landing, gave the pilot a dangerously distorted view. Eventually some improvement was gained by providing flat panels in front of the pilots, in place of the originally curved ones. Because of the width of the flight deck and the need for a gangway forward to the bomb aimer's station in the extreme nose, there was no central control pedestal as, for example, in the B17 and B24. Each of the two pilots had a control pedestal at his outboard hand. The throttles on these pedestals for the four engines were the typical Boeing 'bar' type, as used in the B17. The brake control levers were located close to the captain's right knee.

American single-seat cockpits

As noted, American airforce single-seat cockpits were, in general, larger than those used by other air forces. The control column was set further forward and was higher than those of British and German types. The greater use of electrical systems, as in bombers, meant more switches than levers.

P-39

The P-39 Bell Airacobra, with its engine behind the pilot, was a late 1930s monoplane design that perpetuated the arrangement of many biplanes in which the fuselage-mounted guns projected into the cockpit. The backs of the two 13 mm guns protruded out of the instrument panel, and included two large hand-grips for manually cocking (arming). The drive shaft forward to the propeller passed under the pilot's seat and between his legs so that the control column had to be forked at the bottom. The Airacobra had a car-type door to the cockpit.

A-26 Invader

The usual American side-by-side, two-pilot layout for bombers was not applied to the Douglas Invader (A-26). This twin-engined attack bomber, introduced into the USAAF in 1943, positioned the single set of controls to the left of the gangway to provide access to the navigator/bomb aimer's station in the extreme nose. The engine controls pedestal was on the centre line. A good point, and one

Douglas A-26 Invader. Unlike other American twin-engine attack aircraft the fuselage was wide enough to permit movement between the cockpit and the nose compartment. *Philip Jarrett*

that was so often lacking in contemporary British cockpits, was the 'close-to-hand' fuel cock selectors. In American aircraft these were usually of good size, clearly marked and moving in the logical direction. The Invader pilot also benefited from advances made in the forming of large one-piece cockpit windows: there was only one centre pillar to obstruct the forward view, whereas in other aircraft types there was a multiplicity of small windows.

The instrument panel of the A-26 provides an interesting comparison with that of contemporary RAF aircraft in which, as previously mentioned, the Basic Six arrangement of the principal flight instruments was designed to minimize the pilot's scanning arcs. The seemingly haphazard arrangement of the flight, engine and other instruments, it is presumed, must have been decided upon in the design office after consultation with experienced pilots. And so it would be presumptuous to criticize. After all, hundreds of USAAF and

Lockheed P-38 providing the pilot with extensive arcs-of-view. *Philip Jarrett*

USAF pilots must have coped reasonably well with the arrangement of the instruments.

P-38 Lightning

In the Second World War there were not many single-seater, twin-engined aircraft. Examples included the Westland Whirlwind and Welkin, the de Havilland Hornet, P-38, Me 262 and Arado 234. The Lockheed P-38 was an example of the 'trade-off' game in which available engine power, armament and aerodynamic considerations produced different solutions for the configuration of a new fighter. The Lightning's single-seat cockpit was part of a short fuselage set on the wing between the two Allison turbo-supercharged engines, whose nacelles extended aft to carry the empennage. The location of the pilot provided good arcs of view in most directions. A feature of the cockpit was the spectacle-type aileron control wheel, and not a joystick as used for the majority of fighters. The control column was set to the right of the pilot with a cross-over section to bring the wheel central to the pilot's hands. (Later versions of the P-38 may have had a stick in place of a wheel.)

Floatplanes

The cockpits of floatplanes were little different from wheeled aircraft. However, when they were hoisted back on board a ship an acrobatic performance was needed on the part of the pilot. A typical hoist-in drill in the USN required the pilot, after landing on the water, to taxi the aircraft onto a sled or net being towed astern of the ship. The net was engaged by a hook under the aircraft's keel. Once hauled in close under the jib of a crane, the pilot had to unstrap, climb out and hook the aircraft onto the hoisting cable. This worked reasonably well in a calm sea, but in a rough sea state the aircraft might slide off the net. Then the engine had to be restarted and the aircraft taxied back onto the net.

Nippon

Before 1941 the Western nations assumed, much to their cost later, that Japanese aircraft were of poor quality. By the end of 1941 Allied pilots learnt, sometimes with their lives, that the Mitsubishi A6M Zero, for example, was an excellent fighter. Captured specimens unexpectedly revealed that it was well equipped and had instruments whose quality matched those used by other air forces. Japanese pilots were, on average, smaller than their Western counterparts and therefore were not so demanding on cockpit space. Incidentally, the Zero's twin 7.7 mm fuselage-mounted guns projected back into the cockpit and took up valuable instrument panel space. In some versions of the A6M there was only enough room under the gunsight for an artificial horizon and a turn-and-slip indicator.

Russian

The obsessive secrecy of Russian officialdom meant that information about technical details of aircraft, and cockpits in particular, was limited. A photograph of the cockpit of a Tupolev SB-2 twin-engined bomber of c.1940 reveals controls and instruments similar to those of Western aircraft. The instruments include an artificial horizon similar in appearance to a Sperry type. Interestingly it is arranged with the model aircraft fixed to give an 'inside looking out' presentation, and not the 'outside looking in' that apparently was favoured by Russian pilots. The ignition control has individual, two for each engine, switches, and not combined as in many German and American aircraft in one rotary switch or lever with four positions. The magneto switches are arranged to be 'off' in the down position, as in British aircraft. The Russians could have gone their own way and copied the domestic light switch movement. The aperiodic magnetic compass is similar to the British P type and is mounted between the pilot's feet. The arrangement of the flight instruments appears to be similar to American preferences.

German cockpits

Ju 52 3m

The three-engined version of the Ju 52 of the 1920s became synonymous with the carriage of paratroops and the delivery of stores to the German Army. It was both ubiquitous and hard working. The cockpit was well fenestrated, roomy and utilitarian. Although there was plenty of room on the panels in front of the two pilots, the flight instruments were arranged in no particular order of importance or in relation to their function relative to the others. The engine instruments, not unexpectedly, occupied the centre panel. A large central control pedestal had the throttles and mixture controls on top. The throttle levers were set unusually far apart. In keeping with its 1920s ancestry, the Ju 52 had a complicated arrangement of sprockets, chains and shafts that connected the selector wheel to the flaps. In order to simplify the mechanism and at the same time exercise the pilot's muscles, the flap wheel was behind the second pilot's seat. The wheel had to be about 20 inches in diameter because the flaps were moved by human muscle power. While the pilot was occupied with both flying the aircraft and setting the flaps he had to keep an eye on the flap setting indicator. Again, a cunning piece of design logic had mounted this on the port side of the cockpit. The only hydraulic system was that of the brakes, and according to non-German pilots, it was of little use. Fortunately the Ju 52 was a lumbering but docile machine, so that even if the controls were in odd places there was usually time in which to sort things out. On the subject of brakes, the majority of German aircraft had toe-operated brakes, as did American. The British preferred a hand control lever on the wheel or stick.

Bf 109

The 1940 version of the Bf 109 had a very different instrument arrangement from that of British aircraft. From left to right, starting top left, in two rows of three, they were altimeter, magnetic compass, boost (manifold) gauge, airspeed indicator, turn-and-slip and rpm indicator. The ignition switches were arranged in what might be termed the 'German-American' position. There was one lever on a chain that could be inserted into a quadrant. The pilot could select both off, M1, M2 or M1 plus M2. M meant Magneto. Not to be found in British or American cockpits of that era was the propeller pitch indicator, which in the earlier versions did not have a constant-speed propeller. One item

not found in the RAF, but common in German aircraft of the period was the round counters for the guns. The reflector-type gunsight in the Bf 109 was usually the Revi type. It was offset slightly to starboard. Below the main instrument panel was an auxiliary set of controls and indicators. These included a fuel cock lever, gun armament selector and rounds-used indicator, the gunsight dimmer control, combined fuel and oil-pressure gauge,

Bf109 G-2 The Revi gun sight is top centre on the instrument panel with the round counters to its left. A more comprehensive set of instruments compared with the early versions of the 109 including a radio compass and artificial horizon. *Philip Jarrett*

undercarriage position indicator, undercarriage selector lever with emergency selector below, fuel contents indicator and oil temperature gauge. Not unexpectedly, the Messerschmitt drawing office staff sometimes positioned controls and instruments to suit their needs rather than those of the pilot.

B&V 141B

Throughout the history of the cockpit, designers have essayed unusual locations and shapes. The B&V 141B is one example. This asymmetric single-engined monoplane seated the crew in a nacelle to starboard of the engine. The engine nacelle was extended aft to carry the empennage, the tailplane of which extended to port. This arrangement of crew and engine provided excellent fields of view for the pilot in most directions, except to the left. In Dr Vogt's proposed B&V P-170 three-engined high-speed bomber project, the pilot and navigator/bomb aimer were seated in tandem in the extreme tail.

Fw 190. A tidy arrangement of controls and instruments. The 'bilges' are not in sight. Alongside the REVI reflector gunsight are the round counters for the guns. *Philip Jarrett*

Fw 190

In 1942 a Luftwaffe pilot lost his way and landed his Fw 190 in Britain. The cockpit was found to be well equipped and neatly arranged, with smooth panelling for controls and instruments. To those RAF pilots who had the opportunity to fly the aircraft, the cockpit had nothing like the untidy wiring and details of their cockpits. The Fw 190 was an 'all-electric' machine and included such refinements for the pilot as buttons for controlling the incidence of the tailplane and selection of flap and undercarriage; as well as a thumb switch on the throttle for propeller pitch. A drawing in a contemporary technical publication of the cockpit included references to W/T. What was not explained was how an Fw 190 pilot, or any other fighter pilot, would have had time in which to indulge in a Morse code exchange with other pilots or with the ground. A small point, but it serves to emphasize the general lack of knowledge at the time concerning technical matters.

Arado 234

Had this jet bomber/reconnaissance aircraft arrived on the scene one year earlier, its speed would have presented the Allies with a big problem. The cockpit had some interesting details. The pilot sat close to the bulbous nose transparency with wide arcs of view

Fairey Swordfish torpedo bomber. Just discernable is the athwartships rod in front of the windscreen on which were mounted the deflection marks and lights used when making a torpedo attack. *Philip Jarrett*

forward and to the sides, but not abaft the beam. A periscopic sight in the roof of the cockpit could be used either for bomb aiming or for sighting the rearward-firing defensive guns. For the latter purpose the optical system presented an image of the target as if it were ahead, and therefore the pilot could aim the aircraft as if making a conventional stern attack. When using the other bomb sight located between his feet, the pilot could swing the control wheel and yoke out of the way. The bombsight was coupled to the autopilot.

British cockpits

Swordfish

A number of open-cockpit-type aircraft of the 1930s generation continued in service in 1939. Among the more interesting was the Fairey Swordfish. This single-engined, three-seater biplane looked ancient even when, as a prototype, it arrived for assessment at RAF Martlesham Heath in 1934. The open crew positions of the 'Stringbag', as it was affectionately known in both the Fleet Air Arm and the RAF, provided harsh, cramped and uncomfortable conditions for the pilot, observer (navigator) and telegraphist/air gunner (TAG). The crew categories reflected the aircrew practices of the pre-war Fleet Air Arm (FAA) when, prior to 1938, it was part of the RAF. In those years observers were

naval officers, the TAGs were naval ratings and some of the pilots were RAF embarked for a tour of naval flying. For overwater flights away from the carrier and with primitive radio aids to navigation, a highly qualified naval navigator, who was also familiar with the characteristics of enemy vessels and the most likely position of their 'mobile airfield', the carrier, was most essential.

The pilot's cockpit, below the cut-out in the trailing edge of the upper-wing centre section, was typical of its generation – cluttered and with equipment and instruments mounted in locations convenient to the designer but not necessarily to the pilot. The principal instruments, the type and number of which varied among different marks of the aircraft, were not to the Basic Six arrangement. The primary offensive role of the Swordfish was that of launching a torpedo at a height of 100 ft or less above the water. This required accurate visual judgement of height on the part of the pilot, who could not rely on the altimeter, which might read 100 ft too high or too low. A more sensitive altimeter was introduced later in the war. Mention had been made of the importance of the gunsight, in both size and position, in relation to cockpit design. In the 'Stringbag' the pilot used a special sight when making a torpedo attack. This consisted of two horizontal rows of small lamps mounted on rods attached to the cabane struts. The lamps were spaced at intervals representing five knots of target speed. If the speed of the target vessel was estimated, for example, as 10 knots, then the pilot steered at 90 degrees to its track, keeping the second lamp aligned on the target. This simple but effective torpedo sight solved the 'triangle of velocities' so as to aim the torpedo ahead of the target.

The crews of the Swordfish went to war in their open cockpits flying at low level through intense flak when attacking convoys. Others faced hours of numbing cold when on patrol over the Arctic seas. Many times they hoped that the 100-knot or less airspeed of their 'Stringbag' against a 60-knot gale would be enough get them back to their carrier before they ran out of fuel.

British multi-engine cockpits

All the fuel tank 'plumbing' in the Wellington bomber was disposed on the aft face of the main spar, well away from the cockpit. This meant that the pilot had to depend on one of the crew going aft and correctly operating the selectors. The sudden silence on a dark and stormy night over the ocean as both engines stop is a memorable experience. The Wellington had the engine controls to the left of the pilot and the flap and undercarriage levers to the right.

A typical pilot comment on the Halifax bomber criticized the pilot's position and equipment. Compared with the Lancaster's, the throttle-levers, for example, came far less easily to hand; even though the friction lever was better. The trim tab controls in the Halifax were all over the place. The

Bristol Blenheim IV (long nose). Compared with the Mk I the navigator had a proper chart table under the 'scalloped' part of the aircraft nose. *British Aerospace*

H-P Hampden. This emphasizes the good view afforded the pilot. Note the crude mechanical interlock between the ignition switches and the undercarriage control (Left-middle) *Wallace-Clarke*

undercarriage and flap levers were much too close together. When reaching down for them in the dark, one could be mistaken for the other. This group of levers included the bomb-door control, which perversely did not operate in the expected direction of 'up' for close and 'down' for opening. The blind-flying instruments were arranged in accord with the Basic Six format. However, the other forty or so instruments and indicators were scattered around the cockpit.

The four-engined Vickers Windsor bomber of c.1944 provides another example of cockpit design to which not much thought was given. It provided the pilot with controls arranged to increase his task and to lead to mistakes. The single pilot's place was difficult to climb up into, and just as difficult to vacate in an emergency. Presumably because the RAF had a number of aircraft

types having only one pilot's position, irrespective of the aircraft's size, then at 30 tons the Windsor was to be no exception.

Hudson

Although the Hudson was designed and built by Lockheed in the USA, it is included under the heading of British cockpits because most were operated by the RAF and Dominion air forces. When the first arrived at RAF Leuchars in the summer of 1939, it introduced pilots to an entirely unfamiliar cockpit, as well as handling techniques. Compared with the Anson it was replacing in Coastal Command, the Hudson was a very different proposition. The cockpit had far more instruments than the usual service aircraft. There were more controls and longer engine starting and pre-flight drills. At the end of 1938 potential Hudson pilots had been seconded to British Airways as second pilots so that they could acquire enough handling experience to act as instructors. One pilot recalled:

The handling characteristics, when airborne, I remember as being good, with response to control input both smooth and positive. At 7,500 ft she would skip along at 175 knots IAS.

The cockpit I remember as functional, with most things to hand. An exception was the main wheel hydraulic braking. Here, I felt that Lockheed scored minimal marks – the brakes worked differentially on the rudder pedals, but the amount of braking applied was varied by pulling a long lever rearwards out of the lower part of the throttle pedestal. One or two inches' extension would be very gentle braking, but ten or twelve inches' would lock the main wheels and, if travelling at any speed, tip the aircraft on to its nose. When taxiing one was in the peculiar position (from the left-hand seat) of operating the throttles, which were on your right, with the left hand, while the right hand guarded the brake lever almost down in the bottom of the cockpit. On the take-off run differential throttle was used initially for directional control with coarse and rather ineffective rudder. At roughly 50 to 60 knots IAS, when the tail was raised, the twin fins and rudders gave excellent yaw control.

As was customary at the time, the American engines (Wright Cyclones, and in later marks Pratt & Whitney Twin Wasps) did not have automatic mixture control. The pilot had to refer to the indications of the Cambridge exhaust gas analyser when adjusting the mixture control levers. Prominent in the middle of the main instrument panel, and unfamiliar to most RAF pilots, was the Sperry autopilot control panel. Other unfamiliar controls were the selectors for wing and propeller de-icing and for fuel dumping. Although the Mark I had constant speed propellers they could not be feathered; thereby increasing the pilot's problems in the event of an engine failing soon after take-off. A reassuring feature of the cockpit of the Mk II Hudson onwards was the pair of red propeller-feathering buttons. In one respect in particular the Hudson differed from its American origin in having separate rpm and boost (manifold) pressure instruments for each engine. The preference in the USA was to combine the pointers for two engines on one dial.

Beaufighter

By the end of 1940 RAF Fighter Command started to operate the new Beaufighter. This big twin-engined fighter, with four 20 mm guns and equipped with AI radar, soon made night operations over the UK by the Luftwaffe very unprofitable. The radar operator's position in the back cockpit did not provide a good vantage point from which to help the pilot during the final visual stage of an interception. It would be another two years before the fighter pilot would be able to view a CRT in his cockpit directly and not have to rely completely on the instructions

Bristol Beaufighter c 1945. This illustrates the massive increase in ten years in the number of instruments and controls required by military aircraft. The small CRT (to left of the basic-six panel) is a radar display. *Smiths Group*

passed to him by the radar operator.

H.A. Taylor's comments on flying the Beaufighter included the following:

[It] stood waiting, in its ugly, functional dignity. Its two Hercules engines, disproportionate in their size and hiding the pilot's cockpit between them, were 'tick-tocking' quietly as they cooled down after the engine fitter's check run-ups. I signed the Form 700 and climbed awkwardly up the trapdoor steps into the crowded seat where my parachute was already waiting. With a rigger's help I sorted out, adjusted, and secured the parachute and Sutton harnesses and waited for the sharp metallic clang which meant that the trapdoor had been closed and that the rigger was clear.

At a thumbs-up sign from the ground crew I began to go mechanically and quite automatically through the engine-starting drill. In their turn the two Hercules radials burst lumpily and smokily into life as the starter and booster-coil buttons were pressed. After a few moments of warm-up, with the oil temperatures rising, the oil pressures dropping to normal and the revolution-counter needles swinging idly between a thousand and thirteen hundred, it was time to do the final engine runs and to check manifold pressures, magnetos, and constant-speed propeller operation. All this had to be done quickly and with a perfunctory air, so as not to upset the feelings of the engine fitter, who had already completed the same checks to his own satisfaction.

Then the chocks were waved away and, with an inch or two of extra throttle, we rolled off the grass and on to the perimeter track with the brakes wailing thinly as their control-column trigger was squeezed. The Beaufighter jerked and squealed its way down-wind along the perimeter track, enveloped in the brightly blue wreaths of smoke from the exhaust stacks.

Before turning on to the runway in use I went through the long-established pre-take-off drill. Hydraulics 'on'; three trimming controls set to zero, zero and one inch forward; mixture rich; propeller controls fully forward for maximum revolutions; inner fuel tanks selected; dive-brakes in; flaps up; and engine-cooling gills closed and then opened a trifle. All set.

Mosquito

Access to the cockpit of a Mosquito, and getting out in a hurry, was through a small door low on the starboard side in the fighter version and under the nose in the bomber version. Pilot and navigator when encased in full flying clothing and equipment were very bulky. They sat shoulder to shoulder. The starboard side of the cockpit was crowded with the boxes of the AI radar. The radar operator could look up from the CRTs of the AI, alongside the pilot, and help to make a visual search of the target through the windscreen. Night-vision binoculars were also used. To counter high-flying pressurized Ju 86Ps the Mosquito XV was tried. This had a pressurized cabin, the entrance to which was through a small double hatch under the nose. There are few published comments on the type and position of the controls and instruments. It seems that pilots put up with awkwardly located and difficult to operate controls.

The report on the performance and handling of the Mosquito made by the test pilots of the Aeroplane and Armament Experimental Aircraft Establishment (A&AEE) in 1941 criticized many items in the cockpit. They included:

Pilot's seat too upright for comfort

Pilot's head dangerously close to an overhead crossbar

The elevator trim wheel positioned too low

The ignition switches difficult to reach round the control column

Difficult to avoid switching off both magnetos of an engine together

Undercarriage selector lever could be inadvertently moved to up when getting into or out of the seat

Boost and radiator temperature gauges set too low on the panel

Rudder pedals too close together.

The last item should have included the fact that the pilot's seat was not on the same centre-line as the rudder pedals. Not all pilots were aware that the skewed seating posture, which put more weight on one buttock than the other, might induce a false sensation of turning when flying at night or in cloud. This could be fatal when coping with an engine failure close to the ground and at night.

Pilot Safety and Comfort

Parachutes

Fashions in parachute harness varied among the air forces of the Second World War. There were the single-harness fastening favoured by the British, whereby one turn and a bang with the hand released all four parts of the harness, whereas the American harness had three individual release hooks. An innovation adopted for some RAF squadrons was the Irvin suit, which combined a flying coverall with integral harness to which a chest-type parachute pack could be fastened. This type of personal safety equipment had the advantage that there were few projections and hooks for catching on equipment when moving about in the cramped conditions of RAF bombers. Crews of B-17s and B-24s were further encumbered by having to wear armoured jackets (flak jackets) and steel helmets when operating through intense German flak and fighter attacks.

Ejection

Air staff requirements in the late 1940s, particularly in the UK, included: 'In the last resort a reasonable means of escape in an emergency must be provided for the crew.' The safety and recovery of aircrews was to be assured by the provision of parachutes, escape hatches, jettisonable cockpit canopies and blast-deflection devices.

When normal operating airspeeds began to increase above 400 knots mechanically assisted means of escape, such as ejection seats, had to be developed. Ejection seats were developed and fitted to aircraft in Germany in the Second World War. Test pilot Schenk, who in the He 280 V1 suddenly found that he had no control of his aircraft, was among the first to use an ejection seat 'in anger'. This was in 1942. The compressed-air-operated seat was the first of a number developed for the Luftwaffe's final generation of aircraft – the He 162 jet and the piston-

SAAB twin-boom, pusher, fighter c 1944 emphasizing the danger from the propeller should the pilot have to bale out. *Philip Jarrett*

engined Do 335 Pfeil, for example. But the Me 262 did not have an ejection seat for the pilot. In 1943 the Saab J21A fighter, twin-boom, pusher-propeller engine arrangement, was designed to have an ejection seat for shooting the pilot clear of the pusher propeller. In April 1944 the crew of an He 219 ejected safely. The original Meteor and Vampire were designed with conventional pilot's seat. In the event of trouble the pilot had to roll the aircraft inverted, jettison the canopy and drop out and make a normal parachute departure.

Outside Germany the pioneer in reliable and practical ejection seats that could be fitted to a wide range of aircraft was James (later Sir James) Martin of Martin Baker Ltd. The company's records show that the need for escape devices was not confined to jet aircraft. Both the Spitfire and the Hurricane were the subject of research into ways of assisting a pilot to abandon aircraft. As early as October 1944 a swinging-arm, pilot-ejection system was demonstrated in model form. Later a full-size system was tested in a Defiant, and a number of successful flights were made in which a dummy was swung out and up from the aircraft on the end of an arm pivoted near the fin and assisted by a compressed spring.

Following the lead set by Germany, Martin Baker decided that the best way of projecting aircrews clear of an aircraft in an emergency would be by the forced ejection of the seat, using an explosive charge. James Martin had to consider the sudden loads imposed on a pilot when the charge was fired. How many Gs could be withstood without him suffering severe injuries, particularly to the spine? On 24 January 1945 Bernard Lynch, an experimental fitter, volunteered to be shot up the seat rig in a succession of tests, each to a greater height. Close to ten feet he experienced considerable pain. Later tests imposed spinal damage. However, if the subject's spine was kept naturally erect, with the vertebrae square to each other, it could withstand accelerations of 20 G. The Defiant was replaced as a test vehicle by a Meteor Mk 3 so that the effects of ejection at speeds of 400 knots and higher could be assessed.

Armour plating

In the first year of war few aircraft were equipped with armour protection for their crews. As the air war became more intense, pilots in particular were given armoured seats or bulkheads, and armour was added to protect other vital parts of the aircraft. Armour 8 mm thick formed the back of the pilot's seat in the Bf 109. On the Bf 109G the windscreen was 90 mm thick. A 60 mm thick armoured glass windscreen was fitted to the night-fighter version of the Me 110.

Pressurized compartments

Above about 15,000 ft pilots experience increasing discomfort with every additional 1,000 ft. However, provided they are supplied with a regulated supply of oxygen, are in heated cockpits or wear electrically heated suits and do not have to move about too much, or exert themselves, they can retain some effectiveness, even when flying at 30,000 feet. At that altitude the air pressure has dropped to 4.4 psi and the outside air temperature is down to around − 44°C. The Spitfire was designed in the mid-1930s for attacking invading bombers at around 15,000 ft. The A&AEE report on the handling tests of the Mk I Spitfire refers to the fact that, although no heating system was provided, the cockpit was kept warm by the heat from the engine and exhaust up to 25,000 feet. Gloves were not needed. However, towards the end of the Battle of Britain, in the autumn of 1940, British and German fighters sometimes fought above 25,000 feet. Pilots suffered severely from the extreme cold. Just a small hole in the cockpit let in a numbing blast of freezing air.

Vickers Wellington VI with cylindrical pressurized cabin for the crew. The pilot sat with his head inside the small transparent dome on top of the fuselage. Abandoning the aircraft in a hurry was difficult. *Vickers*

In addition to the discomfort of the cold, the windscreen and canopy iced over. The cockpit and the pilot's flying clothing were never intended for an air war at 20,000 feet and higher.

The final year of war ushered in an entirely new era of aircrew protection and comfort. Up to then only experimental test aircrews and high-altitude-research crews had been given specialized life-support equipment. Later in the war special versions of the Spitfire had pressurized cockpits to permit sustained operation at extreme altitudes. The air pressure in the cockpit of the Spitfire VI at 37,000 feet was equivalent to that at 28,000 feet altitude. As the pressurizing air supply was warmed, the temperature was kept at 8°C even when the outside temperature was down to minus 42°C. However, this was not a true pressure cabin within the general meaning because the difference between the outside pressure and that inside the cockpit was only about 2 psi. The compressor driven by the R-R Merlin 47 could provide only just enough volume of air

to overcome the leakage through the numerous small holes.

The Wellington V and VI were attempts to develop a high-altitude bomber for the RAF. The crew members were sealed in a pressurized cylinder with limited external vision. The Luftwaffe introduced a pressurized crew compartment for the high-altitude P version of the Ju 86, and later for the Ju 388. These were used for photo-reconnaissance. The presence of these aircraft over the UK prompted the development of high-altitude interceptors, such as the Mosquito XV and the Welkin. Another example of a pressurized crew compartment was that of the two-seater Heinkel 219 Uhu developed for a 40,000 ft operating ceiling.

None of the British and German methods of providing an acceptable working environment for the crew was entirely satisfactory, and in no way was there a precursor of the modern pressurized airliner. However, in the Boeing B-29 the crew could operate in a virtual shirt-sleeved environment except when attacked. Three sections of the hull were completely pressurized. When they were operating close to a gun-defended target area, or were attacked by interceptors, the pressure would be lowered so as to mitigate the effects of being hit. The technology of the pressurized Boeing 307 civil airliner of 1939 applied to the structure of the B-29 showed the way to the pressurization of civil aircraft after the war.

The advent of the jet aircraft introduced many more problems associated with life support and safety. Among the many 'trade-offs' or compromises, and often the difficulty of having to chose between one solution and another, was the problem of providing environmental protection for the human crew. The basic question that had to be answered was whether to provide special life-supporting garments or provide a pressurized cabin. The first solution encased a crew member in a helmet and a bulky pressurized suit. The second answer posed many structural and space problems for the aircraft designer; but it did permit a 'shirt-sleeve' environment for the crew. A typical cabin pressure would have been equivalent to 10,000 ft. Modern civil passenger aircraft keep the cabin pressure at about 8,000 ft.

Emergency controls

Some aircraft in the Second World War with only a one-pilot cockpit were equipped with an emergency set of controls at another crew position. Examples are the Martin Maryland and Baltimore and the Douglas DB-7 Boston. The

Martin Baltimore for the RAF with emergency controls in the navigator's nose compartment. *Philip Jarrett*

Douglas Boston III in 1942. Typical American tandem arrangement of navigator, pilot and radio operator; the last having a set of emergency controls. *Philip Jarrett*

Martin Maryland. Tandem seating with navigator in nose, pilot's cockpit in the middle and radio operator/gunner aft. The emergency controls were in the aft cockpit. *Philip Jarrett*

emergency controls of the Maryland and Baltimore were located in the navigator's isolated position in the nose. In the DB-7 the emergency flight and engine controls were in the wireless-operator's position aft. The Martin 139s used by the Netherlands air service in the East Indies in 1941 had a complete set of instruments and controls in the cockpit located at the aft end of the long canopy. These were used by the second pilot/air gunner during cruising on long flights. As mentioned, one type of French bomber of the late 1930s had the second pilot's control position separated and on a different level from that of the first pilot. Presumably this arrangement was intended to avoid both pilots being killed or injured simultaneously. The flight engineers of RAF Lancasters and Halifaxes were trained sufficiently to take over from the pilot and maintain straight and level flight.

Resisting G

By the end of the Second World War the air forces on both sides had developed many different technologies aimed at improving the lethality and versatility of aircraft. Engines, electronics and weapons had made a massive leap up the curve of advancing technology. One particular technique, which came in the last year of war, would become of increasing importance with the advent of jet aircraft able to impose much higher G loads on both pilots and aircraft structures than those of the previous generation. This was the G-suit. The pilots of high-performance fighters were frequently experiencing what we now call G-LOC (Loss Of Consciousness because of G). The USAAF developed the G-3A suit. This enabled pilots of P-51s, for example, to 'pull' 7G without blacking out. The suit automatically inflated to exert pressure on the pilot's abdomen, thighs and calves at 2G, and increased its pressure in step with further increases in G.

Contact flying

Pilots who trained in the USA and Canada became accustomed to the 'chessboard' appearance of the terrain. The regular pattern of fields and roads along with clearly defined railway lines and rivers simplified navigation. Also, the more predictable weather was an advantage. In contrast the visibility for much of the time in the United Kingdom, to which the new crews graduated, was poor. The visibility could change significantly during the time it took to take off, circle the airfield and commence an approach to a landing. Navigation and airmanship tasks included 'reading' the confused ground pattern of small fields, villages, narrow twisting lanes and streams and numerous railway lines. Adding to 'overseas' pilots' problems was the standard RAF arrangement of station buildings and hangars. From the air one station looked like another, particularly in East Anglia. Therefore special 'European familiarization' schools had to be established.

Another type of 'contact' flying, and one that was often made very difficult because of the cockpit type and position, was that of finding an aircraft-carrier and landing on. Deck landings had always been hazardous, and they were made more dangerous with the introduction of high-performance fighters and torpedo-bombers into the US and Royal Navies. Keeping the carrier in view during the downwind leg of the landing pattern when flying a Corsair, for example, took discipline and skill. If the pilot looked to the left at the ship for too long, there was always the possibility of experiencing a form of vertigo. After turning from the base leg and aligning with the deck the landing attitude of this long-nosed fighter deprived the pilot of any direct view ahead. The same problem was found with other aircraft when adapted for carrier work; such as the Spitfire. In poor visibility much of the landing pattern was flown on instruments. Only when close to touching down could a view be had of the deck, and then it might not be aligned in the expected position. All the time the pilot had to avoid letting the aircraft get too fast or too slow, climb or descend, reduce power or increase power too much. The last thing the pilot wanted was to have to share a view of the landing signals officer's (LSO) instructions with the engine and the frames of the windscreen. The pilots of F4U Corsairs sometimes adopted a mild side-slip final approach to the deck so that they could keep the LSO in sight.

Long-range flying

Much has been written about long-range sorties by RAF aircraft in the Second World War when targets located in the remote recesses of Europe were attacked. The USAAF conducted even longer-range operations, particularly in the Pacific theatre. These have been well documented, but what is sometimes overlooked is the arduous environment of the cockpit. For example, the cockpits of RAF aircraft compared with American were cramped and crowded with equipment. The crews were bundled and trussed up in flying-suits, life-jacket, parachute harness, leads for communication and oxygen – so much so that movement to relieve numbing of the posterior and thighs was difficult. The North Atlantic ferry service, which moved new aircraft to the UK, often meant a feat of endurance on the part of the crew. The pilot and navigator/radio operator of a Mosquito sat shoulder to shoulder hour after hour as their aircraft was urged through turbulence, intense rain and severe icing. Aircraft and crews were lost because they broke up in severe storms or were brought down by ice, which formed within a few minutes. So suddenly did the ice form that there was often no time in which to find an altitude where there was warmer air.

Unless the visibility conditions were ideal and the winds favourable, the crews of the Atlantic ferry services had anxiety about their position and fuel remaining added to the monotony and discomfort of flying for ten hours or more between Gander and Prestwick. They were very dependent on receiving accurate weather and visibility data and being able to fix their position by a combination of dead reckoning, astro-navigation and direction-finding radio aid. At any moment they might receive a signal to the effect that their destination airfield was closed down because of fog or that the navigator realized that the wind direction and speed that had been assumed for the flight plan no longer applied. Life-or-death decisions had to be made: press on and hope the fog lifts, turn back, or divert. Every option had the question attached to it of how much fuel remained in the tanks.

Sensations

The skewed seat of the Mosquito has been mentioned as a possible cause of loss of control. The Wellington bomber also had a built-in hazard, as did nearly all wartime aircraft. A number of Wellingtons dived into the ground at night about three minutes after take-off. At the time the cause was not obvious. In 1949 Professor A.R. Collar investigated the RAF's wartime accident reports and concluded that the pilots concerned had not been given sufficient instruction in instrument flying. Collar pointed out that, in daylight, a pilot assessed the angle of climb after take-off from the pressure of his back on the seat and his view of the ground. However, on a dark night, with few if any lights on the ground, a pilot was not always able to tell the difference between a steady climb and acceleration using seat pressure alone. At the top of climb-out, when the aircraft was levelled off, there was an increase in speed. This gave a sensation of pressure on the pilot's back that might lead to the assumption that the aircraft was still climbing. Therefore the pilot would push the control column forward to achieve as he thought level flight. In a circle of cause and effect the aircraft might be pushed over into a fatal dive.

Research programmes conducted between 1939 and 1945 included studies of human behaviour, particularly under stress and long exposure to the cockpit environment. However, much of what was learnt and might have improved cockpits could not be applied because of the pressure of war. Among the data on human performance are the following, gathered by the USAAF. Of 460 accidents and incidents classified as 'pilot error', 50 per cent were attributed to confusing one control with another; 18 per cent to operating a control incorrectly; 18 per cent to failure to check, unlock or operate a control; 3 per cent because a pilot could not reach a control and 11 per cent from miscellaneous causes. Sometimes these facts were carried forward to the design of the next generation of aircraft. But sometimes they were not.

Fatigue

Research into aircrew fatigue, particularly that of pilots, was an important subject in the Second World War. The Cambridge cockpit studies in which pilots 'flew' a Spitfire simulator produced data on the effects of long exposure to noise, aircraft movement and concentration on instruments. Not unexpectedly the commonly perceived deterioration in skill after many hours in the cockpit was verified by the results. Specific end deterioration is a human condition that has been the cause of many approach and landing accidents. At the end of a long and arduous flight there is a natural tendency to relax: 'We've made it back. We'll be on the ground in a few minutes.' The modern motorist is a frequent victim of specific end deterioration; as highlighted by the incidence of accidents close to a driver's home.

Advancing the technologies

From Spitfire 1 to the MB V

The quest for greater speed, operating height and firepower produced successively more complicated aircraft, the Spitfire XIV, for example. This mark was far in advance of the simple Mk 1 of the 1930s. The cockpit had more instruments and switches to match the greater performance, and an attempt was made to tidy up the proliferation of switches and buttons by mounting them in an orderly row. Although the Griffon engine in the Mk XIV, with its five-bladed propeller, is not directly part of the cockpit story, nevertheless it is mentioned because it was far more bulky than the Merlin of earlier marks of Spitfire. This added to the taxiing problem of avoiding ground collisions.

The Hawker Tempest was a larger and more potent aircraft than its ancestor the Hurricane, but apart from having more

With the MB V Martin Baker produced a cockpit in which much thought was given to the layout of instruments and controls. An example that other designers at the time might have followed. *Martin Baker*

Although the DH Hornet fighter arrived too late for WWII nevertheless the cockpit is representative of the era. The reflector gun sight uses the windscreen as a combining glass on which to reflect the aiming images. This is tidier than most British cockpits of the time and the 'bilges' are not in view. *British Aerospace*

controls and instruments, the cockpit was little different from that of the earlier aircraft. A contemporary account of flying the Tempest criticized the cockpit. The bilges were in full view, as were the structural members of the fuselage. Splayed heel-trays ran from under the seat to each of the rudder pedals, and the only inconvenience of not having a floor was in dust, draughts and the possibility of accidentally dropping something. With the seat adjusted for normal pilot height the boost gauge could not easily be seen. The rudder trim control was not to hand and difficult to reach except by the finger-tips. The undercarriage lever on the sloping panel on the left was in contact with the calf of the pilot's left leg. The aperiodic magnetic compass, mounted in the traditional between-the-knees RAF position, was masked by the control column.

Few of the aircraft design offices in the Second World War had the resources or time to allow in-depth studies aimed at improving the control interface. There were many cockpit layouts proposed by pilots. They, after all, were in the best position to comment based on their experience of sitting for many hours in discomfort, unable to obtain accurate instrument readings or employ safe instrument-scanning techniques, unable to see ahead clearly in precipitation and so on. One designer in particular made a big effort in this respect. This was Martin Baker, whose MB V was not only one of the most advanced of all piston-engined fighter aircraft, it had a cockpit in which ergonomic considerations had been applied. The designer of the MB V was unconstrained by tradition. He included many new ideas for the structure, the fitting of the instrument panel and access panels in the fuselage and wings. The cockpit was no exception. He started with a clean sheet of paper, whereas other designers figuratively looked over their shoulder at the cockpits that had gone before. In contrast, the cockpit of the MB V had few 'odd corners' into which

loose objects might hide. The instruments and controls were in orderly arrays and anticipated the fighter cockpits of a later generation.

Cockpit CRT

One particular instrument not found in production aircraft cockpits in the years leading up to the Second World War was the CRT (cathode ray tube) used to present radar information. The CRT in the 1930s was a useful laboratory instrument. Its use was expanded with the advent of television, when it replaced the iconoscopes of the pioneering systems. Those who led UK radar development in the late 1930s appreciated from the start that if the Luftwaffe used night attacks the position and height data provided by the chain of defence radar stations (CH system) were not accurate enough to enable a controller to position a night-fighter within 500 yards of an intruder. Therefore resources had to be applied not only to developing ground-controlled interception (GCI) radar, but most importantly radar equipment compact, reliable and powerful enough to fit into a night-fighter. In the first few months of war some RAF night-fighter Blenheims

AI MkVI radar display unit to the right of the gunsight in an RAF Typhoon. This is an early example of an attack radar in the cockpit of a single-seat fighter. *Crown Copyright*

This is believed to show the special Serrate system used by some Mosquito night fighters 1944-1945. Serrate was used in conjunction with AI MkIV to home onto German night-fighter radar emissions. The AI's two CRT displays are hidden by the rubber visor. The indicator of the Monica tail-warning is mounted below the altimeter on the main instrument panel.
Crown Copyright

were fitted with airborne interception (AI) radar. This was operated by a specialist in the back cockpit, some of whom were civilian scientists. The two small-diameter CRTs had to be hooded so that the operator could interpret the azimuthal, height and range displays on the CRTs, and give the pilot steering information such as 'Turn port 10 degrees. Range four thousand.' Using a CRT for providing more information directly to the pilot was always in the minds of the radar scientists.

The Luftwaffe and the US Navy in the Second World War applied pilot-operated AI to single-seater fighters. The former tried the Neptune series of interception radar in the Bf 109 and the Fw 190. The US Navy used the very successful type APS-4 in the F6F Hellcat. The RAF was not completely convinced that one man could handle an AI radar on his own, although the concept was investigated and flown in a Typhoon. In the radar-equipped night-fighters of the Second World War we find the origins of the arguments in the post-war decades over the respective merits of single-seater and two-seater interceptors. The radar operators in German and British night-fighters were usually highly skilled at 'talking' the pilot into an attacking position. Eventually the pilot indicator (PI) for the AI radar was introduced into Mosquito night-fighters. This enabled the pilot to share some of the workload, as well as speeding up the information link, and was a precursor of a radar display in the single-seat cockpits of the future.

Autopilots

Typical of the wartime generation of autopilots fitted to American aircraft was the Minneapolis-Honeywell C-1 system with its distinctive control and selector unit and with two rows of small lamps to indicate when the pilot could engage the system. The C-1 was coupled to the Norden stabilized bombsight. In contrast, British multi-engined aircraft were equipped with the less sophisticated Smiths pneumatic autopilot that had been developed in the early 1930s. An improved version, which was coupled to the gyro-magnetic compass, provided automatic course keeping, a feature that had been incorporated in German autopilots before the Second World War.

Automatic landing

In 1944 three technologies were merged in experiments conducted jointly in the UK by the USAAF, the RAF and the Tele-communications Research Establishment. They were Rebecca/Eureka, SCS.51 and Ground Control Approach (GCA) radar. Together they formed the precursor of the automatic landing systems developed after the war. Its importance to the story of the cockpit is that they provided the pilot with a homing, orbiting, approach and landing system that was independent of another crew member and the need to listen to a continuous signal from the ground. The experimental equipment, in the cockpits of a Boeing 247D and B-24, included on the one dial of SCS.51, an early ILS (Instrument Landing System), a distance-to-go indicator (an early DME), a localizer needle and a glide slope needle. In addition there was a unit for orbiting control and indication. With this system a pilot could home to base, orbit at a selected radius, turn onto the correct approach path and then descend along a 3-degree glide slope. The orbiting feature arose out of the RAF's and USAAF's requirement for a system that could cope with masses of bombers returning to base. Air traffic control could not safely handle a large number of aircraft at the same time, particularly in poor visibility.

More importantly to the history of the cockpit was the extension of the experiments to achieve automatic landing. The 3-degree angle would become the standard from then on for the ILS used by commercial aircraft making landings under pilot control, and also for automatic landings. Another outcome of the 3-degree approach that had a significant influence on cockpit design in Britain was related to the type of undercarriage. Admittedly the Boeing 247D was a tail dragger, but it had a shallow approach close to 3 degrees. The B-24 was also brought in at about the same angle. A Lancaster was tried with the system, using the typical RAF approach at 5 or 6 degrees. The steep approach path followed by a violent change of attitude just before touch-down was unsuitable for automatic landings. A nosewheel undercarriage and a shallow approach, as with a C-54, were essential. British designers reluctantly realized that the tailwheel configuration for future airliners was long past its sell-by date.

GEE and later H2S

By the end of 1941 GEE and later H2S began to improve the effectiveness of RAF Bomber Command. These navigational aids are important in the history of the cockpit because they represent a move away from pencil-and-paper calculations towards instrument systems that when given inputs of information automatically provide an immediate answer. These advances in 'Where are we?' devices were the first step towards the time when pilots would be independent of specialist navigators.

Instruments

In the closing years of the Second World War some aircraft were capable of flying at speeds close to that of sound. Even when flying, say, at 80 per cent of the speed of sound (Mach 0.80) the airflow of some parts of the aircraft could reach Mach One. This could cause buffeting and even loss of control. Therefore the Machmeter became an important addition to the instrument panel.

Instrument panels sometimes exhibited national characteristics. A seemingly haphazard arrangement of the instrument panel was used in some German aircraft. But often this could not be avoided because the characteristic extensive fenestration forward, with views from the pilot's seat downwards, upwards and to the sides, mitigated against a neat athwartships panel. In the He 111, for example, many of the flight instruments were above the pilot's eye level. In 1943 the RAF and the US Navy had a disagreement over the arrangement of flight instruments. The US Navy Bureau of Medicine decided that the best way to solve the problem was to set up a project to do eye movement studies during flight, something that had not been done before. A PBY 5A was used as the test aircraft. A double camera system photographed the pilot's eyes and the instrument panel simultaneously. A frame-by-frame analysis was made of the film of the pilot's eye movements when using first the USN panel and then the RAF panel. The results showed that there was very little difference in pilot performance.

Gyro magnetic distant-reading compass

In the first two years of the war there was one particular item of equipment that set British cockpits apart from those of other nations. This was the pilot's compass. The cockpit of an RAF aircraft in the early years of the Second World War could be easily identified from the large-diameter aperiodic magnetic compass with rotatable grid ring, which took up a lot of space. Any magnetic compass can be affected by magnetic fields generated by adjacent equipment, including airframe components, bombs and guns. After the 20 mm guns in a Beaufighter were fired the P-type compass could be as much as 30° in

error because the steel blast tubes were magnetized by the passage of the shells. American and German aircraft had remotely located master compass units with repeater instruments in front of the pilot and navigator. By the end of 1940 the RAF began to make increasing use of the gyro magnetic distant-reading compass. The master unit was mounted in a position where it was least affected by adverse magnetic influences. A repeater indicator of aircraft heading was provided on the pilot's instrument panel and in the navigator's compartment.

Engine instruments

Engine instruments in American multi-engined aircraft were usually of the type in which one instrument case housed two mechanisms, thereby giving two pointer-on-dial presentations; one for each of two engines. This arrangement economized on space on the instrument panel. The British also had some twin read-out instruments, such as oil pressure and rpm indicators. The American twin-display instruments, for example, when set in a row covering four engines and two different sets of parameters, had to be scanned carefully to make sure that a particular reading applied to the correct engine.

Radio

Keeping in touch with events and being able to confirm an assumed position by means remote from the aircraft, such as radio, had always been high on the pilot's list of essential cockpit equipment. In the first year of the Second World War German single-seater fighters were fitted with an R/T set band with a useful range of about thirty-five miles. The limited range proved a handicap when Bf 109s were required to escort bombers attacking targets in Britain.

At the start of the Second World War the RAF's principal airborne radio equipment for single- and two-seater aircraft was the TR9

Miles Master I advanced RAF trainer. A more complex cockpit than that of the Tiger Moth or Magister. The tube at the top of the photograph is part of the, WW I Gosport 'intercom' between the pupil and the instructor in the back cockpit; and there was no radio. *Aeroplane*

R/T set. This was an HF radio with limited range. A better R/T set had been developed for operating at VHF. During 1940 some squadrons had the TR9 and others the VHF set. Suprisingly, in the RAF in the 1940s R/T communication between fighters and bombers was not usually available. A prime example is the ferrying of single-engined fighters from Takoradi on the Gold Coast to Cairo across 3,500 miles of the inhospitable heart of Africa. A ferry pilot, in the event of trouble, had no R/T contact with the formation leader flying a medium bomber.

The limited production capacity of the radio industry in the UK was one reason why pupil pilots in the RAF, even at the more advanced stage of their tuition, were without the benefit of R/T. Inexperienced, and

sometimes experienced, pilots, when faced by a sudden deterioration in visibility, were very much on their own. The men and women of the ATA, who ferried aircraft of all sizes and complexity for the RAF, more often than not also flew without any form of radio communication with the ground.

Leading the target
When a target is flying directly towards or away from you then the only aiming correction needed is an allowance for 'drop': that is, the increasing amount by which a bullet or shell is affected by gravity the further it travels. However, when the target is also moving across the line-of-sight, allowance also has to be made for this by 'aiming off', or 'leading' the target. The

Gyro gun sight (GGS) MkII. The operating system included a mirror fixed on a gyroscope which deflected the aiming symbols so that movement of the target across the line of sight was automatically allowed for. With the GGS the pilot only had to hold the target within the circle of six small diamonds and did not have to offset the target, as with the standard reflector sight.   *Wallace Clarke*

successful fighter pilots, the Aces, were usually those who had mastered the art of correctly leading the target and using the pattern formed by the tracer bullets. In the 'Hollywood' air wars pilots are seen blazing away unaware that in the real world a 20-second burst of fire could use up all the ammunition and might also ruin the gun barrels. Therefore the scientists set about devising a simple 'spot-on' method of aiming.

Lead-computing gyro-gunsights went into production for Allied aircraft from 1942 onwards. The gyro sights were very much larger than the non-gyro reflector sights, and therefore filled much of the space behind the windscreen.

In addition to obscuring the view forward, the gyro sight started a new trend in throttle design. Hitherto the throttle had been just a simple lever, sometimes with an intercom button and a switch for water-methanol injection selection. The gyro sight required a range input. This could be a twist grip on the throttle lever used by the pilot to open or close up the ranging 'pips' displayed in the sight so as to bracket the target. The firing-range information and wingspan of the target, previously set by the pilot, were fed to the sight's mechanism as part of the lead-computing function. The introduction of air-launched rockets, when the trajectory was far from flat, required modification of the sights to allow for rocket 'droop'. They also posed a problem in single-engined aircraft because the target was sometimes obscured by the engine during the attack dive.

Pilots of RAF Typhoons attacking German armour and vehicles in Normandy in 1944 found that it was difficult to aim the air-to-ground rockets. A number of modifications to the gun/rocket sight and additions to the instruments were progressively introduced. These included a modified reflector sight with a greater depression of the aiming line to allow for rocket 'droop', a more precise low-level altimeter, a more accurate indication of 'skid' and a modified gyro horizon for use as an angle-of-dive indicator. The 'skid' indicator was important because, along with the effects of G, any misalignment of the aircraft at the moment when the rockets were fired could result in impact errors of 50 m or more.

In June 1944 the Hawker Tempest V was given a new design of windscreen and improved gyro gunsight. The windscreen frame, along with the reflector glass and brackets of the GM2 gyro-sight, restricted the forward view; particularly when attacking ground targets. In low-visibility conditions there was also a significant loss of light through the reflector glass of the sight, as well as a loss of contrast between the aiming graticule image and the view ahead. Modifications included eliminating the reflector glass and all but the aiming spot, and reflecting the latter directly off the windscreen so as to improve the view of the target significantly. Further improvements included a new design of clear-view windscreen, and this was also applied to the Tempest Vs when they were allocated ground-attack tasks.

CHAPTER SIX

Civil Aviation 1945-1955

Cockpits for peace

Civil aviation carried on in the USA during the war years. The well-established, for its time, network of airways used by the airlines became a vital part of the nation's war effort. The DC-3, and later on the DC-4, not only maintained a reasonable level of public air services but provided a firm foundation for expansion at the end of the war. However, there were few advances in cockpit technology during the war. The instruments and controls in the cockpits of the DC-3/C-47 and DC-4/C-54 and of the Lockheed Lodestar and Constellation, developed during the war years, were very much to the standards of the 1930s. The pointer-on-dial instruments were little different from those of five years earlier.

The years 1945-55 are perhaps best identified as the era in which the writing was on the wall for the propeller-driven commercial aircraft. The piston-propeller engines and turbo-prop engines continued in

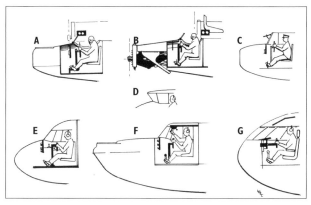

EVOLUTION OF THE FLIGHT DECK

A c 1920 open cockpit derived from WWI bombers. Engine instruments on inboard side of each nacelle.

B Open cockpit trimotor.

C c 1930 with hinged windscreen for flight in low visibility.

D c 1930 reversed rake windscreen to avoid light reflections on instruments.

E c 1940 two-pilot, side-by-side and stepped nose.

F c 1940 flying boat with overhead engine controls to allow access to bow position.

G Windscreen line blended into nose profile as Boeing 307, CW 20 and others. *Author*

DC-4/C-54 military transport whose windscreen and nose profile became the standard for the majority of transport aircraft types for the next 20 years. *Philip Jarrett*

Instrument fashions from the late 1940s. The three-pointer altimeter with its tiny '10,000 ft' pointer sometimes contributed to the misreading of height. It was superseded by the counter-pointer type instruments which had a far less ambiguous presentation.

that began to enter service in this period.

The Second World War had introduced new and complicated machines, none more so than the aircraft. Accidents and incidents in aviation became an accepted part of air force life. Many were caused by straightforward mechanical failure because structures and engines were far more prone to failure than in later decades. Courts of inquiry tended to attribute accidents to 'pilot error'. Those inquiring into the cause of an incident or accident were unlikely to have studied human factors. They more than likely concentrated on the reasons why a pilot had failed to benefit from training and from experience on the aircraft type. They wanted to know why the aircraft had been allowed to enter what was an undesirable area of its performance characteristics, e.g. too tight a turn on the approach with flaps and undercarriage down, thereby inducing a stall. However, a more rigorous approach to the analysis of incident and accident causes was required for civil flying.

The ten years after the Second World War saw a rapid growth in civil air transport. The accident rate, or accident per air miles flown, of pre-war years continued at about the same level. However, passenger complements had doubled and therefore there were more fatalities per accident and a corresponding awareness of the need to improve air safety. Fortunately the loss of life each time was limited because most airliners carried only about fifty passengers. Nevertheless, each disaster made the headlines, along with sensational reporting. Rare were the attempts to understand the technology of aviation. The lay press was interested only in

use into the next decade, but for long-range operations the jet engine became the preferred power. During these years the airliner cockpit gradually changed to meet the changes in engine type and operating practices. The Zero-reader, automatic chart displays of position, such as DECCA, and the introduction of inertial navigation systems and the start of the development of automatic landing systems for passenger-carrying aircraft, all contributed to changes. Propeller reversing and jet thrust reverse controls were among additional cockpit items, along with the weather radar displays sensational reporting so as to increase sales. An example of the general lack of understanding was the argument by counsel at an accident inquiry that because the aircraft was a flying-boat then it should never have been allowed to fly over land and therefore be liable to hit a hill.

Accidents could be allocated to three basic types:

1. Loss of control, resulting in the aircraft stalling or exceeding its performance limits: the former associated with rapid loss of height and therefore disastrous when close to the ground, and the latter causing structural failure. Both the instruments and the shape, position and functioning of the cockpit controls were sometimes contributing factors. For example, an aircraft stalled on take-off because the pilot selected the flaps up instead of the undercarriage. Both levers were close together and identical in shape. Unfortunately selecting the wrong control lever or switch continued to be a common cause of accidents.

2. Collision with another aircraft arising from inadequate fields of view from the cockpit or corrupted air traffic control (ATC) information arising from inadequate cockpit equipment. Many mid-air collisions were attributable to faults in the ATC system, such as false or weak radar returns.

3. Collision with the ground when under full control, resulting from misreading the altimeter; particularly when misread by 10,000 feet. The three-pointer type of altimeter was often the cause. Incorrectly interpreting the navigational instruments, or failing to realize that the instruments had failed or were presenting ambiguous information.

In all three cases inadequate design or lack of good ergonomics of the cockpit and its equipment were often contributory causes.

Managing information

From 1945 onwards more and more information was being provided to pilots. Instead of suffering, as the preceding generation had, from a lack of information, they were now being overloaded with information. Each item of information on its own could be assimilated and acted upon. However, when the input of information started to multiply, pilots had to keep one step ahead of the situation both inside and outside the aircraft. Part of the problem in this era arose from inadequate methods of presenting radio, navigation and aircraft systems status. It would take more than thirty years to develop information and management systems that reduced the incidences of aircrews misreading or misunderstanding information inputs.

The foregoing factors, particularly when related to the landing approach in minimum visibility, were concentrated in the pilot's aural, visual and mental processes. These processes were: to monitor displacements of the ILS needles; watch the rate of descent; adjust the power setting if necessary; check the aircraft's attitude; watch the airspeed indicator and altimeter; try to capture visually the approach lights and so on.

Machine-human interface

In this era of civil aviation the relationship between cockpit design and human behaviour was at a much lower level of activity and understanding than would be achieved thirty years on. Human behaviour at different levels of activity and stress in the cockpit is now well documented. Today there is a wealth of information on how we are likely to behave when at the controls, particularly at different levels of arousal. Every element in the cockpit interface has to be designed or arranged to take account of human behaviour.

As noted, in the early years of aviation

A one-parameter, plus undercarriage-warning, airspeed indicator of the 1950s. *Smiths Group*

concentrated on their overall performance; particularly fatigue, with little or no attention given to the way they reacted to the tools of their work station, such as instruments and controls. Today we have the benefit of a vast fund of information about the ways in which the human pilot sees and perceives. We also know more about the way in which physical sensations and sound affect a pilot's performance.

Accidents waiting to happen

In general, cockpit design, or lack of design, was an accident waiting to happen. To criticize design offices as the only culprits is not fair. It has to be remembered that in 1945 there was no extensive literature from which a designer of the cockpit and its equipment could confidently assume that all but a small percentage of potentially error-inducing items had been eliminated. At this point the reader will want to know why pilot opinion was not embraced as an essential part of the design process. It was. However,

there were few human-factors specialists. Cockpit design proceeded largely without the benefit of either pilot opinion or of human-factors knowledge. Previously scientists concerned with people at work had

Boeing Stratocruiser. Flight engineer's station positioned so that he could operate the throttles on the central controls pedestal between the pilots. Access to the pilots' seats was from the outboard side. *Smiths Group*

there was a trap. The majority of the pilots whose opinions were sought on the layout and equipment of a new cockpit were very experienced aviators. Throughout their careers they had learnt from and survived incidents attributable to inadequate or badly shaped and positioned instruments and controls. Therefore they were not necessarily the best judges, and it might have been better to include less experienced pilots who would not hesitate to comment, 'How am I expected to reach that or see that?'

During the 1930s the impression gained on scanning the array of instruments and controls of a typical airliner, or private aircraft for that matter, was that the designer had applied plenty of TLAR, i.e. 'That looks about right.' Of course there were degrees of good and bad. However, so many cockpits were, like the curate's egg, good in parts.

In 1945 a common civil airline cockpit, in shape and equipment, had evolved from those of the 1930s, in particular from the airliners and military transports of the USA, and especially from the cockpits of the DC-3/C-47 and DC-4/C-54. With German aviation buried for the time being, only France and Britain outside the USA entered the international airline business. Both countries finished the war very much dependent on the USA. During the war neither had had the opportunity or resources to develop civil passenger aircraft comparable to those of the American airlines. In Britain what resources were applied to passenger aircraft design were wasted from the start because of the inability to match the need for aircraft comparable to the large American transports. Russia continued its wartime obsession with secrecy, so that little could be learnt about civil aircraft development there.

In Britain the Brabazon Committee issued a number of specifications for civil passenger aircraft of different sizes. Apart from the requirements of the civil aviation authorities relating to the number and type of instruments and controls and the performance of the radio/navigation system, little or no guidance was provided concerning the design of the cockpits. Progress toward an ergonomic study of the flight deck was sidelined by having to adapt existing bombers, such as the Lancaster and the Halifax, for a civil role. Virtually the only transition step the pilots had to make was to exchange their light blue uniforms for an airline's dark blue. The cockpits and their equipment were as they had been when they were in the RAF. During the war some RAF pilots had written to the technical press complaining about cockpits and their equipment. However, not much was done to collate and publish their comments so as to provide a comprehensive guide to flight-deck design in general.

With the exception of instrument layout, of which more later, American transport

Avro Tudor of BSAA. *Philip Jarrett*

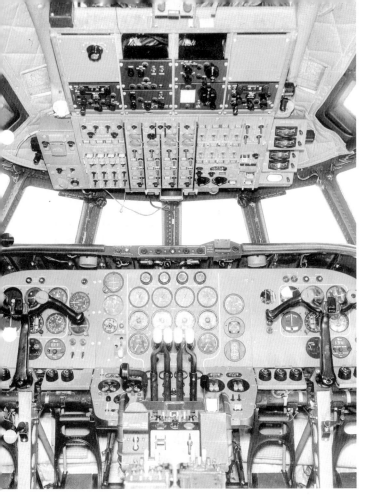

Bristol Britannia. An example of another version of the wheel and pole primary control with the top shaped to avoid obscuring the instruments. *Smiths Group*

Armagnac c 1955. Another attempt to find alternatives for the wheel and column type control. At each pilot's seat were two vertical poles. When moved fore and aft together they controlled the elevator. When pushed down or pulled up differentially they operated the ailerons. *Aeroplane Monthly*

cockpits, with side-by-side pilots' seats, stepped nose and central control pedestal, set the standard. The British airliners, such as the Tudor, Hermes and Viking, followed the American example. The RAF's Basic Six arrangement of the primary flight instruments was carried over to the civil aircraft. Even though it had proved its worth in many thousands of service aircraft, not all civil design offices understood the need to mount it so that its centre coincided with the centre line of the pilot's seat or that the commonly accepted relationship on the panel of the individual instruments needed to be adhered to. Also, they often failed to prevent the flight controls obscuring the instruments.

TLAR continued among the many attempts by British companies to produce a successful replacement for the ubiquitous DC-3. One was the Handley Page Herald. This had mixed parentage and a protracted and uncertain gestation. When it finally emerged, as a twin Dart-engined high-wing monoplane, its cockpit was adversely commented upon in

the technical press. The layout of the instrument panels owed little to any study of the pilot's tasks. The dimensions of the cockpit were limited by the shape of the fuselage nose and, from the writer's experience, one's outboard shoulder, arm and leg were hard up against the side.

Standard cockpit equipment?

In Britain, and to a lesser extent in the USA, each aircraft construction company tended to ignore what others were doing. Only the requirements of the certificating authorities forced a degree of standardization. The airworthiness requirements specified performance over a range of operating modes and the provision of adequate controls and instruments. If the requirements specified, for example, that a means had to be provided for selecting the raising and lowering of the undercarriage and that it had to be within reach of either pilot, that was that. The designer could decide on a switch, a knob or a lever. If a lever, then it could have a ball-shaped end, a spade end or a wheel-shaped end. Adding to the pilots' problems were control columns and wheels that obstructed a view of the instrument panel.

The chain of events

The records show that inadequate design of instruments and controls contributed to many civil transport accidents in this period. The chain of events leading up to a disaster can be very long and include many different factors and elements. A good example is that of a twin-engined passenger aircraft modified to carry an engine in the cabin. The spare engine was needed as a replacement for the failed engine of an aircraft stranded away from its base. The chain of events started with the captain of the aircraft being allocated a room in a hotel near the airport. An early start was needed to avoid having to take off when the air temperature had risen to a level that would reduce the take-off power of the engines. He could not sleep properly because the hotel was alongside the main road to the airport. At the airport he found that the usual co-pilot had been replaced by another, whose English was not very good and made worse over the radio by a strong middle-European accent. The subsequent inquiry revealed that the co-pilot's qualifications were not as they should have been.

By then the combination of lack of sleep and an upset stomach was added to by uncertainty over the position of the load in relation to the aircraft's centre of gravity. Permission was given to start engines. What should have been a routine few minutes' procedure turned into a frustrating thirty minutes as both engines suffered severe oil system trouble. By the time they were airborne the captain was not very happy. The sudden failure of one engine increased his gloom. The co-pilot was instructed to advise ATC of their problem and request immediate clearance back to the airport. This is where unfamiliarity and poor diction resulted in ATC neither understanding nor being able to help. The overloaded and badly trimmed aircraft crashed short of the airfield. Accidents such as this emphasized the need to examine every aspect - not just the pilot's actions, and not just the cockpit instruments and controls.

Cockpit equipment other than instruments and controls were also contributory and sometimes primary causes. A new type of airliner carrying eighty football supporters, at that time a large number of passengers, crashed. The subsequent inquiry examined a number of possible causes. During the approach to land the aircraft suddenly entered a 45° climb and stalled. One conclusion among a number was that the pilot's seat had slid back and caused the pilot to apply full up elevator. This and other 'seat' incidents and disasters forced designers to pay greater attention to the seat mechanism, and to allow greater freedom of configuration so as to suit pilots of different body dimensions.

A time-bomb

The C-54/DC-4 was a major contributor to the growth of civil aviation in the immediate post-war years. The cockpit and the controls and instruments were to the standards of the time. Thousands of pilots had completed an incredible number of flights since the aircraft entered service as a military transport in 1942. The DC-4's accident statistics were average for this era. Of course, there were problems with both engines and airframes, and some of the instruments and controls were difficult to see and operate. One set of controls in particular could easily be mishandled. These were the fuel selector valve-control levers. They were difficult to see and awkward to reach, and a pilot could easily move the wrong one. For example, the cross-feed lever might be left slightly open, thereby allowing fuel to flow from one tank to another without the crew knowing. Twenty-five years on, a fatal crash to a DC-4 occurred when, during an approach to land, Nos 3 and 4 engines lost power because of fuel starvation. The potential hazard had been known for many years to some authorities and operators, but not to all. Nothing was done either to alert everyone or to redesign the fuel-control levers.

In 1947 The USAF published a report by Fitts and Jones on errors made by pilots when operating controls. They studied 460 examples. They found that confusion between engine and throttle controls represented 19 per cent of the total: for example, shutting down No. 1 engine when all the indications were that the controls for No. 2 should have been operated. Eight per cent of the mistakes arose from pressing the wrong feathering button. Sixteen per cent of the errors concerned mistaking the flap lever for the undercarriage lever or vice versa. Forgetting to operate a control or adjusting it incorrectly accounted for 18 per cent. Unintentional operation or inability to reach a particular control accounted for 14 per cent. The obvious overall conclusion had to be that a major contributor to these errors was the general low level of ergonomic thought and design applied to levers, buttons and switches, and to their shape and location.

The view ahead

What the pilot sees or perceives (they are not the same thing), especially when looking at the scene outside the cockpit, is an example of where human behaviour interacts with

Early version of the Viscount with an aperiodic magnetic compass suspended from the overhead and with the mechanical drive mechanisms to the windscreen wipers in full view. Although toe brakes are provided there are also brake levers on the control spectacles. *Vickers*

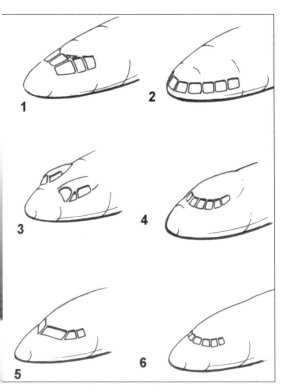

A number of different nose shapes and cockpit fenestration arrangements for the Constellation were studied before Lockheed decided on the production version.

1. Cockpit above cabin deck level.
2. Cockpit below cabin deck level.
3. 'Bug eyes'; impractical.
4. Blister shape as Viscount.
5. Traditional stepped nose.
6. Prototype and production nose.

Author

ergonomics. Of primary concern is the pilot's ability to gain the maximum amount of information from what can be seen. Therefore adequate fields of view (FOV) are obviously very important. How the pilot interprets, i.e. perceives, the view ahead, particularly during the approach to a landing, depends very much on the adequacy of ground features, such as approach and runway lights, as well as on the size and shape of the cockpit windows.

An important factor in visual perception is our knowledge of the identity, characteristics and relationships among the objects and features of the world around us: for the pilot this is concentrated in the view ahead. During a critical phase of flight, such as a landing in poor visibility, the pilot has a mental image of the expected perspective shape of the runway. This image is primarily based on the visual experience of hundreds of previous landings, and is triggered by a glimpse of only a small part of the view ahead and features on the ground. Moving objects and changes to the view ahead form the ever-changing perspective view of surface features during the final stage of a landing. Our knowledge of the world we perceive is our most valuable tool in interpreting instantaneous perceptual information and changes to that information; both subtle and gross. This knowledge usually enables us to react to the information quickly and correctly, but sometimes it does not.

In the immediate post-war years some operators in the UK were using DH-86s and Ju 52s, that approached at about 60 knots (100 feet/sec). In a horizontal visibility of

Viscount cockpit with direct vision (DV) windows for use should the pilots be unable to see through the windscreen. *Vickers*

DH 106. Comet. The two pilots and the flight engineer were crowded well forward in the nose. *Smiths Group*

300 ft, three seconds was little enough time in which to correct the approach path on first sighting the runway threshold. When aircraft were put into service that approached at 100 knots there was even less time in which to refocus the eyes to the view ahead from the 20 inches (40 cm) used for concentrating on the instruments. Not until the safety authorities in the UK insisted that operators had to set criteria for an instrument landing would there be a reduction in landing accidents. Under the new rules account had to be taken of speed, visibility and most importantly the accuracy of the ILS at every runway.

A very important human dimension that has to be related to the cockpit is the eye reference point (ERP). In the early 1950s this was not always given proper attention. If the pilot is to have an adequate FOV of the approach lighting and runway during a landing, and at the same time see all the essential instruments, then the seat must be adjustable so that the pilot can have his eyes at the design ERP.

The field of view in some of the post-war transports was worked out by someone sitting in a mock-up of the cockpit and its windows and measuring the angles subtended by their eyes. The author was involved in such an exercise and also prepared the FOV diagrams. The chief designer was happy, and apparently the certificating authorities made no comment.

One day an airline captain sat in the prototype and commented, 'If I'm in a 30° bank to the left my view of the horizon is cut off on that side.' The assumption had been made by the armchair pilots in the drawing office that the required FOV need only apply when flying straight and level.

Expectation

Another aspect of seeing relates to perceiving the expected and not the actual. This is a common human failing. When all or some of the elements of the real world are hidden by others, or by insufficient visibility, pilots expect them to appear eventually. As mentioned, this reliance on expectation can have disastrous consequences if based on false or insufficient clues. On occasions many of us act on a first glance and assume,

which is part of perception, that what we were expecting to see is actually there. An extreme example is the pilot making an instrument approach in low visibility who assumes that the rows of lights ahead mark the runway, whereas they are the highway lights to one side of, and parallel to, the runway. Occasionally the real world does not appear or change in expected ways, and then we may become confused, frightened or disoriented and react incorrectly. The result of these can be errors on the part of a pilot. To avoid errors or to reduce their adverse effects careful attention must be paid to the detail design of instruments and controls.

Within the overall subject of perception within and outward from the cockpit, a distinction has to be made between the way in which a pilot visually perceives the real

Although the nose and fenestration of the Sud Aviation Caravelle was derived from the DH 106 the type and arrangement of the controls were very different. *Philip Jarrett*

Sud Aviation Caravelle with cockpit and nose structure derived from the DH 106 Comet. *Philip Jarrett*

world and the artificial world of instrument displays. The importance of visual perception, or rather the correct interpretation of perceptual inputs, is particularly applicable to the pilot's control and judgemental tasks whenever using simultaneously real-world and artificial-world information; although, in the absence of visual enhancement systems, the two are not used simultaneously, except when combined in a HUD (Head-up Display), because the pilot alternates between the 'inside' and the 'outside' views. Nevertheless, each time the source of information is changed the pilot has to adjust quickly to different visual tasks. These include adapting in milliseconds to changes that have occurred in the real world and in the artificial world presented by the cockpit instruments since the last scan. For this reason and others, psychologists attempt to understand as much as possible about how the pilot sees and perceives the real world. This subject is also of great importance in relation to analogue and pictorial representations provided by instruments.

Lateral influences

To some degree the right-hand preferences of the majority of pilots influences the design of the cockpit. Since the advent of the side-by-side, two-pilot cockpit, transport aircraft pilots have become accustomed to both right-hand on the engine controls when flying as P1 and left hand when in the P2 position. Human laterality in aviation, as a population characteristic, is little different from that of other highly trained skill groups. Training and adaptability to the special control skills overcomes most handedness problems. There is a tendency among some people, who declare themselves to be clearly handed, to establish a set of careful actions which enables them to conform to their 'declared' handedness. Only when they are surprised or under stress do they revert to their true handedness, with the result that they might confuse left and right.

Human adaptability is such that only a few pilots who are left handed, for example, have any particular problem. Experiments with aircrews were conducted in which it was observed that a number used their left hands unconsciously for doing certain things. Some pilots, though they were classified as right-handers, confused left and right to varying degrees in varying situations. In one example a pilot had the handedness characteristic of ambidexterity. However, he had been left-hand preferring as a child but had subsequently practised many manual skills, e.g. handwriting, with the right hand. Only after he had been selected, medically examined and trained as a pilot was it shown that he had to refer to his wedding ring in order to identify left and right.

Overall, the individual factors that influence aviation practice tended to produce a preference to scan from left to right, circle to the left, lean to the left, turn to the left and fly right-hand on the primary control in single-seat cockpits. However, in those aircraft types in which the pilot sits to one side of the centre-line these factors have less significance.

One aspect of laterality in aviation is concerned with vision, and in particular the way in which the world outside the cockpit is scanned. The scanning patterns used when keeping a visual lookout for conflicting traffic or targets might be influenced by lateral characteristics such as those influenced by writing and reading from left to right. However, research seems to show that other factors are more important, such as the more likely area of the view ahead in which other aircraft or a target will appear. The early keep-right airway rule may have encouraged more attention to the port bow.

In the side-by-side flight deck each of the two pilots has to learn to adapt to a visual scanning pattern appropriate to the side of the aircraft on which he or she is sitting, and in some respects this is analogous to the car driver's visual task when driving either on the left or on the right of a car. The way in which the transport pilots scan the outside view might be influenced by the fact that each is seated off to one side of the centre-line of the cockpit. For example, from the left-hand-seat position, conflicting aircraft that appear to the right will be more difficult to detect than those that appear to the left. In the same way, the pilot in the right-hand seat may not always see another aircraft approaching from the left.

The scanning of instrument panels is to some extent influenced by the left-to-right order of numerals and print, and the numbering of engines and their associated instruments from left to right. However, the instruments of the pre-electronic age were often arranged without consideration of the pilot's need to be able to scan them quickly at intervals. The Basic Six panel and the Basic T arrangement of the essential flight instruments were intended to improve and simplify the scanning task, particularly when making an instrument approach to land.

Accidents and left-right confusion

A feature of many aircraft accidents has been the effects of pilot stress and fatigue, which in conjunction with a series of incidents, none of which in isolation was serious, resulted in disaster. Under stress or fatigue, dormant lateral habits such as confusing left and right, might have dominated a pilot's behaviour, thereby inducing a turn in the wrong direction or moving controls in the wrong direction. Also, under stress, a pilot might transpose numbers on some vital control input, for example when changing the barometric setting of the altimeter.

Some of the more important examples of confusion between left and right occurred with the identification, from instrument readings, that an engine on one side had failed, followed by confusion of action whereby the wrong engine was switched off. In the 1950s the primary cause of three successive accidents to one type of twin-engined transport aircraft was the pilot's misreading of the engine instruments. In all three accidents the pilot shut down the 'good' engine and not the other whose instruments indicated that it was failing. The engine instruments in this particular type of aircraft were of the twin-pointer configuration. The oil pressure reading for both engines was combined on one dial to the left of another two-pointer instrument, so that when the starboard engine oil-pressure needle indicated the onset of failure the pilot thought it was the port engine that was failing.

Port and starboard, left and right

The influence of nautical terminology was most apparent with the use of 'port' for left and 'starboard' for right by British aviation. Left side and right side were used by other countries and were eventually used more frequently in Britain. Port engine and starboard engine were usually adequate for twin-engined aircraft, but with the advent of four engines it became customary to number the engines from left to right, looking forward, so that on the far left was No. 1, and not, as with a ship's stations and compartments, from right to left.

Sometimes aircraft designers introduced an example of lateral confusion when they positioned the flight engineer and his controls facing aft so that his left hand was to the right side of the aircraft, and all the controls and instruments were arranged as a mirror image of the parts of the aircraft to which they referred.

Inside the side-by-side cockpit the principal groups of controls and equipment

DH Dove.

are usually arranged in a mirror-image pattern about the centre-line, but in a number of different lateral sequences, depending on their function. For example, the primary controls carry buttons and selectors on the hand-grips arranged mirror image to enable the pilots to operate them with the hand most used on the primary control, i.e. the outboard hand. The side-stick control has introduced another set of lateral relationships, as will be mentioned. The primary instrument panels, one for each pilot, are usually to an identical arrangement of instruments and therefore are not a mirror

image. The principal engine-control levers are arranged in topographical relationship to the engines, with engine No. 1 controls on the extreme left, and with the instruments for each engine in related vertical rows.

The helicopter provides a clear example of a complete reversal of what at one time was a well-established stereotype. This is the positioning of the principal pilot to the right of the cockpit so that the right hand is on the cyclic-pitch-control lever and the left hand is on the collective-pitch control. One reason for this may be related to the preference of the majority of pilots to use their right hand

Lockheed Constellation. Wide arc-of-view in the horizontal plane but limited in the vertical. *British Airways.*

DC-3 cockpit: angles of view from the captain's (P1) eye reference point. The view of conflicting traffic approaching from the right is severely restricted. This contributed to the causes of numerous near misses and collisions in areas of high traffic density. *Author*

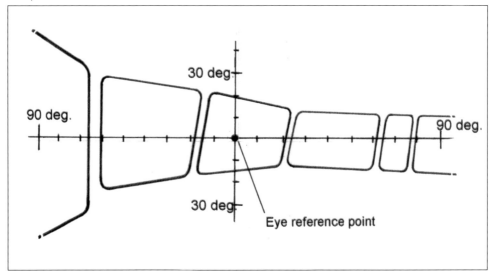

for the control requiring the greater degree of precision and coordination.

See and be seen

Pressurized fuselages became the standard for large passenger aircraft in the 1950s to enable them to operate above most of the turbulent layers of air. A typical cruising altitude would be 20,000 feet. Pressurization imposed a limit to the size of windows, particularly for the cockpit. The arcs of view were restricted in both the vertical plane and in the horizontal by the window frames. They were further reduced by the distance of the pilot's eye reference point (ERP) from the glass – that of the captain to the left and of the second pilot to the right. Frequently during a flight one of the pilots could be 'head down' consulting a chart or operating manual. If, for example, the captain in the left-hand seat was adjusting one of the instrument settings, the other pilot could easily fail to detect another aircraft closing on the port bow. If it was not spotted before it was within half a mile then there was less than ten seconds in which to react to the threat. Even when the closing speed was only about 50 knots the pilots of a DC-7 failed to detect a Constellation cruising ahead of them at the same altitude. Both aircraft crashed.

When flying at high altitudes and deprived of objects on which to focus, such as clouds, the earth or other aircraft, a pilot's eyes are focused at about two metres. Therefore objects further away are undetected. This 'space myopia' applies also when making an approach to land in fog or even in darkness. The first sighting of the runway can be delayed, or the chance of quickly and correctly interpreting visual clues can be reduced.

Flight-deck crew

The DC-4's take-off weight was less than 80,000 lb, and this was important in relation to airline cockpit design in general. In 1948 the Federal Aviation Agency decreed that aircraft above that weight had to have a third flight-deck crew member; such as a flight engineer. A series of crashes to the stretched version of the DC-4, the DC-6, were attributable to cockpit workload factors. Arguments on this subject between pilots and airlines were to rumble on throughout the 1950s. The 80,000 lb demarcation was arbitrary as far as workload was concerned. An aircraft of half that weight could, because of poor cockpit design, impose just as high a workload.

The provision of a flight engineer had for many years been considered necessary in large multi-engined aircraft because of the need to constantly monitor the 'health' of engines and to control the distribution of fuel contained in a number of dispersed tanks; as well as monitor other systems, such as electrical power. The pilots usually had enough on their hands in just flying and navigating the aircraft. In addition, particularly for long-haul overwater flying away from land-based navigational aids, specialist navigators and radio operators were required.

Now that 'workload' has been introduced as a primary factor in cockpit design and pilot performance, it is necessary to define what it means. Essentially it is derived from comparing the time available in which to complete a task with the time needed to complete the task. If there are many tasks needing attention, but a limited time available, then a pilot either has to attempt to complete all of them or concentrate on the most important. In attempting to monitor, for example, the ILS and other flight instruments, and at the same time adjust the trim and engine controls, and also talk to an air traffic controller, some or all of the individual tasks will be hurried and even neglected.

DC-7 'Super 7'. *Philip Jarrett*

Cockpit variety

During this era incidents and accidents resulted from pilots having to change from one aircraft type to another type, sometimes on the same day. As each aircraft manufacturer had its own ideas about which way a lever or knob should be turned, these could become accidents waiting to happen. In one mixed fleet the Ju 52 had instruments and controls arranged in a very different way from those of the Viking or even from other types of aircraft. A vital engine control in the Ju 52 had to be moved in the opposite sense to the same control in a Viking.

One very experienced pilot considered that the instruments and controls of the Viking were so badly arranged that they induced accidents. Although the Ju 52 had a moderate touch-down speed, about 60 knots,

and therefore was not too demanding on either the pilot's skill or runway length, braking to a standstill after landing was not easy or simple. The three throttle levers also acted as brake levers. When pulled right back against a spring the brakes were applied, the middle lever giving equal hydraulic power to both sets of brakes, and the outer levers providing differential braking. As was usual with German aircraft of 1930s vintage, the brakes were weak and could not be relied upon. Some versions of the aircraft had two levers that could be pulled out toward the pilot's knees to apply the brakes differentially or equally. When taxiing a Ju 52 in winter there was always the chance that an engine would stop completely if its throttle lever was pulled back to the braking position. Of course, the cockpit of the Ju 52

DC-7. Indicator and controls on the overhead panel above the windscreen; these include the contents indicators for the 7,800 gallons of fuel carried in the wing tanks. *Philip Jarrett*

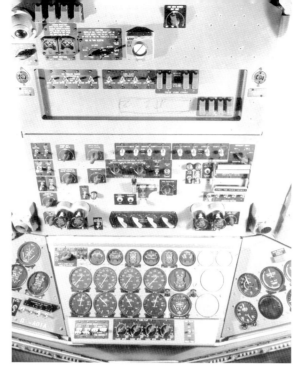

Below: DC-7. Captain's flight instruments. *Philip Jarrett*

Below: DC-7. Second Pilot's flight instruments. *Philip Jarrett*

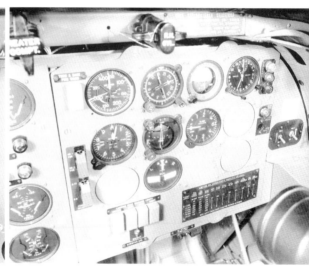

Below: DC-7. Weather radar at Captain's outboard knee. An improved version visible without the need for a hood. *Philip Jarrett*

Below: DC-7. Weather radar at second pilot's outboard knee. A viewing hood was necessary because of the poor definition of the CRT display in high ambient light. *Philip Jarrett*

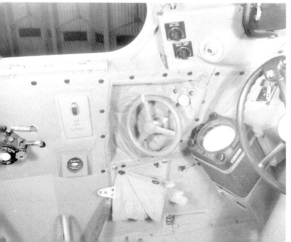

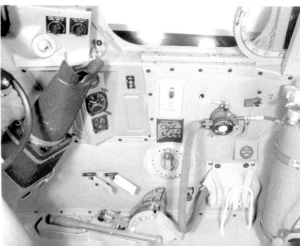

DC-7. Central control pedestal details. There are two sets of throttle levers with the propeller controls between them. The majority of the radio/navigation controls are also on the central pedestal. *Philip Jarrett*

DC-7. Vertical face of central controls pedestal showing the autopilot selector panel, radio controls, mixture and carburetor air levers, undercarriage lever (centre), flap lever (right) and aileron trim wheel. *Philip Jarrett*

was to 1930 standards and therefore should not be taken as being representative of the design standards of the early 1950s.

In the cockpits of some of the new airliners of the early 1950s many of the pre-war TLAR decisions concerning instruments and controls were perpetuated. Instruments were positioned in relation to each other without thought being given to the pilot's scanning task when under stress; such as when making an instrument landing or when a major engine failure occurred. In some cockpits important controls were within the reach of only one of the pilots or were awkwardly placed. Even when an attempt was made to position controls in a logical order, not enough thought was given to the possible danger of one lever being confused with another.

The instrument panel

For many years instrument panels were 'happenings' rather than the outcome of deliberate thoughts about the relationships between one instrument and the others on the same panel. In general, in relation to the human operator, instrument panel design is concerned with enhancing the effectiveness of the individual units that make up a panel as well as that of the panel as a whole. In the USA there was a different approach to arranging the instruments. Many American civil aircraft, both big and small, had what seemed to British eyes a strange arrangement of the flight and engine instruments. However, that was what thousands of pilots had become used to from the first time they were shown how to fly on 'needle, ball and airspeed'. This preference persisted until the advent of the Basic T. This is a good example of making the most effective use of individual instruments by placing them in an

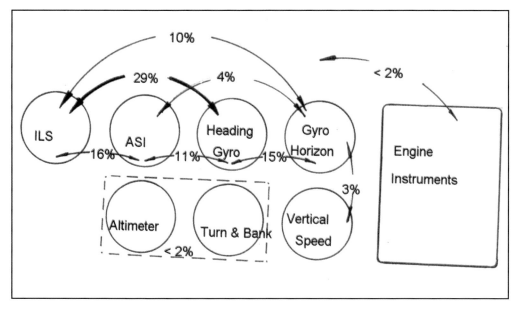

Before agreement was reached on the Basic Tee arrangement of the four most important flight instruments an analysis was made of a typical layout of the instrument panel of a typical American transport aircraft. This determined how the pilot scanned the instruments during an ILS approach. 29% of time was devoted to scanning between the ILS indicator and the heading indicator. Less than 2% of time was given to the altimeter and turn-and-bank instruments and to the engine instruments. Of course the last were being monitored by the second pilot. *Author*

arrangement that eases the pilot's task of integrating the discrete displays of speed, attitude, height and heading.

The development of better instrumentation continued throughout the era so as to keep pace with the rapid expansion of civil aviation. During an approach to land the pilot had to interpret the crossed pointers of the ILS indicator in such a way that the aircraft was kept on the glide slope and the localizer beams. Attending to the ILS as well as monitoring attitude, airspeed, vertical speed, heading and height imposed a high workload. In turbulence, a cross-wind and other distractions, the workload was even higher. Therefore Sperry introduced the Zero Reader. This was based on the artificial horizon, to which were added a vertical and a horizontal bar. By zeroing the displacement of the bars from the symbol representing the aircraft on the centre of the dial, the aircraft could be flown smoothly back onto the

approach path. For example, if the vertical needle was to the right of the symbol representing the aircraft, and the horizontal needle was above the symbol, then the control demand was bank right and raise nose until both bars intersected the symbol. Further developments led to the attitude director indicator (ADI). By controlling the aircraft so as to bring the aircraft reference symbol over the intersection of the pitch-and-bank director bars the aircraft would then be on the selected heading, at the required height and vertical speed.

The increase in air traffic in the post-war years required an extension of the airways systems, and in parallel the need for better navigational and flight instruments. The remote reading compass and the radio bearing indicator were combined so as to produce the radio magnetic indicator (RMI). This enabled a pilot to read the aircraft's magnetic heading as well as the bearing of a

The C-47/Dakota/DC-3 cockpit. This 1950s version has the instruments arranged in no particular order of importance or relationship. There was wide variation in instruments among the DC-3 cockpits. *Smiths Group*

radio beacon. A further development combined electromechanical and electronics to produce the horizontal situation indicator (HSI). This provided an easily read picture of where the aircraft was in relation to radio navigational aids This, together with the ADI, became the first 'pictorial' display. An important event in this era were the trials in 1950 of the Sperry inertial navigation (IN) system. This combination of gyros and accelerometers provided a system that was independent of electronic signals transmitted either from the ground or from the aircraft. The basic principles had been

not overcome the loads imposed on the controls. The simple arrangement of rods or cables that directly connected the hand and foot controls to ailerons, elevator and rudder had to be elaborated. Decade by decade as aircraft came into use that were larger or faster than before (or both), methods were devised for multiplying the pilot's muscular effort. The simplest solution was to set back the hinge line of a control surface, such as a rudder, so that part of the surface projected into the airstream, thereby balancing out part of the load applied to the main surface. When this proved unsuitable, designers would apply servo tabs. These moved in concert with the main surface but in the opposite direction. Sometimes, for example, the control wires or rods from the cockpit controls went to the tabs and were not directly connected to the elevator.

The new large civil jet transport aircraft imposed even greater demands on power and precision of operation, and therefore hydraulic- or electrical-power-operated control surfaces came into use. Irrespective of the type and complexity of power-operated controls, an important step in the history of the aircraft cockpit is the elimination of the one-time direct link between pilot and aircraft. No longer could the pilot 'feel' the air loads on the control surfaces and in turn the loads imposed on the aircraft's structure when manoeuvring. To provide 'feel' and to prevent the powerful control systems being used to overstress the aircraft, artificial loads in the form of springs or Q systems had to be added. The latter responded to the dynamic pressure of the airflow.

around for many years, but it would take another ten before a production standard system was perfected, and then, at first, only for application to military aircraft.

More muscle power

At certain combinations of speed and control surface area the pilot's muscle power could

Autoland

In the immediate post-war years the number of accidents resulting from attempts to land in insufficient visibility encouraged the development of landing guidance systems. Ground control approach radar, used by the air forces, was supplied to civil airfields. When a DC-3 crashed at London Heathrow airport when the pilot attempted a GCA landing in 600 ft visibility, the civil aviation authority declared that GCA was 'not a blind-landing aid, it was only a guide to pilots'. With a GCA approach and landing the pilot was entirely dependent on the accuracy of the radar and on the skill of the operators. The pilot was not fully in the control loop; whereas with the ILS, provided the beams were accurately set up, the pilot was fully in the control loop. The required technological upward step from ILS was fully automatic, 'hands-off' control.

Development of military autoland systems continued after the war; especially for the RAF's V bomber force. The research was eventually extended to include civil passenger-carrying aircraft operations. With approach and landing speeds increasing, sometimes by as much as 50 per cent, and the need to maintain operational effectiveness irrespective of the visibility, the development of automatic landing was pushed ahead. After the war the Royal Aircraft Establishment (RAE) in Britain perfected vastly improved systems of approach and runway lighting (e.g. the Calvert). These gave the pilot the maximum guidance during a landing in poor visibility conditions and helped to overcome space myopia. They helped to reduce the number of landing incidents and accidents arising from faster approach speeds and aircraft that were larger and less manoeuvrable.

Weather radar

In this period of civil aviation expansion, aircraft continued to be damaged or even lost because of entering a region of the intense precipitation, severe sharp-edged gusts and up-and-down air movements of a storm cell. Radar came to the rescue in the shape of a system that could look ahead and detect potentially dangerous atmospheric conditions. At first the airborne sets were bulky and the CRT display had to be viewed through a hood. As an example, with one experimental weather radar the display unit was 40 inches (102 cm) in length and 10 inches (25 cm) square. This took up a lot of room in the cockpit. Eventually CRTs were developed that could be viewed in daylight and were small enough to be included in the main instrument panel.

Lessons learnt

By the end of this pioneering era in civil aviation, a vast body of information and experience relating to the cockpit and the pilot's task had been accumulated. This would be applied to the design of the next generation of transport aircraft. Unfortunately some of the shortcomings of cockpit design and operating procedures that had caused so many accidents in the first ten post-war years were still around in 1955.

CHAPTER SEVEN

Military Cockpits 1945-1955

Old wine in new bottles

The decade after the Second World War is selected as a specific era in this book because it covers the transition from piston-engined propeller power to gas turbine power for fighters and bombers. But the change to turbine power for ab initio training aircraft was a decade away.

Although the aviation gas turbine engine was developed in the 1930s, the many problems to be overcome, particularly the metallurgical, delayed the introduction of a practicable jet aircraft until nearly the end of the Second World War. In Germany, the USA and Britain during the final years of the war, design offices began to scheme advanced aircraft combining the advantages of jet propulsion with the latest ideas in aerodynamics. Although better ejection seats and canopies, giving maximum arcs of view, were developed, in general there were few

Instrument panel for the Vampire jet fighter c 1947. Apart from a Mach meter, an RPM (meter reading up to 20,000) and cabin pressure indicators, this could be a contemporary piston-engine aircraft panel. *Smiths Group Archives*

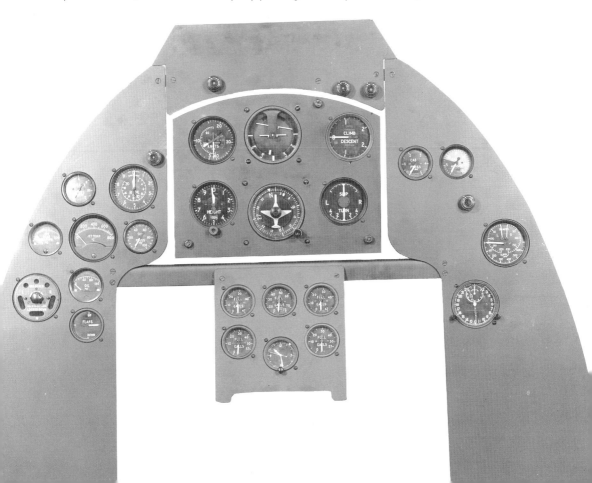

innovations in controls and instrumentation. As in previous design eras, designers had to concentrate first on solving the aerodynamic, structural and engine problems. Instrumentation and control details had to take a backseat.

Because new aircraft, systems and equipment took many months to develop, even in wartime, post-war technology emerged from that of the final war years. Even though by 1943 the jet engines were beginning to push the piston engines off the drawing boards, cockpit technology did not change significantly. To start with, jet aircraft did not achieve an overall performance very much better than that of the piston-engined aircraft. Therefore, apart from shaft speed indicators able to peak at 10,000 rpm, temperature indicator scales up to 1,000°C and Machmeters, existing cockpit equipment could be used.

Germany won the race to get jet aircraft into production and into action by a short head. The most effective were the Me 262 and the Arado 234. Their potential adversary, the Gloster Meteor, arrived too late in the war to engage with them in combat. Its cockpit also was 'the mixture as before', plus instruments specific to the jet engine.

Meteor

The Gloster Meteor, the first large-scale production jet aircraft fighter for the RAF, introduced an entirely new cockpit environment. The most notable feature was the absence of the low-frequency vibrations, around 3 kHz, and sounds which many pilots had endured when flying Spitfires and Tempests and other piston-engined aircraft. No longer was the view ahead shared with a bulky radial or in-line engine. In the Meteor the pilot had a virtually unobstructed view ahead from the cockpit, which was set close to the nose of the aircraft. Adding to the excellent visibility from the cockpit when taxiing was the level ground attitude provided by the nosewheel undercarriage.

Gloster Aircraft, as with its experimental Whittle-engined jet, was not able to devote too much time and resources to detailed refinements of the Meteor airframe. This was that of a conventional twin piston-engined aircraft. The cockpit and its equipment had to be provided from what was available. Therefore it was little different from those of the piston-engined fighters. Compared with the fourteen engine-starting actions for the Me 262, the starting check list for the engines of the Meteor was simpler. It required only seven lever and button selection steps. In 1945 the turbine engine was still in its infancy, and therefore care had to be exercised so as not to allow the jet pipe temperature to reach an excessive value, usually around 500°C. The pilot also had to keep the rpm for each engine away from a value at which the engine resonated to such an extent that it caused the turbine to shed blades.

The fuel consumption rate of the Meteor, as with other jet aircraft, was much greater than that of a piston-engined aircraft of comparable power. This meant that among the cockpit instruments those concerned with fuel flow and quantity were of vital importance. A Meteor pilot had to avoid 'idling' on the ground at all times and had to keep one eye on the fuel quantity remaining and pay strict attention to the 'Bingo' radio reminders from the ground that 'his time was up'. The Derwent engines of the Meteor Mk IV, for example, burnt around 200 gallons of kerosene each hour of flight. Even when taxiing to the take-off point each engine used twenty gallons. At the end of a sortie up to 40,000 ft only sixty gallons out of 325 might remain with which to complete an approach to the airfield and landing and allow for a 'wave off' and a go-round-again circuit.

The type and arrangement of the flight

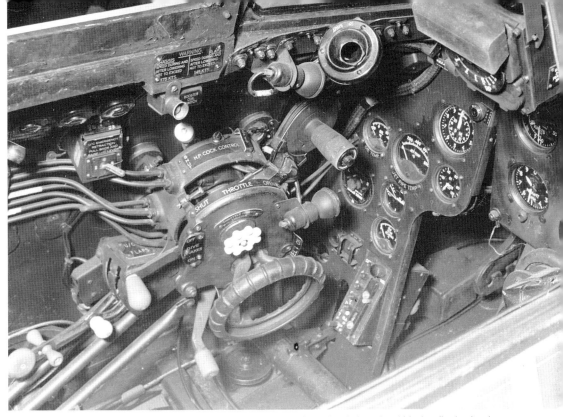

Detail of the cockpit of a DH Vampire showing the twist-grip on the top of the throttle lever by which the pilot bracketed the target when seen through the gyro gunsight. *BAE*

instruments were typically RAF c.1944. The early marks of the Meteor had the Basic Six panel set below the gyro gunsight. Successive developments of the basic Meteor design, such as the AW NF 11 two-seater night-fighter, exhibited a number of differences in cockpit equipment related to the role of the aircraft. For example, the Mk IV and later types had pressurized cockpits along with the warning in the Pilot's Notes not to throttle back too much at high altitude, thereby losing cockpit pressure. The DH Vampire followed the Meteor into RAF service. Among its cockpit equipment was a large twist-grip on the throttle lever for setting target range on the gyro gunsight and a rear-bearing-temperature indicator. The latter emphasized the need in those days to monitor engine health closely.

One of the first departures from the RAF Basic Six panel. This is the principal instrument panel in a Folland Gnat arranged around an integrated system of attitude and horizontal situation indicators. *Smiths Group Archives*

Unusual postures

Now and then an attempt was made to get away from the conventional seated position for the pilot. If the pilot could lie prone or supine then the effects of G might be reduced. Another benefit would be aerodynamic, because the frontal area of the cockpit would be less, thereby reducing drag. However, those benefits were outweighed by a number of negative points. When prone the pilot's weight, including the head, had to be supported by a specially shaped couch and chin rest. Although the effects of G on the blood system might be less during a positive G manoeuvre, the pilot's head would be forced down onto the chin rest. As the Wright brothers discovered, the prone position resulted in neck ache. Lying prone with the head at an angle to the body would have made it extremely difficult to use the gunsight, let alone scan the few instruments that could be fitted in around the pilot's head. A fundamental requirement for air-to-air combat was the ability to keep an all-round lookout for the enemy. This was nearly impossible when lying prone. Another problem came with how to operate the rudder control, because when lying prone the

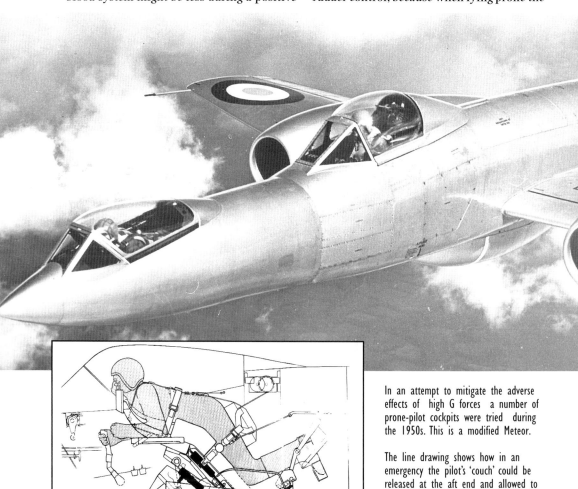

In an attempt to mitigate the adverse effects of high G forces a number of prone-pilot cockpits were tried during the 1950s. This is a modified Meteor.

The line drawing shows how in an emergency the pilot's 'couch' could be released at the aft end and allowed to swing downward so that he could drop below the aircraft. *Aeroplane Monthly*

Irrespective of the seat angle, pilots found that controlling vertical speed so as to effect a smooth touch-down was not easy. These aircraft were being experimented with in the days before the advent of the necessary sophisticated control and instrumentation systems.

F-86

The Meteor, with its unswept wings, represented the first-line strength of RAF Fighter Command. In contrast, the USAF was given the North American F-86 Sabre. Its swept wings owed much to the

Leduc 021 ram jet of 1953. The 'pilot's position', rather than 'cockpit', was in a jettisonable nose cone. The directly forward view was enhanced by a prism on the upper surface of the cone. *Aeroplane Monthly*

ankles provided only limited movement.

Despite the drawbacks, a number of experimental prone-pilot aircraft were flown. They included the appropriately named Bobsleigh by Reid & Sigrist and a converted Meteor F8. In the latter the pilot lay prone on a couch at an angle of about 40° to the horizontal. In the event of trouble the couch could be released downward so that the he could fall free of the aircraft. Apparently none of the flight-test reports by different pilots extolled the idea. As an experiment a Grumman F-7F Tigercat was equipped with a seat having three selectable positions: normal upright, inclined back for combat and supine for comfort during long-range cruising.

An awkward rather than unusual posture had to be suffered by pilots of the vertical take-off and landing (VTOL) aircraft that were evaluated in the 1950s. The Convair XFY-1 of 1954 and the Ryan X-13 of 1955 sat on their tails when on the ground, as did some other experimental VTOL types. In some the pilot's seat was fixed so that during take-off and landing he was on his back. In others the seat could be rotated to a horizontal position when required.

aerodynamic developments of German scientists, whose knowledge and research results were used as a guide by its designers. At the time it was the best of the breed and gave the Communist MiG 15 pilots over Korea a nasty shock. The cockpit of the F-86 was more cramped than the usual American type because room had to be found for the six 13 mm guns mounted in threes on each side of the fuselage. One British test pilot commented that the instrument layout was neat and logical in presentation. That may have applied to the F-86, but not to the F-86D, which had a big radar CRT on the main instrument panel, resulting in a somewhat untidy layout. At the time the instruments may have seemed to be arranged in a logical arrangement. However, as later research in America would show, they were not necessarily arranged so as to optimize the pilot's scanning task. The importance of the F-86 in the history of the fighter/attack cockpit is in the protection and comfort afforded the pilot. There was an ejection seat; air conditioning and pressurization, the pilot wore a G-suit and there was alloy and steel armour-plating in front of and behind the cockpit. This outstanding aircraft entered service equipped with a Mk 18 gyro gunsight that contributed to the shooting skills of the American pilots.

With increased performance, particularly for fighters, came heavy flight-control loads. These had to be reduced by adding power assistance. However, the early systems were the cause of many problems. What happened if the power system failed? The usual arrangement was a direct mechanical linkage from the control column to the control surface, along with a means to keep the stick loads within the pilot's muscular ability. In the F3D-1 a very simple solution was devised. At the press of a button, the control column could be extended upward. This increased the leverage of the stick so that the pilot could cope with the control loads. The F3D-2 had the G-3 autopilot with a control panel that included a small control stick for making limited manoeuvres. There was also a 'panic' button that returned the aircraft to level flight from any attitude of climb, descent and up to 65° of bank. There was also a button for selecting barometric altitude hold.

Among the fighters of the 1950s the F4D is another example of the way in which cockpit design lagged behind other advances in technology. The delta-wing Douglas F4D was not a good aircraft. The control system lacked harmony; the afterburner was erratic in operation; the air intakes were not aerodynamically matched to the engine; the free-floating leading-edge slats did not work when they should; and there were other failings. The instruments and controls in the cockpit were neither arranged nor designed to meet the demands of an aircraft intended as a night and all-weather fighter, An experienced US Navy pilot expressed himself in no uncertain terms when writing about the F4D:

All-weather flying implies much headwork by the pilot and a lot of reference to charts,

displays, radios, lights and switches. The F4D cockpit was jammed and crammed. Most switches were haphazardly located. Most of the instruments were grossly misplaced. Light reflections danced round the multifaceted windscreen and canopy. The autopilot, which could have been a godsend to the harassed pilot, never worked. The control column was short, stubby, hesitant, halting, heavy, jerky in motion and almost completely obscured the radar scope.

The above description includes examples of poor cockpit ergonomics in the cockpit, but they were not unique to the F4D. Many could be applied to the cockpits of other fighters of this era. The question remains: why were most of the instruments grossly misplaced? Were the opinions of pilots who looked at the drawings or sat in a mock-up of the cockpit ignored? Also, why is it that so many descriptions of cockpits by aviation writers include the observation, 'The instruments and controls were arranged in a logical manner', whereas in fact they were often arranged illogically? Perhaps one answer might be that the designers of high-performance jet aircraft at that time had to concentrate on overcoming some very serious aerodynamic problems, and this tended to push cockpit ergonomic considerations to one side.

Post-war bombers

In 1946 Northrop produced the XB-35. This was the first of a number of tailless, blended-body aircraft in which the fuselage and wing were merged, along with the four pusher-propeller engines. Having no conventional fuselage, the cockpit had to be inset into the leading edge at the apex of the swept-back wing. The two-pilot cockpit had the captain's seat and controls on the left, with the pilot's head and shoulders up in a fighter-type canopy. The second pilot's position was on

Cockpit of a B-45 Tornado. Most of the main instrument panel is taken up by the 30 or more engine instruments. Although this is a single seat, on centre-line, cockpit, The throttles are to the right of the pilot. Fore and aft access between the cockpits is by a gangway on the port side. *Aeroplane Monthly*

the right and lower down, and with only a view forward, though transparencies blended into the wing's leading edge. The engine-control levers were pendent from overhead in flying-boat fashion. A massive centre-line controls pedestal separated the two pilots, with the engine instrument panel at its forward end. The eight-jet YB-49, developed from the YB-35, had a similar cockpit arrangement.

When it came to the B-47, Boeing departed from the traditional American flight-deck layout for bombers. In place of the standard American side-by-side, two-pilot arrangement, the B-47 had tandem cockpits

under one transparent canopy, similar to that of a fighter aircraft. Another interesting departure from tradition was the positioning of the gangway to the left of the seats rather than to the right. A similar gangway position was adopted for the B-45 Tornado of the USAF. The first of these flew in the same year, 1947, as the B-47. With the gangway on the left this meant that the engine controls had to be set at the pilot's right hand, as with the conventional side-by-side cockpit, even though it was a single-seater type. The prototype B-52 had a tandem cockpit, but Boeing reverted to the traditional side-by-side for the production series. A distinguishing feature of the central control pedestal was the eight throttles. The pilots of the earlier Convair B-36 even had to get their fingers around ten throttles.

Victor

Contemporary with the American jet bombers were the HP Victor, the Avro Vulcan and the English Electric Canberra. The first two had side-by-side, two-pilot cockpits and not the single pilot's position usually associated with RAF bombers. The cockpit of the Victor was far advanced ergonomically from earlier Handley Page aircraft. The Hampden and Halifax had exhibited that company's TLAR attitude to cockpit design, one that put the demands of the electricians and 'plumbers' over those of the pilot. But so did many other company design offices.

With the Victor, HP took a significant step forward when it designed the 'high-speed' pointed nose and cockpit. Nevertheless, the fenestration technology available at the time forced the use of many small windows. The

Avro Vulcan. Single-grip roll and pitch controls, on push-pull arms extending out of the instrument panel, with engine controls between. *Philip Jarrett*

Victor 'V' bomber with cockpit fenestration faired into the pointed nose. *Philip Jarrett*

Avro Vulcan 'V' bomber with 'fighter' type canopy for the side-by-side cockpit. *Phillip Jarrett*

instrument panels were late Second World War style in the position and number of instruments. The control column for roll and pitch in front of each pilot in the side-by-side cockpit was similar to that of a fighter. The hand-grip could be moved fore and aft for pitch and rotated for roll control. It was mounted on a shaft that moved through a hole in the lower part of the instrument panel. One of its merits was an unobstructed cockpit deck and freedom for the pilots' legs when ejecting. The Vulcan also had a fighter-type control column to give clearance for the legs of the pilots when ejecting. The cockpit was not faired into the lines of the fuselage, as with the Victor, but was proud of the top line.

Canberra

When the EEC designers at Preston completed the preliminary cockpit speci-

fications and drawings for their new twin jet-engine bomber, they had to specify instruments and other equipment available at the time. Therefore the cockpit for this, at the time, very advanced jet bomber was very much Second World War RAF. To what extent TLAR came into the equation is not certain. Roland Beamont, the chief and very experienced test pilot, was closely involved with the design processes, and presumably he was satisfied with the type and location of every item. In retrospect, the appellation 'the back of the clockmaker's shop' seems uncharitable. After all, as with other aircraft of the time, a design office had no manual of good ergonomics to which it could refer for guidance. However, if readers refer to a photograph of the Canberra cockpit they can make their own judgement. In this era, jet fighter cockpit dimensions were, in general, no greater than those of the piston-engined

Canberra bomber c 1950. Externally the aircraft had the clean lines of a typical jet bomber/fighter. However, inside the cockpit things were rather different and were back to the WWII piston-engine era with any place for everything and everything in any place. *British Aerospace*

aircraft, but the number of instruments had increased significantly, resulting in some very untidy and overcrowded instrument panels.

Multi-role cockpits

Since the start of military aviation few aircraft types have been used exclusively in the role for which they were first conceived. For example, the single-seater biplane fighters of the First World War, such as the Camel, were eventually equipped to carry bombs and extra guns for the strafing of troops in the trenches. Some RFC pilots looked on ground-attack sorties as both dangerous and not the sort of flying for which they had volunteered.

Between wars air forces have often had to adapt aircraft to perform more than one operational role because in times of peace nations do not like spending money on armaments. The 'general-purpose' appellation has been used to embrace high- and low-level bombing, reconnaissance ground attack and photo-reconnaissance. During the Second World War most of the new types among the agile, as opposed to heavy bombers, acquired new functions as the air war reduced the need for the pure interceptor. In the last year of war over Europe the Americans and the British deployed some of their fastest and best fighters in close-support of the advancing armies. The one-time 'fighter-only' pilots had to acquire the additional skills of low-level attack.

The shape and equipment of the cockpit of

DH Vampire T-11 trainer of the 1950s. Another 'Back of the clockmaker's shop'. *British Aerospace*

aircraft adapted to additional or new roles, however, did not change significantly. A few more switches for bomb and rocket selection were added and the gyro gunsight modified to allow for the greater drooping trajectory of rockets compared with bullets and shells. Aircraft that had originally been designed to fight at 20,000 ft or higher were now directed by forward air controllers onto the enemy's armoured formations moving on the ground. Unfortunately, because of poor communication, inadequate briefing or just the inability to distinguish between friend and foe among the confusion of the land battle, there were 'blue-on-blue' incidents when aircraft attacked their own side. The experience of the air war over Europe in the later stages was to have a great influence on both the design of future aircraft and on cockpit equipment and design.

In the 1950s increasing attention was being paid to the need for aircraft whose primary function was that of strike, or 'ground attack'. The air war of the future was envisaged as being in two parts – one close to the stratosphere, the other close to the 'nap' of the earth. The latter predicated aircraft with a cockpit interface able to convey to the pilot far more information than before. More and higher-quality information could only be acquired by adding more and more electronic sensors, such as radar, and in consequence more and more displays and controls in the cockpit. The greater complexity also resulted in vast increases in aircraft cost, which in turn required more rigorous pilot-training programmes so as to make the best possible use of what were being termed 'weapon systems', rather than an aircraft to which weapons were 'add-ons'.

During the Second World War protective and survival equipment for the pilot was, in general, limited to a safety harness, oxygen supply, 'Mae West' and parachute. By 1950 pilots were being given greater protection. Ejection seats, personal life-support clothing and protective 'bone dome' helmets gradually became the standard; albeit the first generation of jet-fighter pilots continued to wear the 'soft' helmets of the piston-engined days. As late as 1954 RAF pilots of Vickers Supermarine Swift jet fighters still wore the 'soft' helmet. Even before the jet age, pilots were sometimes severely injured by 'bird strikes' that smashed through the windscreen and injured them. In turbulence jet aircraft pilots could be injured or even knocked unconscious as their heads were banged from side to side against the canopy. The 'bone dome' and its visor became an essential item of wear.

Fumes and sound intensity

The demise of the piston engine for first-line military aircraft removed the hazard of carbon monoxide fumes in the cockpit. The jet engine's exhaust contained only a small mount of CO, and was well away from the cockpit. Piston-engine rpm rarely exceeded 3,000 whereas even the first-generation gas turbines could double that, so that the pilot was subjected to a different range of frequencies and intensities. As comparative examples there are the sound level of 120 decibels at piston-engine frequencies in the cockpit of the USN's F-4U, and the 120 decibels at much higher frequencies affecting the crew of a jet-engined B-45. Irrespective of the variations of sound intensity among different aircraft types, the key figure is that of 140 decibels, above which both air and ground crews will suffer from disorientation and nausea unless wearing ear sound protectors. The imposition of 100 decibels continuously for eight hours eventually causes hearing loss. In both piston- and turbine-engined aircraft the intercom system not only relays speech, radio and audio warnings; it generates noise. Unwanted noise distorts information and keeps the sound level dangerously high.

The ejection seat

The Meteor and Vampire were designed with a conventional pilot's seat. In the event of trouble the pilot had to roll the aircraft inverted, jettison the canopy and drop out and make a normal parachute departure. After 1945 the frontiers of altitude and speed were pushed further and further outward as engine and airframe developments were advanced. The USAF was allocated massive financial and material resources for the development of supersonic and stratospheric aircraft. In relation to cockpit development, the ejection seat programmes included studies of the He 162 seat and the significant contribution to saving lives made by the ejection seats developed by Martin Baker in Britain. On 24 July 1946 Bernard Lynch was ejected in a Martin Baker rocket-powered seat from a Meteor flying at 280 knots at 8,000 ft. Both improved ejection seats and environmental protection for pilots followed. It was in this particular era of aviation that emerged the concept of the escape capsule. A complete cockpit could be forcibly ejected and then lowered to the ground by parachute. All crew protection and survival systems were integral with the capsule.

Through the canopy

Canopy became the usual name for the transparent enclosure of the cockpit. But the synthetic glass had to be tough. During the ejection sequence the first thing the pilot had to do was jettison the canopy. Then pull down a face blind that triggered the seat charge. In the F9F-6 Panther of 1948, for example, the pilot and seat could be ejected right through the canopy. In earlier versions of the F9F pilots were killed because under extreme G forces they could not reach for the canopy ejection handle.

Avro Vulcan c 1960: fighter type control columns and WWII type instruments and panel layout. Ejection seats for the two pilots but not for the other crew members. *Rolls-Royce*

V bomber escape

Ejection seats were provided for the two pilots in the RAF's Victor and Vulcan bombers but not for the other aircrew. Traditionally the pilot or pilots have remained at the controls in the event of trouble in order to give time for their crew to bale out. Regrettably, when the two V bombers were designed the configuration of the cockpit and adjacent crew compartment did not permit the installation of ejection seats for other than the pilots. After the Vulcan had been in service a few years Martin Baker designed a modification which would provide ejection seats for the crew 'in the back'. But this was not applied because of the cost. The excuse was that the Vulcans were to be taken out of service. However, they were not phased out for another ten years or more.

The drill for making a successful non-ejection-seat escape from a Vulcan was as follows. The two outboard seats could be turned inwards, and if necessary the occupants could use an inflatable assister cushion to counteract G force so that they could stand and then step down to face the exit door. The one in the middle position had to push the seat back and struggle around the other seats to reach the door. The exit door had to be forced open by pneumatic rams and held open against the airstream. The exit had to be done in an orderly slide down the door. However, if the undercarriage was down they would hit the nosewheel leg. They were told that they could slide down and use the door struts to swing around the nosewheel. This difficult task had been demonstrated in a wind tunnel. In the event of a sudden, unexpected, airframe or total engine failure the exit procedure set out in the 'book' could prove to be very theoretical. The difficulties the crew would have in abandoning aircraft must have preyed heavily on the minds of the pilots. Following the deaths of many aircrews trying to escape from trouble by ejecting at high Mach numbers, during which they sustained horrific injuries from wind blast and erosion and thermal injury, the USAF equipped the B-58 Hustler with an escape capsule for each of the three-man crew. These enabled the crew to operate in a 'shirt-sleeve' environment.

Black boxes

For the first two decades of the military jet aircraft the cockpits were usually equipped with instruments whose design was only slightly advanced from that of 1945. In the 1950s avionic display units were often 'shoe-horned' into the cockpit; as in the F-86D. Not only had space to be found in the cockpit for the display units, but it had to be found somewhere in the fuselage for the associated 'black boxes'. This was achieved either by crowding out other equipment or by 'stretching' the fuselage. An example of the latter solution is the Lockheed Shooting Star, which had been designed before the advent of search-and-attack radar systems. The fifteen black boxes with which it was later equipped were equivalent in volume to ten large suitcases.

Jet aircraft were not only becoming much faster than their 'prancing-piston' predecessors; they were increasingly more versatile and therefore far more expensive. These expensive and sophisticated machines required better instruments and extensive avionics systems, as well as the means to find and attack targets of all types. At the same time the opposition was acquiring the means to track and shoot down aircraft, particularly if they were operated at low level. The CRT, of course, had arrived in the cockpit in the early 1940s in the shape of AI, ASV radars and other electronic aids to navigation and target finding, such as GEE and H2S. Some German AI displays in 1945 even had colour to discriminate between different types of the information. But they were not accessible to

A typical 1950s instrument panel with a number of different functions and systems' controls and indicators crowded together and in no particular order of importance or relationship. However, a better arrangement was prevented to some extent by the limitations of the available space. *Crown*

DECCA electro-mechanical pen-on-chart navigation display. *BAE.*

the pilot. By the end of the Second World War the CRT was being positioned for direct viewing by the pilot. However, it sat alongside the conventional pointer-on-dial instruments, and remained for many years the only representative of the revolution in avionics that would eventually burst onto the scene in a proliferation of alphanumerics, symbols, maps, weather and other data, at first in monochrome and then in multi-colour. Pen-on-chart navigational position displays, such as DECCA, became available in this era. However, their bulk and setting-up controls were only suitable for large cockpits.

In 1954 the US Navy published its thoughts on the cockpit of the future. The projected design featured one large combined information and weapon-aiming electronic display. This was mounted above a 'desktop' control panel that included a side-stick primary flight control. Although it expressed the Navy's desire to improve the total cockpit interface, it was in advance of the available avionic and display technologies. With the pilot's legs under the 'desk' the major part of the interface would have had to be swung out of the way or ejected before the seat ejection sequence was triggered.

A bumpy ride

One requirement common to many specifications for tactical strike reconnaissance aircraft in the 1950s was the ability to penetrate enemy air space by flying at around 1,000 ft or even less. At that height an aircraft flying close to Mach 1 was expected to be immune to radar detection. In the 1950s terrain-following electronics and other ground-avoidance devices were not available. The crew's task during a low-level penetration sortie, particularly over undulating territory, was exacerbated by the effects of gusts. Gusts not only increased airframe structural fatigue, but they gave a

bumpy ride for the crew; at times they would be subjected to severe vibration through the seats. This was recognized as a major crew fatigue inducer in low-level penetration sorties. Even sprung seats were tried, but these did not come into general use for another twenty years, and then only for helicopter crews.

Off the deck

In the history of the cockpit perhaps the most dramatic environment for the pilot was that of landing on and taking off from the deck of an aircraft-carrier. Accidents, particularly when landing on, were unfortunately a daily feature of carrier operations in both the Royal and United States Navies. In the last three years of the war the piston-engined aircraft, such as the Spitfire, Hellcat and Corsair, with their higher landing speeds, demanded a very high standard of skill from naval pilots. With the advent of jet aircraft operating from carriers the accident rate increased to nearly unacceptable levels.

When the jet aircraft came into service at sea the combination of even higher approach speeds than those of the piston-engined era reduced the time in which both the pilot and landing signals officer (LSO) could react to errors. In addition the much slower response of a jet engine to throttle changes had to be allowed for. Adding to the problems were inadequate flight-deck illumination and approach-guidance equipment. A USN admiral recalled that

All the ingredients for an accident were present: an inexperienced young (or old) pilot attempting to land aboard ship at night in bad weather, flying on instruments at very low altitude over the water in a descending turn on final approach, without radar control, while looking for the ghost-like figure of the LSO in his lighted flight suit, waving lighted paddles at an airplane he could hardly see in the dark. It was the extreme test for man and machine and naval aviation.

Obviously something had to be done to reduce the attrition rate of both pilots and machines. The Royal Navy, with less money with which to replace aircraft and pilots, developed the angled deck, the steam catapult and the mirror landing system. The USN embraced these technologies with alacrity, and the accident rate went down. But the pilot was still having to eyeball the ship, the LSO or a mirror landing system to obtain guidance information in relation to the aircraft's trajectory. Although naval pilots were trained to keep their eyes on the carrier deck, rather than the cockpit instruments, an occasional glance down at essential information was necessary. In those few milliseconds the smooth sequence of control actions and awareness of how the approach was progressing could be lost. Hence the development of head-up instrumentation. Before attempting a landing onto a carrier, pilots were trained to land on at airfields marked out to represent the flight deck of a carrier. In this era, other than films taken from the cockpit during landing on, there were few suitable simulators (see Chapter 12).

The advent of jet aircraft provided naval pilots with a wonderful view of the flight deck. But there had to be some revised thinking about the process of landing on. An important part of the landing technique is that of lift control. With a propeller-driven aircraft, a demand for more lift can be answered by opening the throttle so that the airflow over the wings increases the lift. Conversely when the throttle is closed lift is reduced and drag increased by the propeller disc. However, with a jet aircraft lift can only be increased by opening the throttle to increase speed. But the slow acceleration of a turbine engine, compared with that of a piston engine, means that a landing cannot be controlled by large throttle movements.

Therefore the air brakes become a major control and ideally should be infinitely variable.

Forward air control

With the perfection of techniques for attacking ground targets from the air using fighter/attack aircraft armed with bombs, machine-guns and rockets came the role of the forward air controller (FAC). The FAC could direct pilots onto targets and give a commentary on the results of their attacks. No longer did pilots set off armed only with a tactical briefing before take-off, and thereafter without further information on the target. This introduced a new era in the cockpit and one in which greater effectiveness was made of the aircraft as a weapon system.

This method of giving the pilot or pilots precise and up-to-the-minute information about their target was used to great effect at the Falaise Gap attacks during the Allied invasion of France in 1944. It had its faults, and blue-on-blue attacks would be an unfortunate aspect of the air wars for the future. A typical exchange between pilot and FAC might be as follows:

FAC: 'I'm close to the target. Make dummy run at the armour on the hill at the bend of the river.'

Pilot: 'Roger.'

The fighter pilot sees the target as he makes a dummy run and then goes round again to position for an attack with guns and rockets.

'I've got them but I also spotted a tank half hidden just to their right.'

FAC: 'I told you I was close. That's me.'

Nautical influences

In the RAF in the last three years of the Second World War the introduction of electromechanical navigational aids, such as the air position indicator (API) based on minutes of latitude and longitude (one minute of latitude equals one nautical mile), hastened the change-over to working in nautical miles and speed in knots for all commands, and not just for RAF Coastal Command. The Royal and US Navies' air services had always used the nautical units. However, not until the formation of the USAF in 1947 did all American military crews start to use the nautical units.

The influence of nautical terminology was most apparent with the use of 'port' for left and 'starboard' for right by British aviation. Left side and right side were used by other countries, and eventually were used more frequently in Britain. Under the stress of aerial combat, particularly in British and American bomber aircraft in the Second World War when attacked by fighters, a 'clock' system was used in which twelve o'clock represented a position directly ahead.

For a few years, in the late 1940s, aircraft designers introduced an example of lateral confusion when they positioned the flight engineer and his controls facing aft so that his left hand was to the right side of the aircraft and all the controls and instruments were arranged as a mirror image of the parts of the aircraft to which they referred.

CHAPTER EIGHT

Civil Cockpits 1955-1970

Human senses

Before we review the era in which air transport fully embraced the turbine and the jet, some more words on the human sense organs are appropriate. These are the organs used to determine what is happening and what may happen. They are included as an introduction because the human pilot is the most important programmed and reprogrammable computer in an aircraft. The pilot provides a sensor and control interface between an aircraft's systems and between the aircraft and the environment in which it is operated.

The human computer uses aural, visual and movement sensors and provides effectors for control actions by finger, hand and foot actions. Other sensors are used to detect changes in the environment, such as temperature and humidity. Of all the sensors, the visual is obviously of most importance. Visual sensing of the real world and of the artificial world of the cockpit instruments is not just a matter of looking. Seeing is not necessarily the same thing as perception.

From our earliest years we learn to react to moving objects and to the apparent relative movements among the numerous objects that make up our view of the world. We quickly learn that some actions are way in the future encounters when visual inputs are received. Occasionally the real world does not appear or change in expected ways. This can cause confusion and disorientation, and a pilot may react better than others whenever

we react to the real world. With experience we learn the most effective actions and we react in the same incorrectly. To avoid errors or to reduce their adverse effects careful attention must be paid to the detail design of instruments and controls. Unfortunately not all who designed cockpits in the first fifty years of civil aviation appreciated the pilot's visual problems.

The pilot's view of the world outside the cockpit, particularly when flying close to the ground during an approach to land, is usually made up of familiar shapes, colours and relationships. But sometimes these elements are unfamiliar or confused because of obscuration or distortion by the atmosphere and light level. When all or some of the elements of the real world are hidden by others, or by insufficient visibility, pilots expect them to appear eventually. Reliance on expectation can have disastrous consequences if based on false or insufficient clues.

The human pilot has many undoubted control skills compared with those of the machine. However, during extreme turbulence the pilot can become completely disorientated and unable to exercise corrective control actions. The severe accelerations imposed on the aircraft and on the human body during violent turbulence adds to the pilot's mental and physical confusion. If at the same time the nose of the aircraft starts to vibrate at around 4 Hz, the view of the instruments, particularly those needed for regaining control, will be blurred.

The jet cockpit

As experience was accumulated from the handling of large jet transports, such as the Boeing 707, it highlighted how different they were from propeller-driven aircraft. Not only were some of the jet transports larger, all were faster. Together these two factors meant a significant increase in aircraft momentum. When making a landing in a piston-engined airliner any divergence from the localizer and glide slope could usually be corrected quickly, particularly as the piston-engine-propeller combination would respond within a second or two of the throttles being pushed fully forward. With a jet, on the other hand, the pilot had to anticipate divergences. The pilot could not afford, for example, to let the aircraft get too far below the glide slope because its momentum would keep it diverging even when the pilot applied up elevator or increased thrust. Adding to the problem was the slow response of the turbine engines to a thrust demand. In the first-generation jet transports six to eight seconds might elapse before full power was available. The effect of momentum applied also to attempts to regain the localizer. All this meant that a jet transport had to be flown so that it was settled as early as possible on the optimum approach path. For this and other reasons, the cockpit design parameters appropriate to piston-engined aircraft had to be considerably revised for the jet aircraft.

Instruments

For about the first half of this period of transport aircraft flight deck development, a typical suite of ten primary flight instruments consisted of the following:

Two attitude director instruments (ADIs)

Two airspeed indicators (ASIs)

Two altimeters (ALTs)

Two horizontal situation indicators (HSIs)

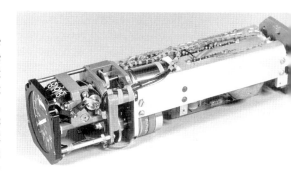

The tip of the iceberg. An electro-mechanical per-centage engine-speed indicator with case removed. *Smiths Group*

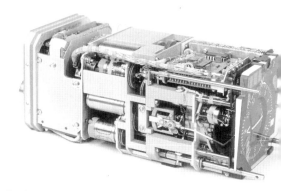

By the mid 1960s a limit had been reached in packing electronics, servo motors and their electro-mechanical systems into one case of acceptable length. This is an example of a multi-parameter instrument that combined VOR, DME, RMI and ILS; parameters that previously had been displayed by separate instruments. *Smiths Group*

Two vertical speed indicators (VSIs).

Each group of ADI, ASI and ALT, one for the captain the other for the co-pilot, had an independent pitot-static system for the ASI and ALT and a vertical reference gyro for the ADI. Both pilots had to make frequent cross-checking to avoid following an erroneous reading if one of the instruments failed. However, in the USA the safety authority (FAA) did not insist on standby instruments. Not until 1967 were these installed in Boeing 707 aircraft.

The introduction of jet aircraft, with flight characteristics different from those of the piston-engined/propeller types, highlighted the lack of standardization in the way in which the primary flight instruments were arranged in front of each pilot. The SAE in the USA proposed one standard, the International Federation of Air Line Pilots another, and the American pilots association (ALPA) had its own ideas. Up to then the only standard panel arrangement was the RAF's Basic Six, which had been introduced in the 1930s and applied to the majority of the air force's aircraft. There was much debate over which layout was the best. The USAF had settled on what became known as the Basic T. Eventually the parties to the debate agreed on the Basic T for civil use. The underlying philosophy of the Basic T was the positioning of the attitude director and the horizontal situation indicator on the vertical line and with the airspeed and altimeter completing the cross-bar of the T. There were variations among different aircraft types for the location of the turn-and-bank (T&B) indicator and the radiomagnetic indicator (RMI). Furthermore, the position of the vertical speed indicator (VSI) was not agreed to by all.

In the late 1950s instrument designers concentrated on two areas. Firstly, they improved the individual pointer-on-dial instruments so that they provided clear and unambiguous information under all lighting conditions, from the darkest night to the extremely bright unfiltered sunlight at high altitudes. Secondly, and of great importance to the future, they combined three or more parameters in one display. A good example of this was the attitude director instrument (ADI). However, there were limitations to the complexity and number of small electric motors and feed-back devices that could be packed into an instrument case. As it was, some instruments were 8 inches (200 mm) from front to back. These took up valuable space behind an instrument panel. They were also expensive to service and repair. Above all the format of a display, that is the alphanumerics and the symbols, could not be

changed easily or quickly, and definitely not in flight. If for no other reason electronic displays needed to be invented.

The big jet transports could experience a 'jet upset' during which they went completely out of control. Steep diving angles and 360° rolling would topple the gyros in the instruments, such as the attitude directors. Therefore, instruments had to be developed that could cope with any aircraft attitude.

Linear displays

From time to time designers of cockpits have considered vertical or horizontal linear 'tape'-type instruments. They have been used for displaying both flight and systems parameters. Compared with a circular-scale instrument they took up less space on a panel. However, although they were very acceptable for indicating an instantaneous value against a fixed lubber line, they were not as effective as a moving pointer in giving 'rate' information. A pilot needed to know at what rate a parameter's value was changing in order to anticipate it reaching a certain level. Some pilots liked the tape type, others did not. There were arguments over the direction in which the numerals should be printed on the tape. For example, in an altimeter, should the tape move downwards with increasing height or upwards? Most preferred that the tape should move down so that the lubber line appeared to move upward past increasing values when the aircraft was climbing. The Concorde prototype had tape instruments but the operator, BOAC, insisted on the 'conventional'. When ordering the Boeing 747 Pan American specified circular-scale instruments for the engine systems panels, whereas TWA settled for 'tape'.

Another factor that had to be argued over with linear-type instruments was the danger that in a four-engined aircraft a pilot might confuse, for example, one engine's temperature with another's. In some cockpits two groups of four linear scales were side by side, making eight columns. Those that advocated this type of instrument pointed to the advantage of being able to see instantly that one parameter was out of line with the others. But even with four circular-scale instruments a pilot, when scanning a panel, just as easily spots that one of the pointers is out of alignment with the others. This and other arguments were to continue into the coming era of the 'glass' cockpit to be described in the chapters that follow.

Flight trials were made of electro-luminescence technology for instruments. This technology was very acceptable for producing vertical tape instruments, particularly for engine indications. The biggest problem came from direct sunlight on the face of the instrument. Although sunlight also affected viewing conventional pointer-on-dial instruments, they could still be read because the white pointers against a black dial were both larger and more distinct than a narrow electroluminescence column.

Light and Dark

The flight deck environment is one that exhibits, in certain flight conditions, sharp and sudden changes in the level of ambient light. As an aircraft flies through a succession of clouds and clear sky in bright sunshine, the level of natural illumination of the instruments changes rapidly from one condition to the next. If the aircraft is being manoeuvred, with changes of heading, in bright sunshine, particularly at high altitudes, then there are sharply bounded areas of intense black shadow and bright sunlight moving across the panels. At night, although the level of external ambient light may not vary much, there is a conflict between the desirable level of instrument lighting so that they can be read and the pilot's need to maintain a visual lookout for

other traffic. Furthermore, because instruments have to have some form of protective and transparent screen over the dial and its moving parts, this can be a source of unwanted reflections of cockpit lights, such as warning lamps. In daylight even the pilot's white shirt can produce unwanted specular reflection.

Lighting of instrument panels is a subject of many conflicting needs. Of these, colour has been one of the controlling factors in the evolution of instrument design. Until it was acceptable to use other than red lighting, the design of multi-parameter displays, such as attitude directors, was restricted. It was not possible, with red light, to differentiate clearly between the different parts of, say, an attitude director having a reference aircraft symbol, horizon and roll indicator, ILS director pointers, command symbols and warning flags. With red lighting all these symbols and flags and lines were hard to distinguish one from the other. Once it became acceptable to use white light as a source, either flood, integral or instrument back-lighting, the instrument designer was free to use a multi-colour presentation. This had an influence on subsequent instrument design as well as on total panel arrangements because colour enabled more parameters to be displayed on one instrument face.

More electronics

From the mid-1950s onwards there was a rapid growth of electronic systems for enhancing the safety and efficiency of flight by improving the information given to the pilot. Weather radar, which provided a clear indication of the best course to avoid centres of excessive turbulence, became a familiar feature of the cockpit. Although it became an undoubted essential instrument, it had to be used with care. Attempting to look ahead and find a way through a number of storm cells could lead the aircraft up a 'blind alley' with

HS 125. Weather radar display, engine instruments and undercarriage lever on central panel. Primary controls shaped to avoid obscuring instruments. *BAE*

no way out. Therefore all weather radar manuals essentially advised pilots to go round and not try and go through storms.

In Chapter Three the radio range was mentioned. It remained in use until after the Second World War. However, because it confined aircraft to one of the four radiating beams from each transmitter, a flight from, say, A to B could not be flown directly but had to go via C and D over a succession of dog-leg tracks. The radio-range system was not perfect because during storms it could be adversely affected by electrical activity in the atmosphere.

The need for what eventually became known as area navigation (R-Nav) encouraged the development of radio aids from which aircraft position could be determined without recourse to pencil, chart, radio bearings and calculations. The RAF was given GEE in order to eliminate the unacceptably large circles of uncertainty of position, particularly when approaching a target. GEE for civil use, and subsequent developments such as LORAN and other area navigation systems, required the user to interpret the indications on a CRT display or listen to a series of dots and dashes, as with CONSOL, for example. They could not be used directly by the pilot. GEE was followed by DECCA. At first the pilots of an aircraft fitted with DECCA had to interpret the indications of the decometers and relate them to a special chart in order to ascertain instantaneous position. To reduce the workload Decca developed the DECCA Flight Log, and by 1955 airline pilots were able to glance at a pen-and-roller blind-type display and determine their position instantaneously with considerable accuracy.

A further development was the Decca/HARCO Navigator system, which also gave the pilot an immediate and continuous visual display of aircraft position. A chart moved under a pen that marked both the position and the track of the aircraft. It contributed much to the efficiency of air transport. However, its display unit was an electromechanical device that took up a lot of room on the principal instrument panel. There was also DECCA Omnitrac, which gave an automatic chart display that could be coupled to the autopilot and flight director. It gave time and distance to waypoints derived from VOR/DME and other data inputs. This detailed description of just a few of the R-Nav systems is intended to emphasize the move toward providing pilots with an instantaneous and unambiguous indication of aircraft position.

These R-Nav systems were the subject of much argument in the years after the Second World War. Although this book is about the cockpit and in particular its instruments, it is important to recount how a combination of politics and national interests impinged at one time on the future development of the cockpit interface. Essentially, the United States insisted that its improved radio-range system (VOR/DME) should be the principal international navigational aid, especially for defining airways. Attempts to advance R-Nav systems, with their directly interpretable displays of position, were not successful, and for the next ten or more years pilots and air traffic controllers had to rely on the VOR/DME system to define airways, and pilots had to hope that its accuracy at any waypoint was sufficient to ensure safe separation from other traffic.

Without going into technical details, the target for the avionics industry in the 1950s was in effect a system similar to our present GPS. Away from accurate radio navigation aids airliners had to depend on classic dead-reckoning techniques and long-range aids, such as LORAN, which usually required the inclusion of a non-pilot specialist on the flight deck. Another R-Nav system is inertial navigation (IN), which originally had been developed for the military. The Litton IN system was approved by the FAA in 1968 for installation in Boeing 707s. An important attribute of IN is its independence from the need to transmit or receive electronic data. It is self-contained. Provided it is correctly set up at the beginning of a flight it continues to provide an instantaneous indication of aircraft position in latitude and longitude coordinates. This data can be used by other aircraft systems, such as the autopilot. Its principle of operation is analogous to someone who walks at a varying pace and keeps changing direction when moving across a featureless landscape. If the walker is endowed with a fabulous memory and a built-in sense of direction, and memorizes the elapsed times between each change of direction, then he or she is able to put a finger on the map and say 'That's where I am now'. An IN system was another step in the reduction of flight-deck crew complements. For example, American Airlines dispensed with navigators on its trans-Pacific routes.

The first-generation jet cockpits

The fenestration of the Comet's cockpit was blended into the smooth shape of the fuselage nose. This simplified the structural design of the pressurized fuselage and therefore was similar in principle to that of

Below the central instrument panel in this version of the Tupolov 134 is the opening into the navigator's position in the extreme nose. Note the extensive upward arcs-of-view provided. *BAA*

VC.10 flight deck. The central controls pedestal prevents easy access to the pilots' seats. Compared with the Tu 134 the upward view through the small windows is restricted. *BAE*

the Boeing Stratocruiser. As the flight deck was positioned well forward, its athwartships dimension was narrow and therefore the two pilots sat fairly close together. Although the aircraft's structure, shape and performance were at the leading edge of technology, the cockpit equipment was mostly 'off the shelf' from a 'piston engine' instrument store. Of courses, there were Machmeters and engine instruments having a much greater range of rpm values and temperatures than those of a piston-

BAC 1-11. Aileron, rudder and elevator trim controls are concentrated to the left of the two thrust levers. In many other aircraft they are dispersed. The coaming is curved and therefore not the recommended straight line to give a horizontal reference. *BAE*

engined aircraft. After the excitement of the Comet's record-breaking route-proving trials and the first series of passenger-carrying flights had abated, the cockpit came in for criticism from the pilots. The cramped flight deck required a 'musical-chairs' evolution whenever a member of the crew had to change position.

The non-stepped nose of the Comet imposed a structural penalty, for in order to provide adequate vertical arcs of view the windows had to be much larger than with a stepped nose. In 1945, when the Comet was on the drawing board, not much was known about how either to make or to use large areas of multi-layer heated transparencies for windows. Also, at that time there were few pressurized passenger aircraft from which to gather in-flight experience of structural loads. The few military pressurized aircraft had limited window area, or, as in the B29, a multiplicity of small windows. Therefore de Havilland entered dangerous and uncharted waters when it chose a cabin differential pressure of 9 psi, a small value until you relate it to a window more than one foot square; when the total load is getting on for a ton. So not only had the windows to be tough, their framework had to be an elaborate one-piece forging. The nose of the Caravelle was derived from the DH Comet, but the cockpit had a different arrangement of instruments and controls and in some ways was more advanced.

Among the cockpit design conflicts, for all aircraft and not just for the Comet, that had to be resolved related to the pilot's eye position or eye reference point (ERP). Ideally it needs to be close to the glass in order to maximize the arcs of view. However, that would conflict with the need to be able to view the instruments and be too close to the controls. This design factor can best be appreciated when seated behind the wheel of a car. With the eyes about 15 cm from the glass the horizontal arc of view is very wide -

at least 100° through the forward window. In a typical airliner this dimension on the pilot's centre-line is around 50 cm.

Boeing 707

The Boeing 707 rapidly filled the hole left in the commercial aircraft world by the grounding and modification of all Comets. DH paid the price that many pioneers have had to pay by being first on the scene. Boeing was able to learn from the Comet's problems and from its operating experience. The cockpit of the 707 was in keeping with the nascent commercial jet age. Compared with the Comet, its erstwhile rival, the nose was of the traditional stepped type so as to give optimum arcs of view. One Boeing 'trademark' feature was not carried over from the 317 and its bombers. This was the positioning of the throttles outboard of each pilot. In the 707 they were mounted on the central controls' pedestal.

The introduction of the commercial jets not only provided faster cruising speeds and operations at 25,000 feet or higher above most of the turbulent layers of air, they also presented a number of problems in the cockpit. To start with pilots were used to a nearly direct relationship between throttle movement and power. For example, for every inch of movement of the throttle of a piston engine an engine might deliver 300 shp, whereas a jet engine's throttle movement did not necessarily have a straight-line relationship with power. For example, over about a quarter of lever movement from the idle position there was a non-linear response of power. Only at about the half-way point did engine power increase in step with throttle opening. Added to this was the slow speed-up of the jet engine compared with a piston type, particularly over the first quarter of throttle opening. This could mean that a sudden demand for increased thrust to avoid undershooting an approach could take

Cessna Skylane c 1967 selected to show the push-and-pull engine control knobs (centre) in place of levers. Both the pitch and rudder trim wheels move in the expected directions. The 'wood' finish to the switch and radio panels emulates the fascia of an automobile. The airspeed indicator has an elaborate array of indices and sectors to enable the pilot to select the optimum speed for different flight conditions. *Philip Jarrett*

up to eight seconds before the aircraft responded, and then it might be too late. Eventually the engine designers were able to provide a linear relationship between throttle position and thrust.

In any year in aviation there have usually been a number of projected aircraft designs. But only a few have progressed further than the drawing board. In 1957 the long-established British company Handley Page designed a long-range executive transport aircraft. This was the HP 113 project. It was an advanced design, having swept wings

with laminar flow control by suction. The forward section of the fuselage would have been that of the Canberra. The existing controls, instruments and crew positions would have been retained. Handley Page made provision for a conventional windscreen in place of the one-piece canopy of the original. More than likely pilots would have insisted on changes to the instruments and controls because the cockpit of the Canberra was very much to the standards of the early 1940s.

From time to time cockpit design offices

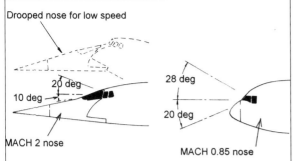

Transport aircraft noses for Mach 2 and Mach 0.85. The drooped nose was adopted for both the Concorde and its Russian copy. *Author*

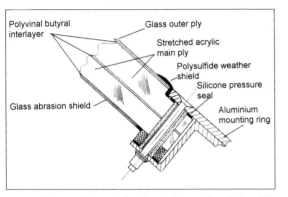

The materials used for the windscreen of a Boeing 747 designed to keep out rain, snow, hailstones and birds. The outer and inner glass surfaces protect the main plies from abrasion and scratching. *Author*

have essayed the 'bug-eye' cockpit in which each of the two pilots has an individual fighter-type canopy. Although this provided wide fields of view one of its disadvantages was the difficulty each pilot would have had in cross-monitoring the instruments and controls. For this and other reasons the idea did not find favour with the airlines.

The non-stepped windscreen nose went out of fashion in the early 1960s. The principal civil transport manufacturers since then have tended to adopt a stepped type nose with a V-shaped windscreen for the flight deck. Although not necessarily aerodynamically perfect, this profile affords the pilots the maximum arcs of view. The advent of supersonic passenger aircraft, such as Concorde and the unsuccessful Russian SST, introduced the variable, drooping, nose:

up and sharply pointed for Mach 2, drooped to expose a more conventional forward flight-deck windscreen.

Supersonic instruments

The future for instrument technology was predicted in a number of papers in the 1960s. This was also the time when Boeing was actively scheming its riposte to Concorde. It was proposed that the Boeing SST would have three electronic TV-type displays in front of each pilot. One would electronically generate attitude information and the other the horizontal 'map' situation display. The third would be a monitor of Mach number against altitude or flight level, presented in graph format. The other instruments would be the then current state-of-the-technology counter-pointer type, combining a pointer on circular scale with a numeric counter read-out.

In 1969 the Sperry company was commissioned by Boeing to develop a CRT-type attitude director indicator (ADI). This and other advanced display technologies were intended for Boeing's SST. The Sperry ADI system provided a 7 in x 7 in monochrome CRT on which was displayed attitude and command symbols superimposed on a picture of the real world from a forward-looking TV camera. In the next decade the CRT would replace the electromechanical ADI and other instruments. This 1969 development was the start of the road to the 'glass cockpit' of the 1980s.

At this stage of instrument development the technology to differentiate parts of a display by different colours was not sufficiently developed. However, as the gestation period for a supersonic transport was likely to be at least ten years no doubt the Boeing SST's flight deck would have been in full colour by 1980.

Cockpit Wars

In the 1950s, as in the 1930s, pilots were being coerced into accumulating excessive flying hours in each 24-hour period. High cockpit workload, because of inadequate attention to the ergonomics of the instruments and controls, contributed to fatigue, and vice-versa. Eventually the regulatory bodies imposed restrictions on the number of hours in relation to the intervening rest periods. At the same time more resources were applied to improving cockpits so as to reduce fatigue and maintain an acceptable level of arousal on the part of the pilot.

With the advent of the jet airliner, pilots in general, through their representatives, insisted on three pilots for all jet transports. The triangular arguments between pilots, certificating authorities and airlines was protracted. It was exacerbated by the fact that the new jets had included a flight engineer's position with controls and instruments at the drawing-board stage. In effect airlines were faced with a demand for a four-crew cockpit. Irrespective of the arguments, the fundamental cockpit design requirement was one of providing adequate instruments, controls and navigational aids so that under the most critical circumstances of a flight the aircraft could be flown safely to its destination. Because there were many different types of commercial operation, ranging from short-haul to long-haul and from fully controlled flying to operating over areas devoid of radio aids, there were corresponding variations in crew complements among the different airlines.

Autoland

The combination of frequent low-visibility conditions at European airports in the 1950s and 1960s and the loss of revenue caused by the disruption of scheduled flights prompted the development of civil automatic landing systems. During the war and earlier the RAE and the RAF had been researching ways of enabling an approach to land to continue when the visibility was as low as 100 metres. Since the First World War automatic landing had been the subject of hundreds of patents and experimental flights in France, Germany and the United States. However, few were found to provide the required level of redundancy, to ensure safety, for passenger-carrying operations.

Autoland did not change the cockpit significantly. An additional control and indicator panel was fitted so that the pilots could monitor the automatic progress of the aircraft as it descended down the 3-degree glide slope. If the pilot in command decided that it was unsafe to continue the approach for any reason an automatic go-around could be triggered. Autoland was specified at the drawing-board stage for both the DH Trident and the Vickers VC 10. It was a technical success and British airlines had the satisfaction of being able to keep to their schedules despite thick fog. However, automatic landing in this era did not find favour in the USA. There the philosophy for safe landing was one of providing the pilot with the maximum amount of information that would enable a landing to continue by reference to instruments and what could be seen of the approach and runway lighting patterns, the pilot remaining 'hands on' throughout the approach and landing. Autoland became an acceptable system for maintaining airline schedules irrespective of the weather, and from that time forward the majority of new passenger airliners were figuratively equipped at the drawing-board stage with automatic landing.

Para-visual Display

The Para-visual Display (PVD) was developed in the 1960s to provide guidance for the pilot once the aircraft had touched down automatically in low-visibility conditions. Attempting to steer an aircraft moving at more than 100 knots and not being able to see more than 100 m presented the pilot with a formidable task. You would not want to drive your car along a turnpike at 120 mph in 100 m visibility. The PVD director display provided left-right guidance to enable the pilot to keep the aircraft to the centre-line of the runway. The modern PVD indicator presents 'follow me' left-right director information by a rotating 'barber's pole' in the pilot's peripheral vision when looking forward. An important attribute of the PVD is that the pilot does not have to view it from a particular, fixed, head position.

HUD or Autoland?

Head-up Display (HUD) development for civil use and Autoland engendered much debate over their individual merits and their relationship to each other as operating procedures in the cockpit. Their place in this book is justified because both introduced changes to the controls and instruments of the civil flight deck.

As with military HUDs, the pilot had to adapt in milliseconds from focusing at infinity through the combining glass of the HUD to focusing on the head-down instruments. When making an approach to land in a civil aircraft, pilots had to transfer their attention from the analogue displays of information, such as the Sperry Zero Reader or the needles of the ILS indicator, to any clues outside the cockpit needed to progress safely down the approach path. The proponents of the see-through display, such as HUD, argued that it enabled a pilot to continue an approach to land at the decision height in one of the ICAO low-visibility categories. The HUD also provided attitude, a horizon and an aiming point superimposed on the ideal touch-down point, as well as 'fly to', or director, symbology. The design target

was a display that included all the information needed to continue safely down the 2.5-3-degree glide slope.

On first consideration it seemed that pilots were being given a very useful tool. However, the debate over the merits of HUD were protracted and opinions became markedly polarized. On the one hand there were those who supported the idea, but on the other hand others argued that the better way to control an aircraft to a safe landing in reduced visibility was the automatic landing system (autoland). Autoland had been developed in the UK by the BLEU (Blind Landing Experimental Unit) and continued with by the two principal British avionic companies (Elliott and Smiths).

However, civil HUD applications were few, and it was not until the 1980s, as will be described, that airline operators specified HUD for operations involving approaches and landings to airports set in mountainous terrain and subjected to frequent periods of poor visibility. With both techniques the questions that raised the most argument were: 'What happens if there is a failure of either the ground-based system or one of the systems on the aircraft?', and 'What guidance is available to the pilot in such an event?' The design target for autoland was safe landings in zero visibility. However, the minimum was set at ICAO category 3b, 50 m horizontal visibility. Below 50 m the pilot needed guidance after touch-down from additional electronic systems in order to keep to the centre-line of the runway.

Built-in error-inducing devices

Compared with a piston-engine/propeller-driven aircraft, a jet, even with flaps extended and gear down, has less drag. Once down on the runway the jet airliner needs more than flaps and wheel brakes to slow down. Reverse thrust was provided, but this was not always enough and so spoilers were

A Boeing 747 c 1969 in the years before electronic displays made a significant change to the look of the flight deck.
Philip Jarrett

added. These flap-like surfaces can be extended on the upper surface of the wings to increase drag, but they also massively dump lift. Once the wheels are on the runway dumping lift increases the wheel-braking effort.

A typical spoiler control has two elements – an arming lever and an actuating lever, or one lever with two positions. When the DC-8 was designed the spoiler control was a two-position lever. A DC-8 came over the threshold and at sixty feet up from the runway the captain told the co-pilot to arm the spoilers. Instead of just moving the lever to the 'arm' position the co-pilot moved it all the way to the deploy position. The sudden loss of lift and increased drag made the aircraft hit the ground so hard that the No. 4

engine pod tore off. Attempts by the crew to recover the situation were unsuccessful, and the aircraft crashed. The subsequent investigation revealed that the manufacturer's aircraft manuals inaccurately suggested that the spoilers could not be deployed in flight and there was a mechanism to prevent it. Not only was there no such mechanism, there was no guard or detent to prevent the spoiler lever from being accidentally moved past the 'arming' position.

Cockpit width

At a gross take-off weight of 350 tons the Boeing 747 was more than 200 tons heavier than the 707. Some 'big' aircraft of the past

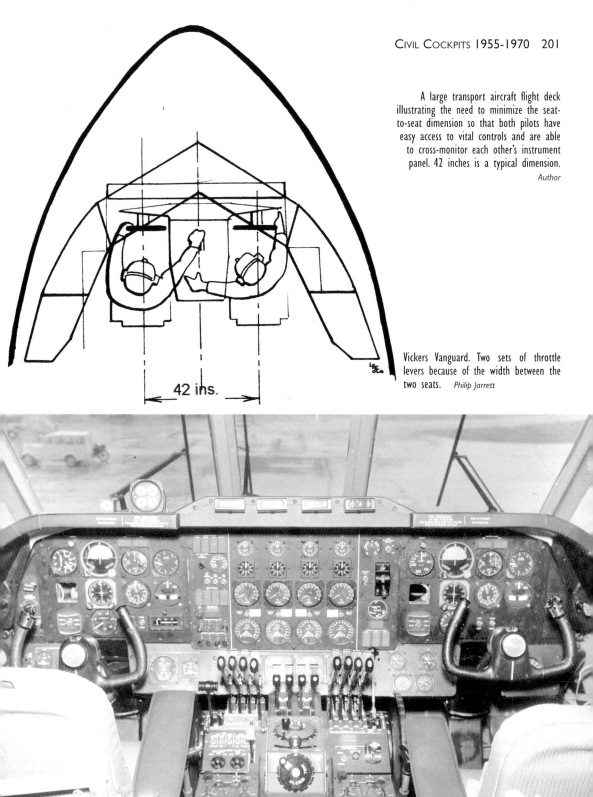

A large transport aircraft flight deck illustrating the need to minimize the seat-to-seat dimension so that both pilots have easy access to vital controls and are able to cross-monitor each other's instrument panel. 42 inches is a typical dimension. *Author*

42 ins.

Vickers Vanguard. Two sets of throttle levers because of the width between the two seats. *Philip Jarrett* have had spacious cockpits in keeping with their size, e.g. Sikorsky's Bolshoi, the Dornier D X and the Staaken bombers. However, the dimensions, particularly the width, of the 747 cockpit were made not much larger than that of the 707. An important cockpit function, particularly when there is some doubt about the accuracy or reliability of an instrument display on one panel, is the cross-checking of one pilot's instruments by the other pilot. With all large aircraft the controls on the central pedestal need to be within reach of either pilot. Therefore, and to avoid unnecessary duplication of engine thrust levers, for example, the distance between centre-lines of the pilots' seats should preferably not be much greater than 42 in. The distance between the pilots' seats in the Lockheed 188 Electra of 1957 was much greater, and therefore there had to be two sets of throttle levers.

CHAPTER NINE

Military Cockpits 1955-1970

Dramatic changes

In this period of military aircraft development, and particularly the fighter/attack cockpit, the introduction of new weapons and integrated weapon-aiming systems for air-to-air and air-to-ground missiles changed the look of the interface. Developments in both sensor and computer technology had to be matched by new concepts for control and instrumentation. Throughout this era CRT displays became more versatile, and the pointer-on-dial instruments were progressively consigned to secondary functions, or only retained as standby units in the event of a major avionics failure. Vertical and horizontal 'tape' displays for engine parameters continued to be advocated and sometimes used, but in general they lost out in the end to cirscale instruments or to the increasing use of CRT displays.

Multi-role

Throughout the history of military aviation multi-role or multi-purpose, or even general-purpose, have been used to describe many

Early version of the BAe Hawk with its typical 1960s trainer/attack cockpit. The different case sizes of the principal flight instruments precludes a symmetrical layout. However, as long as the information provided by the individual instruments is clear and unambiguous, design for the sake of aesthetics is of far less importance. *British Aerospace.*

Lockheed F-104 Starfighter. The attack radar scope is forward of the stick. There are two 360° 'spherical' type attitude indicators to the right of the display of bearing and distance to navigational beacons. *Philip Jarrett*

mechanical instrument development made steady progress from 1914 onwards, but not until the 1940s was there any marked increase in the speed of development. Eventually these types were overtaken by the electronic. In the 1950s inertial navigation (IN) systems were added to existing military aircraft types and analogue computers began to take their place on board. Avionic systems could 'talk' to each other, and a push-button selection of systems became the standard. The pilot only had to press a few buttons and the radar, for example, would switch from air-to-air mode to air-to-ground mode. From about 1955 onwards avionics began to revolutionize the look of the cockpit.

By the end of the 1950s the fighter/attack cockpit was beginning to lose its Second World War look. From then on more and more instruments and controls were added to match the increasing versatility of aircraft. The increasing complexity of aircraft, particularly the avionic systems, was forcing up the costs to a level far above the amount of money given out by the politicians. No longer could an air force have the luxury of hundreds of a dozen or so different first-line aircraft types. Each of a smaller number of types had to perform many different roles; as also did their pilots. Attempts to produce 'lightweight' fighters, such as the Folland Gnat, resulted in airframes and electrical power systems that could not cope with additional equipment necessary for extending the original concept to embrace other roles, such as interception using radar or even upgrading weapon aiming by installing a HUD. The Gnat cockpit was a tight fit from the word go. There was little room available for more elaborate stores

different basic types of aircraft. For example, aircraft originally intended as pursuits or fighters were modified so that they could carry bombs or torpedoes, as was the RAF's Beaufighter. Both the German and American air forces adapted existing designs so that they could perform additional functions. But these involved add-on changes. This could be done fairly easily because aircraft were a collection of disparate electronic boxes, electrical systems and weapon-aiming and release devices. All these were hard wired. Each stood alone and the pilot had to coordinate their functioning. Radar, for example, was often either air-to-air or air-to-ground. It could not be switched from one to the other. Or if it could be it was not as effective as it should have been in either role.

Avionics

As with most advances in aviation, avionics development has been a gradual process. However, there are degrees of gradualness. Pointer-on-dial mechanical and electro-

Folland Gnat 'compact' fighter. All the principal instruments were electro-mechanical. The current HUDs were too large to fit above the instrument panel. *Smiths Group*

management, weapon selection and modern aiming systems. The proof of war, such as India versus Pakistan, virtually killed off the concept of the small lightweight fighter and its equally small cockpit. Even the big aircraft with a big cockpit presented problems when it became necessary to upgrade. The English Electric Lightning cockpit was designed before the advent of the electronic head-up

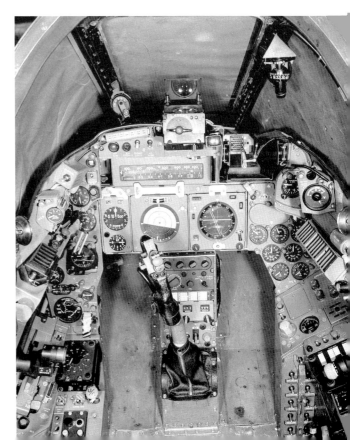

English Electric Lightning c 1960. Horizontal 'tape' airspeed and Mach number above large electro-mechanical attitude and horizontal situation displays. Against the windscreen is the gyro gunsight. The shape of the nose forward of the instrument panel did not afford room for an electronic HUD. The attack radar display unit fits into the space to the right of the gunsight. To the left are the twin throttle levers and the lever for the air brakes. *British Aerospace*

An important item in the history of th military aircraft cockpit. This is one of th earliest head-up displays (HUDs) and not mu larger than the gyro gunsight it replaced.
Smiths Group

SaaB Draken cockpit showing the large displa screen of the attack radar and the vertic scale airspeed/Mach indicator. *SaaB AB*

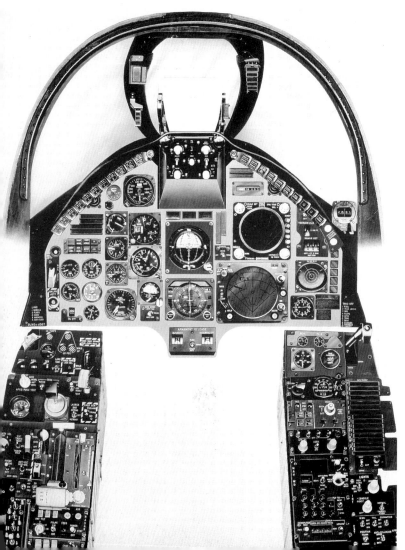

Principal instrument and control panels in a A-7E Corsair II. *LTV*

display, so there was no room between the bottom of the windscreen and the top of the instrument panel for a HUD display unit and the combining glass.

Jet aircraft in this era were achieving higher speeds and ceilings than before. They were also far more versatile and therefore more expensive than the piston-engined types of earlier times. The pilots of these expensive and sophisticated weapons needed better instruments and extensive avionics so that targets could be found and attacked in all visibility conditions. They also had to have systems that could detect and counter the enemy's guns and missiles. The CRT had arrived in the single-seat cockpit in the last year of the Second World War. It was positioned alongside the conventional pointer-on-dial instruments, and would for many years be the only representative of the electronic display revolution that by the end of this era would provide pilots with a proliferation of alphanumerics, symbols, maps, weather and other information.

HUD

By the mid-1960s the HUD had become an essential part of the cockpit interface. The HUD's computer took information from a number of different sources, such as the air data system, aircraft attitude and heading, and weapon-aiming data, and presented it in

SaaB Viggen c 1969. Large electro mechanical spherical attitude indicator moved from the usual centre line position to make room for an electronic tactical and weapon-aiming display. *SaaB AB*

the pilot's forward line of sight. An air data system typically senses, measures, computes and transmits to other systems pressure altitude, outside air temperature, Mach number, equivalent air speed (EAS), angle of attack (Alpha), yaw angle and dynamic pressure.

One of the spurs to the development of the HUD related to the poor visibility conditions that obtained for much of the time in Europe. The Harrier and Jaguar squadrons of the RAF, for example, were required, in the event of a Soviet advance westwards, to 'take out' tanks and bridges in the face of surface-to-air-missiles. Attacks would have been at low level irrespective of the visibility. In those circumstances a pilot would have had to fly 'head up' in order to navigate and avoid obstacles. There would be no time in which to refer to 'head-down' cockpit instruments. In the 1950s there were significant improvements in the performance of anti-aircraft defences. 'Set-piece' attacks, with the aircraft flown to precise attack patterns, were no longer acceptable. For example, loitering close to a target in order to assess the best approach track could not be indulged in when the defences had sophisticated fire-control systems for their weapons. Pilots could afford to make only one pass at a ground target, as fast and low as possible The weapon-aiming system had to provide instantaneous guidance. During low-level, 'nap of the earth', flying the air space was sometimes contested by birds. For example, a SEPECAT Jaguar flying at 460 knots at 200 ft hit a bird. The windscreen was penetrated and the combining glass of the head-up display was smashed. Fortunately the pilot's helmet visor was down and he was not injured.

Although the HUD looked like an improved version of the gyro gunsight, it was far more than that. A HUD unit consists of three principal elements – a CRT, the many lenses of the optical system and the combining glass or glasses. The HUD's computer can provide a wide range of symbology and alphanumerics from which the pilot can select those appropriate to a particular flight mode. However, the final information process is non-avionic because it is just an optical display. There is therefore a limit to the vertical and horizontal fields of view. In a typical 1960s-generation refractive-optics HUD these were typically 12° and 18° respectively. Diffractive optics using holographic technology provided increased fields of view. A notable example is the GEC Avionics Lantirn (Low altitude navigational targeting infra-red for night) HUD.

No longer did the pilot have to scan a number of discrete instruments in order to build up a complete picture of what the aircraft was doing, where it was going and what was needed to be done in order to achieve a specific goal. As with the multi-function electronic head-down displays that came later, the pilot could select the display to match the immediate operating phase, i.e. en route, cruise, navigation, target search, target acquisition (ground or air) and attack. The HUD could display any of these at a touch of a button, as well as provide a continuous indication at the periphery of the display of aircraft angle-of-attack, altitude, vertical speed, Mach/airspeed and heading. The first generation of HUDs were of the cursive type, but this limited the quality of the display. Eventually the raster display technique was adopted, which is similar to the domestic TV with its parallel lines forming the picture. This enabled the 'pictures' from the FLIR (forward-looking infra-red) and LLTV (low-light TV) to be presented head up and not just on head-down instruments on the main instrument panel. The HUD forced a rethink about the shape and volume of the fighter/attack cockpit. As with the ejection seat, it needed space in which to install the display unit. As

Early 1960s cockpit standards (SEPECAT Jaguar) to which have been added a GEC-Marconi COMED (Combined Map and Electronic Display) and a Smiths Group HUD (Head Up Display). The former provides a continuously moving 'map' type display with the aircraft position shown at the centre. *Smiths Group Archives*

Harrier GR MkI cockpit of the 1960s in the decade before the move to wall-to-wall electronic displays replaced most of the 'clocks'. The HUD and the COMAD were developed in parallel with the Harrier and were essential equipment to enable the pilot to make the most effective use of the aircraft's unique capabilities. *British Aerospace*

Typical symbology reflected from the combining glass of a head up display. Aircraft is banked left. Speed 180 knots. Heading 130 degrees. Barometric height 1,800 feet. *Smiths Group*

Improving from experience

By the beginning of this era in military aviation the jet had all but ousted the piston-engine – propeller combination. Even at the close of the piston-engine half of high-performance aviation history not all the built-in fault-inducing items in the cockpit had been eliminated. Although greater attention was being paid to instrument design and the type and position of controls, incidents and accidents were still a fact of air force life. The jet cockpit inherited many shortcomings of the piston-engine age. It was not just the controls and instruments that might, through poor design and arrangement, cause trouble. An example was a decision to install a different type of pilot's survival pack in the cockpits of a fleet of fighter/attack aircraft. Only after a pilot was killed, because he was unable to reach the ejection seat handle, was it realized that the new survival pack might have been the cause. This was confirmed when all the pilots found that they would not have been able to reach the seat handle.

mentioned, not all the 1950s generation of fighter/attack aircraft, such as the Lightning, had room above the instrument panel. From 1960 onwards decisions over dimensions and volumes had to include two key elements – ejection seat and HUD.

LTV Corsair II c 1970. The cockpit, radome and air-intake are close together in the nose of the aircraft. *Smiths Group Archives*

Early version of an RAF Nimrod maritime patrol aircraft's cockpit. Subsequent avionic up-grades have replaced most of the 'clocks'; with large electronic displays. *BAE*

TSR 2

The progress of new British aircraft continued to be bedevilled and sometimes stopped dead by a combination of politics, lack of funds and changes on the part of both the civil administration and the air staff. The TSR 2 is a notable example of an aircraft design and testing programme launched with such high hopes by the British aircraft industry in 1956. Had it gone into production it would have given the RAF a tactical/strike/reconnaissance aircraft with technology far in advance of the Canberra that it was intended to replace. Although the TSR 2 was scrapped soon after a series of

successful test flights, it is included in this book because it is a good example of how a design team has to accept a series of compromises.

As with most aircraft, the cockpit and its equipment reflect the operational tasks for which the aircraft is designed. For the TSR 2 this included flying at low level supersonically, reaching Mach 2 at the tropopause, delivering nuclear or conventional munitions from low level in poor visibility, completing all-weather photo sorties out to 1,000 nm, having good gust-effect alleviation in the interest of the crew, the windscreen able to resist a 3 lb bird-strike at 750 knots and the crew able to escape throughout the performance limits of the aircraft. And even more directly affecting the design of the cockpit were the requirements relating to protection against extremely low air pressures and temperatures at the limiting altitude, as well as atomic flash.

An initial major design decision that had to be reached concerned the respective merits of side-by-side seating for pilot and navigator/electronics officer, or a tandem arrangement. The side-by-side imposed aerodynamic penalties because of the increased fuselage width needed, which in turn affected the design of the engine intakes. And within the cockpit the number and panel space requirements of the avionic systems required for the many different operational roles ruled out the side-by-side. The TSR 2 was to be the RAF's 'Swiss Army knife' with its many different blades and tools. Perhaps in trying to achieve the ability to perform so many different tasks the development programme was handicapped from the start.

Irrespective of how uncertain the TSR 2's future might have appeared at the time, the specifications relating to the cockpit equipment served as a valuable incentive to those involved with developing new types of instruments. For example, at this time strip-type electronic instruments were being developed. They were considered, but the air staff, for logistical reasons, decided to stick with the electromechanical, pointer-on-dial type. Of course, a HUD was to be both a key item as well as the focal point when arranging the instrumentation. The next two items in order of

importance directly in front of the pilot would be the attitude director (ADI) and the horizontal situation indicator (HSI) (navigation display). These had to be side by side and not vertically disposed because room had to be made below them for the large, 10-inch-diameter display, screen of the combined moving map and electronic display unit. A panel of standby flight instruments was to the left of the principal head-up and head-down displays. To the right were the group of engine instruments. An interesting observation, on studying one official description of the cockpit, was the use of the word 'dashboard' instead of instrument panel. This was a relic from the early automobile era and not really appropriate for

TSR 2 c 1964. Another example of instrument technology lagging engine, airframe and aerodynamic technologies. The majority of the instruments are electromechanical. Had the TSR 2 gone into production it is likely that by 1975 the cockpit interface would have been the subject of a comprehensive upgrade programme to take advantage of electronic displays matched to the latest sensor and weapon systems technologies. *British Aerospace*

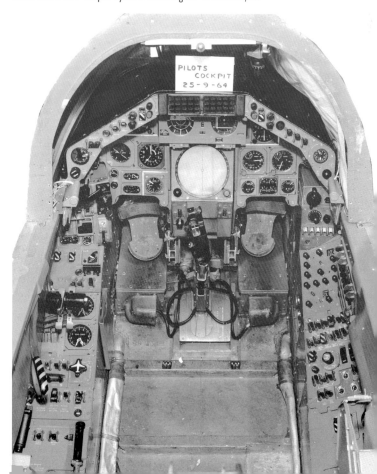

such an advanced 'flying machine' as the TSR 2.

Among a long list of compromises were the angular relationships between the ideal aerodynamic shape of the nose for supersonic flight, the most effective angle for the dielectric cone over the radar dish and the slope of the windscreen. The operational requirements included an 11° downwards view forward with its origin at the pilot's eye reference point (ERP). The windscreen was at an angle of 35° to the horizontal in order to give the optimum arcs of view. This angle in turn affected the location of the HUD because the windscreen also had to act as a combining glass, thereby obviating the need for its heavy supporting frames. For this reason and others a V-shaped windscreen of two panels was ruled out by the need to use the glass for reflecting the HUD symbology.

Within all cockpits for high-performance aircraft there are likely to be conflicts in the vertical dimensions below the glare shield between ejection clearance for the pilot's legs and the best arrangement of the principal instruments. In the TSR 2 it was decided to incline the main instrument panel so as to increase the available area. A major design decision concerned the type and position of the control column. It could have extended back out of the lower part of the instrument panel, or be in the conventional between-the-knees position, or it could be a side-stick. The side-stick was always an option, and not just for the TSR 2, but there was the question of what to do if the pilot's right hand and arm were injured. Would that mean having to eject? Also, a side-stick took up the space usually reserved for secondary controls to the right of the pilot. In the end the conventional position was chosen. No doubt had the TSR 2 entered service with the RAF in the 1970s it would have been retrofitted with the latest types of electronic displays in order to improve the quality and overall ergonomics of the cockpit. As it was, it arrived at a time in the development of avionics when it had to make do with what was available.

Short Belfast with an early type of HUD for transport aircraft. *Smiths Group*

The Big Bear

The Tupolev Tu-95MS, NATO code BEAR, exemplified the advances made by Russian aviation technology since the end of the Second World War. This cruise-missile-carrying bomber was part of the Soviet long-range aviation fleet, and at an all-up weight of around 180 tonnes can be

Boeing B-52 flight deck c 1960. The principal engine panel contains 32 instruments. On the controls pedestal there are eight thrust levers. Two large electronic displays of navigation and tactical information dominate the main panel. This photograph is only typical because throughout the long in-service life of the B-52 there have been many up-grades of the avionics and associated cockpit equipment. *Philip Jarrett*

compared for size with the B-52's 227 tonnes and the 100 tonnes or so of the RAF's Vulcan and Victor. The pilot and second pilot of the Bear, along with flight engineer, navigators and electronic systems operators, were seated in a pressurized section of the hull, with the two pilots facing forwards and the other crew members facing aft or to the side. The complete fenestration of ten windows extended through 180° horizontally and 90° vertically. None of the crew, including the two pilots, was given ejection seats, even though the aircraft could attain a maximum speed of about 500 knots, and if out of control even faster. It is believed that a 'trolley' running on rails could be used by the flight-deck crew to reach the escape hatch. During a visit to a UK air show in 1993, limited access was granted to

journalists. Those instruments that were not deliberately covered up gave the impression that, at the time, they were not to the same level of technology as those in Western air forces. By then the Bear, as a concept, was more than forty years old, and in that time, no doubt, there had been many different versions and many changes to the cockpit equipment in an attempt to catch up with Western technology.

F-11

At the beginning of this era a number of very interesting fighters came on the scene. One was the F-11. Already mentioned was the large size of American cockpits compared with those in the aircraft of other countries. However, the cockpit of the F-11 was not large enough to accommodate an average-size

USN pilot when he wore a pressurized anti-G suit. Because the top of the canopy was faired into the top line of the fuselage the pilot's view on each quarter was not as good as in the F-86 Sabre. A Martin Baker X5 ejection seat was fitted. At that time ejection seats were usually actuated by pulling down a face blind, and not by levers at the sides of the seat or a loop between the pilot's legs. Also around this time control columns were beginning to acquire more and more buttons and triggers as the number of different weapon systems increased. On the F-11's stick there were the gun trigger, bomb release button, rocket trigger, trim control and the nosewheel steering system engagement selector. As this was the 1950s, aiming of guns and rockets was through a reflector sight, alongside which was the indicator for the radar ranging system. There was no autopilot or auto-stabilizer, so that the ability to aim accurately was compromised. Subsequent retrofit avionics included an all-weather attack radar.

Too many cooks

In the early 1960s there was disagreement between the USAF and the USN over the General Dynamics F-111. The Air Force wanted it as a precision bomber, whereas the Navy wanted the twin-engined, two-seater, variable-geometry F-111 as a fleet defence fighter. The Pentagon ordered both services to agree on a common aircraft that would meet both operational roles. The cockpit and its profile were influenced by subsequent arguments and contrary decisions among the two services. The Navy preferred the pilot and navigator/electronics operator to be seated side by side, whereas the Air Force wanted a tandem seat arrangement. The Navy won.

General Dynamics provided the aircraft with a side-by-side cockpit that was part of an escape capsule. The pilot on the left had a limited view aft and to the right. Aerodynamic and structural considerations precluded a canopy proud of the top line of the fuselage. This suited the Air Force because it intended to use the aircraft as a bomber and to rely on speed for defence; therefore there was less need for a view astern. Even had the Air Force or the Navy wanted a raised canopy so as to improve the all-round view, the serious transonic drag problems that beset the aircraft's progress from prototype to production aircraft ruled out any changes to the original cockpit profile. As it happened, the Navy lost interest in the F-111 as a fleet defence fighter or for any other role.

The F-111's instruments were updated in the late 1960s to improve the aircraft's effectiveness and to reduce crew workload. A mission management system was installed that took charge of most of the navigation, communication and target-seeking and attacking tasks from the crew. A key element in the update was a digital computer and a new multi-function radar. The crew of an F-111 can see the ground mapped and displayed with accuracy and clarity on the display screens in the cockpit. They can distinguish between stationary and moving targets on the ground. The sensor/display system also provides guidance for air-to-air missiles should the F-111 have to take part in a dogfight. An important item in the F-111's avionics inventory, and one that directly affects the pilot's handling of the aircraft, is the terrain-following radar. This reduces workload, particularly when flying at 500 knots at 500 ft or less. At that speed and level any hesitation or slow reaction on the part of the pilot can lead to disaster. The F-111's terrain-following system keeps the aircraft at a constant preselected height above the earth's surface, even when it is rugged and undulating.

Mention must be made of the additional primary control lever alongside the throttle levers. This is the wing-sweep control. Which way should it move? Aft to increase sweep-back for high-speed flight or forward for low speed? In the end it was decided that it would move forward for greater sweep-back because it was considered logical that, as with the throttles, if you wanted to go faster then you pushed forward. A pedantic ergonomist would argue that a control must move in the same direction as the thing being controlled.

The escape capsule concept has been considered from time to time as an alternative to individual ejection seats. It was adopted for the F-111 in order to give the crew a 'shirt-sleeve' pressurized cockpit environment in which they did not have to wear a pressure suit or parachute harness. However, they had to wear an anti-G garment. The capsule formed part of the fuselage until it was ejected by rockets that thrust it well away from the aircraft. Parachutes were deployed automatically and inflatable cells cushioned the impact with the sea or ground. The capsule was self righting and could protect the crew until rescued.

F-4F Phantom

For more than thirty years the F-4F was a well-known part of the aviation scene. It served with the US Navy and Air Force, with the RAF and the Royal Navy and in the air forces of many other countries. It performed over a wide range of roles, from interception to ground attack. Irrespective of its operational success, it has a particular place in cockpit history because it is yet another example of a major design decision relating to pilot workload. When the Phantom was only a preliminary specification and the subject of arguments around the table, the

F-4F Phantom. A book on cockpits would be incomplete without the pilot's place in one of the most outstanding and long — lived fighter attack aircraft of the last century. This photograph emphasizes the trend in the early 1960s to crowd more and more weapon-aiming equipment against the windscreen. *Boeing*

big question that had to be answered concerned the number of crew: one pilot or a pilot assisted by an electronics officer? In the 1950s most of the navigation, search, target-acquisition and attack electronics were discrete systems with limited ability to interchange data automatically. Therefore it was decided that the multiple tasks of integration and coordination would impose too high a workload on a solo pilot. And so the F-4F became a two-seater. The respective merits of single-seater and two-seater fighter/attack aircraft would continue to exercise the air staff and design offices in all the major air forces. Eventually advances in avionics and display technologies would make it possible to have single-seater fighter/attack aircraft in which the pilot's workload was kept to an acceptable level.

Even with the workload shared, the two cockpits of the F-4F were crammed with controls, instruments and electronic displays. The pilot's cockpit instrument panel was dominated by the attack radar screen. Under this were the attitude indicator and the horizontal situation indicator. To the right was the instruments panel for the two engines, and to the left the remaining flight instruments. To the left of the pilot's ejection seat were the engine and configuration controls, such as undercarriage, airbrakes and flaps. On the right were the radio and electrical system controls. The designer of the cockpit was faced with a difficult task in getting everything in so that as many things as possible were within reach and sight of the pilot. Perhaps the result can be summed up as 'a place for a lot of things and each in its place'.

Harrier

Leaving the Harrier cockpit out of this book would be unthinkable. This STOVL, in its RAF and Royal Navy, and later USMC, versions broke the mould of operations requiring long hard-surfaced runways. The Harrier was designed to use forest clearings or short improvised landing strips. Along with the 'ski jump ramp' on the forward end of an aircraft-carrier's deck it could make a conventional take-off at maximum operational weight. On return, both the ship's crew and the Harrier pilot had a far less difficult recovery operation compared with the 'controlled crash' landing, halted by arrester wires, of conventional aircraft.

The top line of the profile of the Harrier's cockpit was only slightly raised above the fuselage. Contemporary fighter/attack aircraft had a bubble canopy raised sufficiently above the line of the fuselage to give the pilot a good angle of view over both quarters. Unless the tactical situation is such that air superiority is guaranteed then there is always the danger of being 'jumped' from astern by the enemy, particularly when making a vertical landing. Eventually all versions of the Harrier had a larger canopy giving a wider field of view astern. The ability to vector the thrust of the engine required an additional control lever alongside the throttle. In the Harrier this is moved aft to rotate the four rotatable thrust nozzles downwards from 0° to 110°.

For a vertical take-off the nozzles are moved to the vertical position and the throttle immediately pushed quickly forward. This is done to prevent the engine ingesting its own exhaust. The autostabilizer system helps the pilot to control the aircraft as it rises on four columns of air. Control in roll, pitch and yaw using the control column and rudder pedals is the same as with any aircraft. Progressive movement of the nozzles from the vertical position to the 0° setting changes the Harrier's control, characteristics and performance into that of a conventional aircraft. For a slow and short landing, the nozzles are first set 20° down during the base leg phase. Once lined up for the approach the nozzles are progressively set to 70° down. The nozzle angle is then used to control the angle of attack and the rate of descent and approach speed. In effect the nozzle lever is used in the same sense as the throttle in a conventional aircraft to control the rate of descent. Close to the ground the pilot uses a combination of throttle and nozzle position to effect a touch-down with minimum vertical speed, followed by a short landing run assisted by moving the nozzles to the 110°g braking position.

Other than the vector thrust nozzle lever, HUD and the combined map and electronic display (COMED), the instruments of the first series of Harriers were unremarkable. Both the HUD and the COMED were key elements in the overall Harrier concept because they were essential to the primary operational role of attacking targets at low level irrespective of the visibility and rugged terrain. Combining the HUD system with the weapon-aiming computer improved the probability of a making a successful attack. COMED used aircraft position derived from the inertial navigation (IN) system to drive an optically projected map continuously. The map was combined with symbology and alphanumerics generated on a monochrome CRT. These were derived from the aircraft's sensors and computers. Map and electronic data were therefore combined on the one screen. A special lens arrangement enabled the pilot to view the display clearly, even when it was exposed to bright sunlight. Meanwhile scientists were developing the multi-colour CRT for aircraft use. By 1970 ring-laser gyros enhanced the accuracy of the IN systems on which other avionics, such as COMED, depended.

A-10 Warthog

The A-10 is an example of an aircraft designed around the cockpit. An important design requirement was that of protecting the pilot during low-level attacks against heavily defended targets. To that end the cockpit was constructed of materials able to resist the impact of SAMs and 23 mm machine-gun bullets. When making a low-level pass against a heavily defended target an A-10 pilot knows that the aircraft's control systems are designed and arranged so that they can resist enemy fire or if damaged an alternative method of control becomes available. These details are most reassuring. Figuratively, with the cockpit design worked out, the rest of the aircraft could then be considered. This included positioning the engines above the trailing edge of the wing. An interesting detail is the positioning of the nosewheel leg to one side so that the multi-barrel 30 mm gun is on the centre-line of the fuselage. This position aligns the gun, the sighting system and the pilot's eyes.

A-7

The LTV A7 single-seat attack aircraft was conventional in all its major elements with the exception of the nose. In the majority of fighter/attack aircraft of this era there was about six feet of nose ahead of the windscreen. In the A-7 the pilot sat with his feet close to the small radome that formed the nose of the aircraft.

C-130 Hercules

The C-130 started its illustrious career at the beginning of this era. The cockpit was not designed, as might have been expected, in accord with the stepped-nose shape of most transport aircraft. Instead it had extensive fenestration blended into the nose shape. This provided the two pilots with large vertical angles of view, and enabled activity on the ground to be kept in view, such as when orbiting a target during an attack using heavy machine-guns firing on the port beam.

Ejecting

The ejection seat is vital for the recovery of expensive-to-train aircrew in the event of trouble. As with the parachute, it has a morale-boosting role. A pilot's survival

Rockwell B-1 bomber flight deck. Vertical scale instruments predominate and in this early 1970s giant bomber there are few electronic displays. The two pilots and the other two crewmen are contained in an escape capsule which can be fired clear of the fuselage. *Smiths Group Archives*

following an aircraft failure depends not only on the correct and instantaneous firing of the ejection seat, it also depends very much on the body-mounted clothing and equipment. When ejection takes place above 10,000 ft a self-contained oxygen supply is essential. The sequence of ejection actions does not end when the seat separation and parachute deployment phases are completed. Even if the pilot reaches the earth's surface and has not suffered severe injuries during ejection, the environment could be hostile. Possibly the most demanding situation is landing in the water, particularly if the sea temperature is at or below freezing. If the immersion suit is not torn, and the dinghy inflates correctly and the locator beacon

operates, a pilot can expect to be rescued with some confidence. But there are many 'ifs' following the moment a pilot triggers the ejection seat. Ejection seat development in this era included the ability to eject safely when flying at 1,000 ft or lower.

The next decade

By the end of the 1960s the avionics 'wizards' were close to perfecting production-standard, multi-function, multi-colour, electronic displays. These would further improve the cockpit interface; particularly when the pilot was scanning and mentally integrating the information displayed.

CHAPTER TEN

Civil Cockpits 1970-2005

The Digital Cockpit

Why choose 1970 as a starting-time mark for this chapter? To some extent this is an arbitrary choice because aviation, and its avionics in particular, evolve like everything else with time. Changes in technology rarely suddenly jump into being.

The new has to live alongside the old. Technology usually metamorphoses by evolutionary processes. Digital computers were being developed in the 1950s but did not become production standard equipment for another ten years. The microchip, which came on the scene from about 1970 onwards, made a significant change both to the look of the flight deck and to the relationship between pilot and machine. Therefore, and to be less arbitrary, 1970 is selected because it is roughly the mid-point between the history of the analogue and the digital technologies: between discrete single-function elements and the integrated circuits that evolved into the microprocessor. For example, there were only four digital computers in the Boeing 747 of 1969, but by 1983 there were more than 100 in the Boeing 757. Digital technology made possible the solid-state instruments that over the next thirty years would consign the pointer-on-dial and numeral-counter electromechanical instruments to a 'standby' status.

Perhaps the most important change in the relationship between pilot and aircraft came with the development of fly-by-wire (FBW) systems. With FBW, the link between the pilot's hands and feet and the control surfaces is no longer via mechanical linkages and the servo-mechanisms of the powered controls. The pilot's actions are processed by computers and the commands passed on, as electrical signals, to the control-surface actuators. The FBW computers also prevent an aircraft exceeding its aerodynamic limits.

The nerve centre

The cockpit is the nerve centre of an aircraft at which many things, functions and events are concentrated. The flight decks of modern airliners, military transports as well as business, commuter and feeder aircraft, exhibit common characteristics, such as 'wall-to-wall' electronic displays and keypads for selecting operating functions and modes of flight or for retrieving information. Many have a side-stick in place of wheel and column for roll and pitch control; some have head-up displays similar to those of a fighter/attack aircraft; and most now exhibit the 'black cockpit' concept whereby the avionic systems only display alphanumerics, graphics, symbology and status lights when information is needed or is selected.

This did not all come about overnight, even though, as mentioned already, the progress toward the modern flight deck accelerated with the introduction of the digital computer and the multi-function, multi-colour displays from about 1970 onwards. Of course, experimental and pre-

McDD MD 80 cockpit in a restful shade of green. The instrumentation is not much advanced in technology from that of the DC-9 of the early 1960s from which it was derived. *Philip Jarrett*

production systems were under way earlier, but aircraft operators were sometimes reluctant, usually for financial rather than technical reasons, to make the technological leap forward.

The interface

For a human pilot to be able to monitor and intervene in the operation of a particular system, such as a flight-control system, there has to be an interface. This has to provide both the means of access to the system (such as keypads, switches or manual controls) and an output of information (electronic, electromechanical displays, etc.). Each part of an aircraft's control anatomy has to be

'transparent' so as to facilitate a two-way flow of information and actions across the two faces of the information and control interface. The faces must merge in one direction into the pilot's senses and effectors (hands and feet) and in the other direction into the aircraft's systems.

Part of the complexity imposed by the needs of a human pilot derives from the completely different language used by mankind and machine. The digital systems of modern aircraft use the 0s and 1s of their computers and data buses. The data have to be processed so that the information conveyed can be understood by a human pilot. In the other direction across the

AD-650H

RD-650

These instruments represent the degree of sophistication achieved in electro-mechanical instrument technology in the 1970s. The primary flight instrument or attitude director indicator (ADI) provides attitude, heading, ILS command 'cross' (yellow) and pitch and roll relative to the horizon along with radio altitude. Its ancestor is the Sperry Zero Reader of the 1950s. Below is its companion the horizontal situation indicator (HIS). *Sperry*

interface, the human pilot's vocal and tactile commands and interrogations have to be converted into electrical signals and then as digital data passed to the control systems.

Continuing the concept of the 'brain and nervous system' of an aircraft, the cockpit is that location at which the principal elements are concentrated. These are the pilot or pilots, the control and information interface, and the volume and structure of the cockpit. An important design target is to achieve as nearly as possible a total interactive symbiotic information and control system interface. The complexity, volume and design problems of systems having to accommodate a human pilot are emphasized if we consider

that for the greater part of the flight of a modern commercial aircraft most systems are performing their particular control and monitoring functions automatically. They also automatically communicate or interface with other systems.

Instruments and controls

That part of the interface that conveys information to the pilot comes under the general heading of instrumentation. This includes all devices that convey information, in whatever form, to the human pilot. It includes pointer-on-dial, pointer-and-numerals, vertical and horizontal scales, lights, electronic displays, annunciators, bells and klaxons, voice messages and parafoveal display units. Some instruments provide just information, others advice, attention-getting or warnings. Those displays that provide control guidance, such as the attitude directors, are an important group. Depending on the particular type of aircraft and its aerodynamic characteristics, there are foot-thumpers to warn of wheel skidding, and stick shakers and knockers to warn of the onset of a stall. There are also stick pushers that lower the aircraft's nose before it reaches

The growth of avionic systems for communication and navigation was not confined to large commercial aircraft. This is the cockpit of a trainer equipped with a comprehensive array of instruments and control panels for flight in all visibility conditions and in controlled airspace. *Slingsby*

a speed or attitude at which it will stall. The fenestration required for the pilot's view of the real world can also be considered as part of the instrumentation because it provides the important real-world information input to the pilot. The elements of the interface that convey commands and interrogations include levers, wheels, knobs, buttons, touch-screens, 'soft' keys and keypads as well as microphones.

Structure and space

The cockpit includes the structure, volumes, space, containers, racks, panels and pedestals on which to mount and secure elements of the interface; including provision for the protection and comfort of the pilot. Positioning the cockpit of a transport aircraft well forward in the nose has advantages and disadvantages. It reduces the area of fenestration, thereby optimizing resistance against the loads of pressurization, and minimizes the cockpit width so that the two pilots are close enough for each to reach all the vital controls and be able to cross-monitor the primary instrument panel of the other. In a transport aircraft, with the cockpit well forward, there is more room for passenger seats or cargo. The disadvantages include restricted fore-and-aft dimensions below the windscreen in which to accommodate instruments. With the cockpit of some aircraft more than 6 m above the tarmac and a long way ahead of the main wheels, taxiing the big jets requires a special technique; particularly when negotiating the turn onto the runway so as not to overshoot or undershoot the centre-line before lining up for take-off.

CRT to LED to LCD

The electromechanical, plus some electronic, instruments of the 1960s and 1970s were eventually replaced by instruments having no moving parts:

cathode ray tubes (CRTs), then light-emitting diodes (LEDs) and finally liquid crystal displays (LCDs). Important display developments have been multi-colour and visibility in full sunlight, as well as redundancy techniques to ensure availability of vital data at all times. In place of the comparatively bulky CRTs of the 1970s-generation electronic displays, the LCDs could be housed in a panel only 15 mm thick. This physical characteristic simplified their installation in the cockpit, particularly if the

A typical electronic horizontal situation display. The aircraft's heading is 220° to offset a wind of 20 knots from 260° (bottom right). The track or course is 227 degrees. Ground speed 165 knots. The aircraft is 15 nautical miles (NM) or 5 minutes from a VOR transmitter and is to the left of the selected VOR radial. *Smiths Group*

An electronic display of the horizontal situation to complement that of the attitude director. At the instant shown the aircraft is heading 012°. The required course to the next waypoint 5.7 nautical miles away is 067 degrees. *Smiths Group*

profile of the aircraft's nose was such that there was little room under the lower rim of the forward cockpit windows.

Electronic displays

There is some truth in the world of avionics statement that, 'You can have as many or as few alphanumeric characters, graphics and symbols as you need and all in a broad range of colours.' As one avionics company put it, 'You can have Donald Duck in full colour and animation, if that is what you want.' The designer of the cockpit is faced with an embarrassment of riches. The problem of what type of display to design, and its content, can be resolved by first analysing the perceptual processes and limitations of the human pilot. How does he or she see? What

Electronic attitude director indicator (EADI) or primary flight display (PFD). Over ten different parameters can be displayed which in the pre-electronic displays era would have required up to ten individual instruments. *Smiths Group*

A typical multi-function CRT display. The pilot can select information by using the peripheral 'soft' keys. In this example Primary Flight Display mode has ben selected. The aircraft is heading 118°. Magnetic, is climbing at 1000 ft/min (right hand vertical scale) at a ground speed (GS) of 282 knots with the wings level. *Smiths Group*

does the pilot need to have presented visually in order to complete specific in-the-control-loop tasks?

The undoubted versatility of the electronic displays, particularly as an ADI, had tended toward a situation in which there were solutions looking for problems, when in fact it should have been the other way round. The instruments had been assumed to be sacrosanct. Their format, graphics, symbols and colours and the interrelationships of the display elements were assumed to be immutable. This relationship between display design and the pilot's visual perceptual performance was acquired because of the way in which instruments in general had evolved over the past one hundred years.

Tradition has played an important part in the evolution of instruments. Some might say a far too important part. It is possible to accept that when electromechanical mechanisms replaced earlier instruments there was no good reason at the time to expect fundamental, even revolutionary, changes to display formats. However, electronic display technologies, when first introduced, provided the opportunity to cast off the chains of tradition. That did not happen. Of course, one good reason for retaining the format of the earlier instrument technology was to smooth the transition on the part of pilots from the old to the new.

An example of tradition influencing display design is to be found with the attitude director indicator. Some were given a 'porthole' for the ground/sky background because it matched the arcs of the bank and slip indices. The porthole also replicated the attitude sphere of the electromechanical ADI. But it was far from being an analogue of what the pilot sees of the real horizon when looking forward through the slot formed by the upper and lower frames of the windscreen. Eventually the circular frame

gave way to vertical side-frames to the display. With the advent of the HUD, when used in the ADI mode, the analogue of the world more closely matched the real world.

AMLCD

Today the active matrix liquid crystal display (AMLCD) is the most commonly used technology for presenting graphics, symbology and alphanumerics in multi-colours. The five or six AMLCDs in a typical airliner cockpit provide more than 90 per cent of the information needed by the pilots throughout all flight modes. Among the advantages of the AMLCD are low current demand, so that there is no need for cooling, and a low operating voltage. When compared with other display techniques, it has a low operating cost and high reliability. The response time of the pixels to input changes can be better than 1/100th of a second. The range of colours is equal to or even better than that of the CRT displays it replaces.

In the LCD each pixel is activated at the intersection of the columns and rows of electrodes that form a lattice or matrix. In an AMLCD each cell or pixel is controlled by its own thin-film transistor; hence 'active matrix'. Perhaps the most important attribute is its 'flatness'. An example of AMLCD technology is the modern electronic attitude director indicator (EADI) or primary flight display (PFD) and the electronic horizontal situation indicator (EHSI) or navigation display (ND). Instrument technology had come a long way from Sperry's first artificial horizon.

Previous two pages: Boeing 747-400. The majority of the information needed for all phases of flight is presented on nine electronic displays. In this view the five principal displays are set to show, from left to right: primary flight, navigation, engine performance, navigation and primary flight. The pilots can, if necessary, command any of the displays to show a different set of information. *Boeing*

'The glass cockpit'

When 'wall-to-wall' electronic displays were introduced they gave rise to the term 'the glass cockpit'. This was an example of a carelessly thought-out appellation. It implied that such a cockpit was all windows and no scantlings. The first application of the new technology was to the commercial fleets whose aircraft were delivered equipped with electronic colour displays for attitude indication (AI) and horizontal situation indication (HSI). At one time there was a significant difference between the appearance of an airliner cockpit and that of utility and of general aircraft (GA) used for business and commuting. Some were still coming into service equipped, as one FAA report unkindly categorized them, with 'steam gauges': in other words mechanical and electromechanical pointer-on-dial instruments. Eventually GA aircraft were provided with instrumentation and controls little different in appearance and technology from those of an airliner.

Improved scanning

As has been described, keeping control of an aircraft, particularly in reduced visibility, meant that the pilot had to maintain a continuous scan of discrete instruments: ASI, artificial horizon, altimeter, vertical speed indicator, heading indicator and the ILS indicator. Decade by decade designers were able to combine more than one function in one instrument, until, with the advent of digital technology and electronic displays, the electronic attitude director indicator (EADI) emerged. Attitude was flanked on the one display by airspeed to the left and barometric height and vertical speed to the right. In addition there was a compass rose with heading indicators along with ILS and VOR symbols. These are just typical sets of information because there was considerable variation among the different types of EADI over the format and number of separate items of information.

The EHSI or navigation display (ND) was developed in parallel with the PFD. It can display a wide range of information. This includes: a map that can be north- or track-orientated along with an adjustable scale, the planned track, waypoints and navigational aids, a superimposed weather radar picture, and EPWS (ground proximity warning) generated terrain information.

Flight management

Before this era the words 'flight management' and its concept were not part of the transport jet scene. There were instruments and controls, autopilot, autothrottle, yaw damper system and air data systems. There were also radio and navigation systems. The pilots had to coordinate the functions of these discrete elements because in general they could not 'talk', in the electronic sense, among themselves. For example, the pilots commanded the autopilot to maintain a specific heading and barometric height. But

A typical flight management system display and control panel used in transport aircraft. This unit can be used to command the aircraft's flight systems to execute the desired route and vertical profile to a waypoint. *Smiths Group*

the selected values were derived from a navigation system, such as an inertial navigation (IN), which did not 'talk' to the autopilot. Year by year integration was advanced. Speed/Mach control lock, through an autothrottle system, and altitude- and heading-acquisition locks were added to the autopilot. These advances prompted the autopilot to change its name, in keeping with its greater authority and abilities, to automatic flight control system (AFCS).

By maximum integration of systems, civil aviation arrived at the flight management system (FMS). This can be used as the primary control and information interface between pilot and aircraft. In effect, the pilot commands the FMS, which in turn commands the flight control (FCS) and autothrottle systems. Once the aircraft is established after take-off, in the first stage of en route climb, the duplicated FMS control and display units are used by the pilots to control the aircraft. Command of the aircraft's speed, vertical speed, heading, barometric height and other performance and navigation values can be vested in the FMS. The modern FMS is also used to control an aircraft so as to provide safe separation and efficient use of the air space and save fuel. It is also integrated with air traffic control so that the aircraft complies with the standards for required navigation performance (RNP). As part of the management, rather than the controlling function of a modern ATC system, the actual navigation performance of an aircraft is compared continuously with an RNP. Should the aircraft depart from the RNP then the crew will be alerted.

Using the keypad on an FMS control and display unit (CDU), the pilots can also select an optimum vertical flight profile so that the aircraft is controlled automatically to reach a predetermined altitude or flight level at a specified time or waypoint, by either climbing or descending. This meets the requirement for 'full-profile navigation', i.e. in both the vertical and horizontal planes. This enables an aircraft to be controlled so as to achieve the most cost-effective flight path and to reach at specified times en route waypoints and the initial-approach waypoint at the destination.

In the context of the cockpit interface it is important to stress that the accuracy of an automatically controlled flight using an FMS depends, as do all aircraft systems, on correct and accurate information. It has to depend for its performance on the availability and accuracy of the terrestrial navigational aids that it is continuously interrogating. The FMS can derive two-dimensional data from VHF omni-directional range (VORs), non-directional beacons (NDBs) and distance-measuring equipment (DME). The DMEs are usually collocated with a VOR. The FMS can be given a vertical reference and speed inputs from the aircraft's air data computer. However, the accuracy of these navigational aids can be adversely affected by atmospheric conditions such as electrical storms. And of course long-range aircraft operating over areas devoid of navigational aids such as VOR/DME have to depend on inertial navigation or 'watch, pencil and chart' navigation. The advent of GPS in the 1980s provided an additional and very accurate positional input to an FMS. For example, in 1996 Alaska Airways, which operated over mountainous terrain and in frequently poor visibility, equipped its Boeing 737s with dual GPS and FMS. In doing so it saved flight time compared with using just ground-based navigational aids, and at the same time it improved the interface between pilots and aircraft.

The greater part of the data needed by the flight-deck crew both before and during flight is contained in route charts and airway manuals. An important group of charts comes under the headings of standard instrument departures (SIDs) and standard terminal approach routes (STARS). These are detailed charts showing the precise headings, minimum or maximum speeds, altitudes, frequencies of navigational aids and other data required so that aircraft operate in terminal areas along paths that are defined both horizontally and vertically. At one time pilots had to carry flight bags crammed with terminal area and airfield information and charts, in addition to the aircraft's flight and performance manuals. In contrast, with an FMS-equipped aircraft the pre-flight 'paperwork' and paper is reduced considerably. Much of the pre-flight briefing data is already on board because it is stored in the FMS database and can be accessed and displayed by the control and display unit (CDU) of the FMS.

Four-dimensional flight

To the three dimensions of space we have to add time. The control of a modern commercial jet aircraft involves these four dimensions from airport gate to destination airport gate. Prior to engine start the flight-deck crew will have entered details of their flight plan into the FMS and checked the aircraft's position at the gate with the GPS. They will have checked the status of all systems by reference to the centralized aircraft monitor. During take-off they monitor the display of each engine's data, such as its shaft rpms and temperatures. The pilot with hands and feet on the primary controls concentrates on the view ahead and listens to the co-pilot calling out the vital reference speeds. These are the decision speed V1 before which, should there be a loss of thrust or other major problem, the aircraft can theoretically be brought to a standstill within the remaining length of the runway. After V1 the crew are committed to a take-off. When 'VR' is called the aircraft can be rotated for take-off. The next call is 'V2' to indicate that in the event of an engine failing a safe flying speed has been reached.

During the first-stage climb the aircraft is 'cleaned up': landing gear up and flaps (if used) retracted and the engines adjusted to climb power. Initially, still under manual control, the aircraft is vectored by ATC until it is clear of the airfield zone and assigned a flight level on a specific airway. At some convenient time after take-off, the first track and assigned altitude or flight level are selected on the control and display unit of the FMS, and thereafter the aircraft's trajectory is maintained automatically. The display screen and keys of the FMS unit enables the crew, if necessary, to select from the data already programmed a different route and vertical profile to the next navigational beacon. The aircraft's heading, altitude and speed are displayed on the EADI and the EHSI, the latter giving a pictorial display of the aircraft's current position and its heading in relation to navigational aids.

In summary, the modern FMS linked to the INS and GPS controls flight planning, navigation and aircraft guidance through the AFCS, along with improved aircraft performance, because it provides greater accuracy in scheduling through precise arrivals at selected navigational positions and destinations. It also reduces workload.

Inexorably aviation is moving toward using 'push-button' technology from 'start engines' to 'finished with engines'. Obviously, when a flight is initiated, using the keyboard of the CDU, correct information must be inserted. For example, when determining the correct take-off reference speeds the pilots have to enter the aircraft's gross weight, CG, take-off flap position, engine thrust level, bleed-air configuration, pressure altitude, outside air temperature, wind, runway length, runway slope, surface conditions, emergency stopping distance and any allowable equipment deficiencies. Any one of these items incorrectly keyed in could lead to trouble. Typical errors include: making mistakes when dealing with mixed units such as litres and pounds of fuel,

Boeing 737-400 c 1980 with the electromechanical flight, engine and systems instruments of the earlier 737s replaced by electronic displays. At the forward corners of the central controls pedestal are the control and display units of the flight management system (FMS). *Boeing*

making a keystroke or transposition error when entering weight, and selecting the wrong line on the CDU for an entry. An example of the last item is entering zero fuel weight in the gross fuel weight line of the display, so that the error in the aircraft's take-off weight is equal to the weight of the fuel.

The Big Two

Aviation technology has never stood still. At the end of the twentieth century, after thirty years of evolution based on digital computers, electronic displays and data highways, the modern airliner cockpit and the systems with which it interfaces reached a significant level of technology. The 'Big Two' aircraft constructors, Boeing and Airbus Industries, included, as standard, 'wall-to-wall' electronic displays, data highways, warning and system-status displays.

Multi-screen cockpits

A typical state-of-the-technology civil airliner cockpit includes at least the following features: a two-pilot layout, six multi-function colour electronic displays, and the control and display units of the flight management systems. The electronic displays can be in the best viewing position relative to the eye reference points of the pilots. The electronic displays also enable the pilots to select the type and amount of information to be presented on any particular display screen. For example, the displays can be integrated with the flight management system (FMS) so that optimum flight routeing using selected waypoints can be pre-programmed. An important feature of the 'glass' cockpit is the flexibility of the individual display units. If need be, the crew can, for example, select a different positional allocation from the usual. Instead of the primary flight display (PFD)being shown on the upper unit on the centre-line of the captain's panel, it can be 'electronically' moved to the lower unit. Similarly it may be found more convenient during pre-start drills to use the upper-centre unit temporarily as a check list or to monitor the configuration and quantities of the aircraft's fuel system.

Two of the six electronic displays in the 'fly-by-wire with side-stick' Airbus 320 and 340 are used for the electronic centralized aircraft monitor (ECAM). This displays engine and systems information and warnings. If the aircraft's performance or handling starts to deteriorate, schematic diagrams of the principal systems can be displayed along with diagnostic and remedial procedures. This is an alternative to searching through a bulky aircraft systems manual. Within limits the crew can select a wide range of alphanumerics, symbols and graphical representations with a range of colours to enhance the overall picture.

Fuel quantity

Included in the ECAM system is fuel quantity indication and management. How much fuel has been taken on and how much remains during a flight has always been one of the most important items of information demanded by a pilot, whether in light aircraft or a jumbo jet. The onetime individual fuel-tank-contents indicators have been replaced by the digital computer-based, versatile, fuel-quantity-indicating system. The calculated fuel quantities in the different tanks are sent over the aircraft's data buses and presented on the ECAM display or integrated with a centralized fault-display system. This provides operational and maintenance interrogation so as to determine the 'health' of the system.

Standard cockpits

The airline pilot has to be type rated. Some are certificated to fly one specific aircraft type, and others are rated for more than one type. To change type or gain an additional type rating requires training and checking by the certificating authorities. Boeing and Airbus have developed a common cockpit for a range of aircraft types that allows cross-crew type qualification. Cockpit standardization is carried to the limit so that only the small details disclose the aircraft type. For example, the flight decks of the Boeing 757, 767 and 777 look very much the same.

Even the designers of regional turbo-props have developed a common cockpit: Bombardier's de Havilland Dash 8 series, for example. Each type in the series has the same five 6 in x 8 in. AMLC displays. The symbology and locations for control and display functions have a common relationship to the pilot's eye reference point. The overhead and central console panels are to a common layout.

Civil HUD

A civil version of the military HUD promised to be an alternative to the ILS and automatic landing systems. In 1992 the management of Horizon Air, a regional feeder airline in the USA, analysed the amount of business lost because of disruption through fog. At its hub airport no fewer than five flights stood to be disrupted every time a single inbound was cancelled or diverted when the visibility dropped below the runway visual range (RVR) minimum of 1,800 ft. The operations of Horizon's parent, Alaska Airways, were also affected by frequent periods of poor visibility. Therefore the airline started a HUD development programme with the aim of reducing indirect operating costs by reducing delays and disruption of the airline's hub and spoke schedules.

Using the HUD installed in the 737-200s, take-offs could be started when visibility dropped to as little as 300 ft. After the FAA

had been convinced of the suitability of the safety factors involved, flights eventually received Cat. IIIa ILS landing clearance (i.e. to visibility minimums of 700 ft (200 m) runway visual range (RVR) and decision heights of 50 ft). In the last decade of the twentieth century more and more civil aircraft were equipped with HUD. Exponents of the civil HUD predicted that it could eliminate the need for the complicated automatic landing system element of the AFCS. They argued that tests showed that the ability to look 'head up and forward' enabled a pilot to complete a landing to the same standards as that of an automatic system.

This revolution on the flight deck encouraged a further development of the HUD principle so that the pilot would not only view the symbology and graphics of the HUD but see them combined with a virtual image of the view ahead. In particular, when landing, the approach and runway lighting patterns position is shown. These avionic systems and displays are typical of the modern trend toward maximum choice of what needs to be displayed and on which one of a number of screens. The merging of a synthetic or virtual view ahead with natural vision, as pioneered in Alaska, continues to be a leading cockpit technology.

Business jets

A modern business jet is expected by its passengers to operate at the flight levels and speeds of the big commercial aircraft. To ensure safe and economical operation, a typical ten-twelve-seater, two-crew aircraft such as the Cessna 750 Citation is equipped with a cockpit whose type and number of instruments and controls emulate those of a large airliner. Dominating the main instrument panel are the five displays of the EFIS. On the central pedestal there are two FMS control and display units. Similar instrumentation is to be found in other

Boeing 777 cockpit showing the 'wall to wall' large screen electronic displays. From left to right the electronic displays have been selected to show: attitude director indicator (ADI), horizontal situation indicator (HIS) and engine parameters. The other two display units (not in view) are most likely showing the HIS and the ADI. *Thales*

business jets.

The Gulfstream G550 business twin-jet can fly 6,750 nm non-stop at Mach 0.8. The cockpit is dominated by four large full-colour electronic displays. At each pilot's outboard hand is a small fixed arm on the end of which are a thumb-controlled cursor knob and three buttons for selecting which of the four display screens is to be accessed. The first pilot can move the cursor to Screens 1, 2 and 3. The second pilot's cursor can be moved to Screens 4, 3 and 2. The primary flight display is on Screens 1 and 4. The upper half is dedicated as an ADI and the lower half as an HSI. The ADI display can be presented on a head-up display unit that folds down from the overhead. This is part of the enhanced visual system (EVS) that combines FLIR with the HUD images and can be used for continuing an approach to land below the visibility-based decision height. One of the displays can be selected as an approach chart (plate) on which the aircraft's position can be displayed.

All's well. Or, is it?

The pilots of an Airbus 300 were suddenly confronted with the failure of all the electronic flight and navigation displays when the aircraft rolled up to 40° and fell 3,000 ft. Fortunately the standby air data instruments (such as ASI, altimeter and VSI) were unaffected. Following the incident the FAA demanded a change to the software that generated the symbols, graphics and alphanumerics of the electronic displays. The only comment has to be one of emphasizing that despite every step taken during the development of a new system to prevent a failure one can still happen.

In the 1980s safety authorities increased their investigations into the relationship between the human and the automatic systems. Were pilots losing the ability to apply basic airmanship when things went wrong? Did the modern flight deck induce a sense of 'all is well' when, in fact, the aircraft was about to depart from a safe flight path? Losing the plot and getting out of step with the system has always been one of the root causes of accidents. Pilots have concentrated on a particular instrument or control and become unaware that the autopilot has either disconnected or placed the aircraft in an unsafe attitude. With the modern flight deck, as the interface in a far more automatic aircraft endowed with a degree of intelligence, there is an even greater need to be aware at all times of what is happening to the aircraft's trajectory in three dimensions and time. The crew can be unaware that their situation awareness has deteriorated.

Situation awareness (SA)

SA may be defined in aviation terms as the correct perception of the operating environment, the current aircraft situation and its projected future status in the four dimensions of space and time: in other words, the degree to which the pilots perceive and understand the current and future condition of the aircraft and its systems and its position in the air space relative to other traffic and most importantly to hazards such as high ground or other spot height obstructions. To be at a high level of situation awareness the crew has to be completely aware of the aircraft's trajectory, its energy and the position of the flight controls and all movable control surfaces. In other words, irrespective of the extent to which control has been delegated to the onboard computers, the pilots must at all times be one step ahead. To repeat, 'They must not lose the plot.'

In Chapter Eight examples were given of where poor cockpit design, instruments and controls were the primary cause of, or had contributed to, an accident. In many of the incidents and accidents of those years the pilot had suffered from a lack of situation awareness, although at the time the concept or its implications were not part of the general body of aviation knowledge. The following is an example from an FAA study of a lack of situation awareness in the cockpit.

The assigned altitude was missed by 1,000 feet. The captain was busy trying to program the flight management computer. Pilots are spending too much time playing with the computer at critical times rather than flying the aircraft. No one looks outside for conflicting traffic.

There are three levels of loss of SA(LOSA):

Failure to perceive information or misconception of information

Improper integration or comprehension of information

Incorrect projection of future actions of the system.

'More data but not necessarily more knowledge' is one comment on the modern flight deck. The modern flight-deck interface of electronic multi-colour liquid crystal display screens, alphanumeric keypads and data input control knobs is in stark contrast to the arrays of pointers on dials and numerous switches and buttons of thirty years ago. Mistakes were made in those cockpits: altimeter pressure settings incorrectly selected, the wrong engine shut down or the fuel system mismanaged. However, the very nature of the control interface and the frequent need to exercise recommended scanning routines tended to keep a crew alert. In contrast, today, the 'wall-to-wall' electronic displays and the delegation of much of the detail processes of flight control and navigation to the computers can induce a detached attitude to the aircraft's progress and health. In these conditions a lack of situation awareness needs to be guarded against.

In the 1990s more questions started to be asked by those concerned with the safety of aviation about the interface between the pilot and the computer-based control and information system in the cockpit. During the 1980s and early 1990s hundreds of incidents and a number of fatal accidents were attributed to problems with the cockpit interface. It was considered that pilots in many instances either did not fully understand what the automated systems were doing or did not receive adequate feedback, that is information, about what the aircraft was doing or was about to do.

Misinterpretation

A twin jet crashed because both pilots failed to read correctly the engine parameter indicators. This indicated that the left engine vibration value was above the acceptable limit. They also failed to identify from noise and shuddering that it was the left engine that

was failing. The vibration indications applying to the left engine were read as applying to the other engine, whose power was then reduced. During the approach to land the left engine lost thrust and the aircraft crashed well short of the runway threshold. The vibration indicators were on a panel positioned contiguously to the right of a group of primary engine instruments. The four instruments, in line across the two panels from left to right, were N2 left engine and N2 right engine, Vibration left engine and Vibration right engine. Because Vibration left engine was immediately to the right of the two N2 indications it was read as applying to the right engine. The irony of this, and similarly misinterpreted incidents and accidents in this era, is that even with the advanced electronic displays of the 1980s they were no better in this respect than the pointer-on-dial instruments of the 1950s.

In pre-'glass cockpit' years the crew had to maintain a constant awareness concerning the aircraft's position in space and where it was heading by integrating the readings from a number of different instruments. The modern electronic navigation displays, such as the horizontal situation indicator, provide an instantaneous indication of the aircraft's current position relative to navigational aids, weather and hazards, as well as its position at some future time. However, the quality of the information depends in the first place very much on the precision with which the crew inputs data to the system. 'Rubbish in, rubbish out' is just as appropriate on the flight deck as at the PC. Like some TV programmes, the electronic displays can be compulsive viewing. Therefore the information they provide must be compared with other sources of information. For example,

Typical application of light emitting diode (LED) technology for engine and system information. This includes, for a twin-engine aircraft: N1 shaft speed, exhaust gas temperature, N2 shaft speed fuel flow rate, oil pressure and temperature, oil quantity, vibration level and the pressure and quantity for each hydraulic system.
Smiths Group.

the indicated air speed shown electronically is only as accurate as the air data system from which it is derived, which in turn is only as accurate as the pitot static unit whose probe may have been damaged or blocked.

One of the most dangerous examples of degraded situation awareness is when the flight crew is not aware of which mode has been selected for the automatic flight control system. Unless the displays, particularly the primary flight displays, are continuously monitored, a change in aircraft operating mode can be missed and the pilots are then not aware of the situation. This can happen even though the display system provides attention-getting colour changes and flashing 'boxes' around the mode parameter that has changed.

In one incident the pilot was unaware that he was 'fighting' the AFCS, and should have disconnected it. Essentially the more the pilot 'pulled', the more the AFCS 'pushed'. Despite the proliferation of information in the form of multi-colour electronic displays and aural warnings, this was nor presented in a way that gave unambiguous guidance. In turn the pilot, in many cases, had not been trained to anticipate that such adversarial events could occur.

In the chapter dealing with the flight decks of the 1950s examples were given of errors induced by differences between the way in which information was presented to the crew and in the way in which important selector controls had to be operated. Despite the versatility and flexibility of modern electronic displays, which within reason enable a vast range of symbols, alphanumerics and meanings, there are still, fifty years on, potentially dangerous variations among different aircraft types. Another source of trouble is the complexity and variety of warnings and alerts relating to the major systems. This embarrassment of riches may not always make deciding on the primary cause of a fault a quick task. In some 'glass' cockpits the only indication that there is a problem with a particular system might be a general alert warning on one of the electronic displays because separate indicators for discrete systems have not been provided.

Associated with warnings provided in the form of changes on the displays to colour and shape along with flashing of symbology and alphanumerics, there is a large number of different warning and attention-getting noises: human voice, horns and klaxons, chiming bells, buzzers, wailing sirens and clacking noises, as well as the tactile, such as stick-shakers. All or some may be present. All can be as buzzing and confusing as it was in the 1950s.

Auditory warnings

Making different warning sounds more distinctive, and matching both the sounds and their levels to cockpit noise, were primary considerations in research in the 1980s into more effective means of alerting crews to problems. The repetition of a sound, initiated at a level of intensity that can be heard but not be intrusive, can alert the pilot without startling him or her. Loudness and pitch can be increased for primary warnings, or relaxed for information alerts. Primary warnings can be identified by special sounds or by a voice message alternating with a warning sound. Horns, bells, and sirens are capable of dominating speech and background noise and commanding attention. However, if the cockpit is flooded with sound this may corrupt vital inter-pilot communication or the R/T. It is then that the crew may be tempted to switch the alarm off.

The risk of pilots confusing one auditory warning with another has to be avoided. In one aircraft, the warnings for 'gear unlocked', 'cabin pressure loss' and 'incorrect take-off configuration' were similar. The Joint Airworthiness Requirements (JARs) state that a power spectrum for warning sound levels at various frequencies must be evaluated against the noise background of the cockpit. Furthermore, warning sounds must be clearly distinguishable one from another. The use of human voice messages, in particular including the use of words formed of a vowel between two consonants, requires careful consideration because the meaning can be masked, distorted or lost within the overall noise of the flight deck or helicopter cockpit.

Helicopter noise

Helicopter pilots have noise problems all of their own. The helicopter cockpit has significantly different sound levels and frequencies compared with those of a fixed-wing aircraft. Typical are levels of 20 dBA or more in the cockpit, along with more lower-frequency noise. The helicopter pilot has to react very quickly to the onset of trouble, such as loss of rotor control servo pressure; gearbox chip warning and rotor speed decay. In addition there have to be radio-height and telephone and electrical power wire hazards warnings.

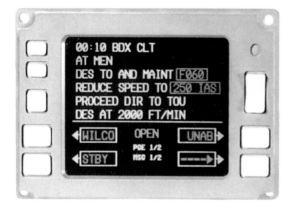

A data link cockpit display unit (DCDU) for presenting messages from air traffic control to the pilot. Compared with R/T it has the advantage of reducing errors caused by voice communication. *Smiths Group*

Aural errors

Contributing to cockpit workload and sometimes to confusion are the R/T messages and instructions from ATC. Despite careful diction, a vital word or numeric value can be confused with another. If pilot and controller use a different version of English, or French for that matter, this is a further potential source of error. In a crowded airspace and a high cockpit workload environment, the potential for mistakes is even higher. In the 1980s, therefore, non-aural datalink systems were developed. These are used to convey ATC messages to an aircraft. A typical data control and display unit presents such messages as 'At EPS (waypoint) descend to and maintain FL50 (a flight level equivalent to 5,000 ft) reduce speed to 250 IAS (250 knots indicated) proceed direct XYZ'. The use of the datalink rather than R/T considerably reduces the chance of errors.

Ground proximity

Adding to the aural warnings on the flight deck is the ground proximity warning system (GPWS). This system is based on a downward-pointing radar combined with barometric height in order to derive the rate at which the distance between the aircraft and the ground is diminishing. It can give a 30-second warning of the need to stop descending or check position and change heading so as to avoid rising ground ahead.

Collision avoidance

Such expressions as 'the crowded skies' have been around for many decades. The North-East Corridor of the USA in the 1940s, in dangerously low visibility conditions, was a nightmare for both pilots and air traffic controllers. By today's standards navigational aids were very limited. Airways were defined by the radio-range stations. There was no such thing as area and airways radar, and the approach radars could only handle a few aircraft at one time. Near-misses were numerous and there were mid-air collisions. Today aircraft can be controlled so as to keep to a defined track and assigned altitude or flight level far more accurately. At the same time the number of aircraft in a given airspace has increased significantly, and the danger of a mid-air collision has not been reduced. In the 1980s traffic collision avoidance systems (TCAS) were developed. These introduced another display unit into the cockpit. It shows range, bearing, closing speed and the relative height of all aircraft within 10 nm. TCAS derives its positional data from the ATC transponders carried by the majority of aircraft. These are the transponders that 'respond' every time an ATC surveillance radar beam sweeps across the aircraft. In doing so they provide the height numerals and identity tag against the aircraft's blip on the ATC controller's screen.

Side-stick

As noted above, some aircraft cockpits feature a joystick for roll and pitch set to the side of the pilot. The Airbus 320 of the 1980s was the first production airliner with side-stick primary controls operating

Airbus side-stick control on the outboard knee of each pilot does not obstruct the view of the instruments and allows a small desk top to be pulled out. The primary presentation of information is provided by six electronic colour displays and by the control and display units (CDUs) of the flight management system on the central controls pedestal.
Airbus Industrie

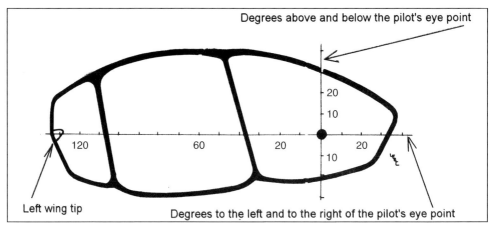

Typical arcs-of-view from the eye reference point (ERP) of the pilot in the PI left-hand seat of the flight deck of a modern airliner. *Author*

through FBW. With no wheel and column in front of either pilot, the look of the cockpit was given a significant change. However, Boeing, for example, from its 707 to the 777, stayed with the traditional control wheel and column primary controls. The Airbus-type side-stick hand-control is not connected mechanically to the control surfaces. A side-stick control can either be of the displacement type in which the small control column replicates the movement of a joystick, but over much smaller angles, or it is virtually fixed and responds to the pressure being applied by the pilot's hand. With both methods movement or pressure is detected by sensors that feed data to the aircraft's flight control system, which in turn commands the power units that move the control surfaces.

Do pilots who fly the side-stick Airbus aircraft find it difficult or awkward if they change seats so that on one flight they may be controlling with the left hand and on another flight with the right? Experience with the side-stick in the A320 showed that when taking off the pilot in the P1 position, left seat, using the left hand for control, tended to roll the aircraft slightly during rotation. This was caused by the natural lie of the forearm and the plane of rotation of the wrist. Therefore the side-stick pitch-demand plane was modified so that as the aircraft

rotated the wings were kept level. A similar but opposite effect and solution applied to the P2 position.

Because the two side-sticks on the Airbus flight decks are not connected mechanically, as with conventional wheel and column type, there was considerable debate among pilots and designers over the relative authority of each unit. Should one pilot be able to override the other's control inputs? One of the logical solutions provided the following:

When one stick is not originating any control commands, the other has full control authority

When one stick is deflected by less than six degrees demands from the other stick are summed with it

When one stick is deflected more than six degrees, a demand from the other stick is again summed, but only up to the limit of a further six degrees.

The designers of the A320 side-stick system emphasize that should there be a conflict of input, the more intelligent pilot would win, not the stronger. However, an irrational pilot could still apply extreme control inputs, although that situation could apply also to all dual-control systems. The electronic primary flight display attitude indicator includes symbols to show the position of the stick relative to its neutral position.

Watching the aircraft

A number of accidents to civil aircraft might have been averted had the crew been accurately and fully aware of what was happening to parts of the aircraft outside their arcs of view. Many involved in-flight fires, such as a wheel and tyre igniting on take-off and exploding in the wheel well. In the last few decades systems have been evaluated for providing flight-deck crews with an external view of the aircraft so that they can assess the nature and extent of external damage and fires.

Security

Starting in the 1960s, the incidence of hijackings and terrorist activity steadily increased. On 11 September 2001 four passenger aircraft were seized by terrorists acting according to their brutal and distorted beliefs. Three of the aircraft were deliberately flown into buildings in New York and Washington, and the fourth crashed after a failed attempt by the passengers to overpower the terrorists, who were intent on destroying the White House. Before these terrible events there had been much discussion on the merits of sealing the cockpit from the passengers. Some pilots were for the idea, others against. After 11 September 2001 the subject was given even greater prominence. Irrespective of the arguments, the provision of a secure door added a new dimension to the cockpit. Long gone were the days when the captain might take a stroll among the passengers.

Pilot opinion

If a group of pilots is asked to comment on the merits or disadvantages of a particular cockpit, there could be significant differences of opinion. Judgements expressed on a cockpit and its equipment are not always the outcome of a scientific process. They may be the result of subjective impressions. Much depends on the attitude of individuals and their particular preferences based on their years of experience. One pilot may severely criticize a particular cockpit, another might be lavish in praise of the same type. Over the decades the basic criteria for the transport aircraft cockpit have emerged. These criteria have been generated from lessons learnt from pilot opinion and during the investigations of incidents and accidents. Of course accidents are the effects of incidents that could not be stopped from proceeding further. To limit workload, maintain a high level of situation awareness and reduce the potential of things that can induce a pilot to make mistakes, flight-deck design criteria can include the following:

An adjustable and comfortable seat for each pilot

A good all-round view in the horizontal plane, including a view of the wingtip outboard of each seat

A downward view over the nose of the aircraft so that on the approach to a landing a sufficient length of approach lighting can be seen

An upward view, particularly of potentially conflicting traffic, when the aircraft is banked in a turn

All primary and secondary controls, selectors, adjusters and switches to be within easy, non-stretching reach of the hands of both pilots

Each pilot must be able to control the aircraft in all its operating configurations without having to change seats

All displays of aircraft attitude and configuration, trajectory, position in three-dimensional space and in time, as well as systems status and health, to be clearly visible in all cockpit lighting conditions.

Airbus 310 cockpit. In front of each pilot are two electronic attitude and horizontal situation displays. In the centre panel are the displays of the electronic centralized aircraft monitor (ECAM) system and on the central controls pedestal are the two flight management system (FMS) control and display units (CDUs). This cockpit represents an interim stage toward the 'glass cockpit'. *Airbus Industrie*

CHAPTER ELEVEN

Military Cockpits 1970-2005

An abundance of avionics

The digital age

The opening year selected for this chapter is 1970. This is the approximate year when the logic gates that make up a typical digital computer for aviation exceeded one million – one hundred times the number in a typical 1960s computer. Within ten years display technology broke through the 'colour barrier', and multi-purpose, multi-colour displays (MPCDs) were in production. The multi-purpose attribute eliminated in one technological leap the need for a pilot to scan

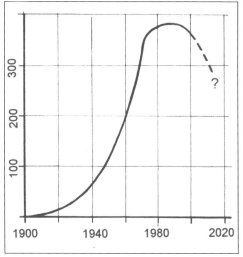

The approximate number of controls and instruments in the cockpit of a fighter or fighter/attack aircraft from the early years of air warfare up to the present. The dotted part of the curve represents the assumption that the number will decrease in the future with the increasing use of more advanced interface technologies, such as DVI and touch screens. *Author*

a number of discrete limited-parameter instruments.

Multi-colour overcame the limitation of the monochrome displays whereby differentiation between parameters, functions and symbology was limited. MPCDs could present as little or as much information as the pilot needed for a specific flight mode. The shadow-mask CRTs used could present up to about fifteen different colours, although in practice eight were usually sufficient. But display technology did not stand still, and within a few years the active matrix liquid crystal display (AMLCD) began to supplant the CRT. The ability to present different sets of information and data on an electronic display integrated with all the major systems of an aircraft means that the pilot can, for example, make a pre-flight check of all systems. The built-in-test (BIT) function of each system can be shown on one of the cockpit displays so that the pilot watches each step-by-step verification of the system's health. During engine start, all the important parameters can be displayed, along with the self-diagnostic functioning of BIT. Thereafter one of the MPCDs can be used as the primary flight display (PFD), another selected for displaying each of the major phases of a flight so as to show aircraft position relative to waypoints, targets, weather and threats. A third display could be selected to show fuel status as a mimic diagram of the fuel tanks and associated plumbing and pumps. Or, at a touch of a key on the periphery of the display, switched to show the status (safe or armed) of all the stores and weapons.

In the modern cockpit the tactile controls, such as levers, switches and buttons, are classified in groups so that those most frequently used and of great importance are located close to the pilot's hands. Today these criteria are accepted as fundamental design standards. But in the past they were often neglected.

At the end of this era the V-22 Osprey with its rotatable wings and engines introduced a new and additional primary flight control. Forward for normal wing-borne flight, aft for vertical flight, similar in effect to the nozzle control of a Harrier.

The first cost of a modern military aircraft often demands a multi-role capability, which in turn imposes the need for a wide range of systems. Both the designer and the air force, for different reasons, may want a single-seater. However, the one-pilot cockpit may finish up as the most advanced, the most sophisticated and the best equipped of its generation, though at high cost and at the expense of high workload for the pilot.

GPS

This is also the era in which the global positioning system (GPS) in association with inertial navigation (IN) provided the pilot with an instantaneous and accurate display of aircraft position. A feature of some hardstandings used by military aircraft is the latitude and longitude painted on the surface. One of the first pre-flight checks by the pilot is to key in the aircraft's geographical position as a datum for the IN computer. Because the system requires a few minutes in which to align itself with the geographical coordinates these can be inserted at any time before a

flight so as to allow a quick-response take-off.

Acronym cockpit

This chapter concentrates on the fighter/attack cockpit because it requires a greater concentration of advanced technologies compared with the cockpits of other types of aircraft. The systems required for all-weather operations and multi-role ability have not only changed the look of the interior of the fighter/attack cockpit but have added a plethora of acronyms to the aviation lexicon: so many, that we are in the aviation age of the 'acronym cockpit'. The many avionic systems are there to extend the pilot's range and accuracy of vision and awareness of what is happening both to the aircraft and to the tactical situation. Many of the acronyms refer to systems that keep the aircraft and pilot as an integral part of the much wider system that embraces information, command and control on the ground, in the air and on the sea.

Hawk 100 with up-front control panel for the HUD and two large electronic displays. *BAE*

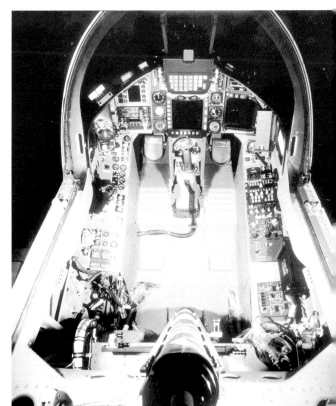

Aircraft, armoured vehicles and ships are usually operated as an integrated force within a particular theatre of war. The modern fighter/attack aircraft costs millions of dollars and therefore a pilot can no longer take off into the 'wild blue yonder' in the hope that a target will be found. Each sortie requires meticulous planning and has to be part of a much bigger operation involving other weapon systems. To achieve a high rate of success there has to be an extensive suite of avionics, and the pilot has to be not only a tightly strapped-in and plugged-in part of the aircraft but an extension of the aircraft as an intelligent computer-based weapon system.

Come night, come fog, rain or snow

Since 1970, if not earlier, the dominant requirement for a fighter/attack aircraft, as a system, is that it and its crew must be able to go to, find, and then attack a target with at least an 80 per cent probability of success irrespective of foul weather and complete darkness, and at the same time be aware of, and able to avoid, the enemy's lethal activities. The costs of a cockpit, both the structure and the interface equipment, can be a significant proportion of the total aircraft cost. Cost usually increases proportionally to aircraft versatility. The greater the number of avionic and weapon systems, the greater the cost of the instrumentation and controls. The greater the performance of the aircraft, the greater the need for more expensive crew

Joint Primary Air Training System (JPATS) cockpit. Compared with earlier primary trainers the majority of the displays are electronic. In the centre of the panel, at the top, is the electronic attitude director and below the horizontal situation display. Other features, intended to introduce the pupil pilot to equipment in first line aircraft, are the black and yellow ejection seat firing handle, the substantial throttle grip and the array of selector buttons on the control column. *Smiths Group*

protection. Modern aircrews are themselves a very expensive item of total cost.

From the second half of the twentieth century onwards the cost of military aircraft and the high cost of pilot-training programmes meant that the safe recovery and landing of an aircraft after a sortie required a

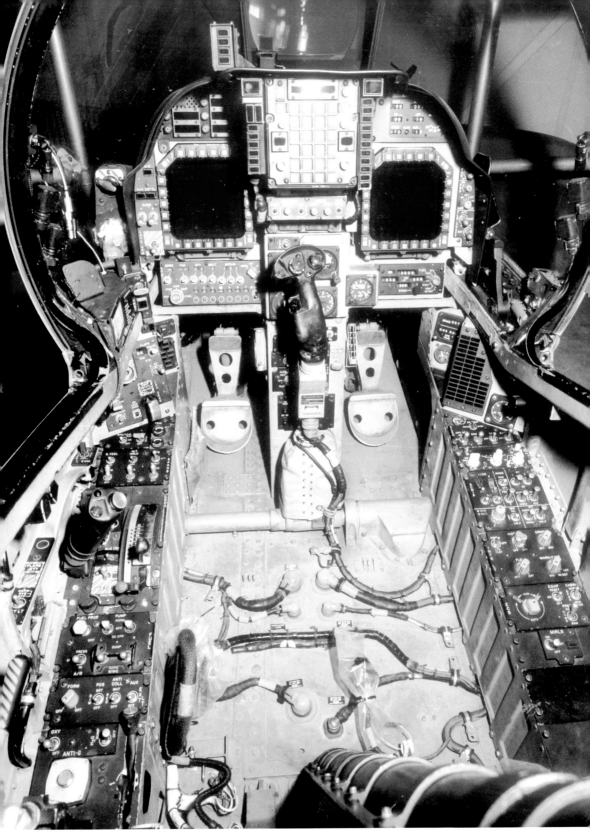

Cockpit of a Sea Harrier F/A2. This shows the addition of two electronic multi-function electronic display units flanking a central panel of electromechanical and barometric instruments. However there is no up-front control panel below the HUD, the controls for which are on the left side of the coaming. *British Aerospace*

well-equipped cockpit. Therefore, today's military pilot is provided with information and guidance in the form of electronic displays and aural inputs dedicated to getting home and landing safely, irrespective of the visibility conditions. It was one thing to hit the boundary hedge in a $10,000 (1940s money) P-51 attempting to land in fog, but a very different matter writing off $10 millionsworth of Mig-29, plus the cost of training the pilot.

Designing the fighter/attack cockpit

Situation awareness

An aircraft can be equipped with a most comprehensive range of avionic aids. The pilot is given information on the state of the major aircraft systems, on where the target is and how to get to it. And when the enemy's defence systems have 'locked on' to the aircraft the HUD can provide primary flight data, the target-seeking radar can display its information and the ECM display indicates locations of surface-to-air missile batteries and the presence of their radar emissions. The status of fuel tanks and associated plumbing and engine performance are displayed in graphic detail. The weapons panel of the stores management system shows which offensive stores are available and have been selected. A profusion of status lamps, communications-management panel lights, IFF-selection panel lights, along with annunciators and voice communications from controllers and other ground-based radios, assail the pilot's senses. Overall there is plenty of information. But if it is presented in a confused manner the pilot is not aware of the total situation inside the cockpit and outside the aircraft.

Situation awareness is a key factor when considering cockpit systems and equipment. It can be enhanced by the provision of a limited set of data on top-quality displays. This is where the 'need to know' rule has to be rigorously applied. It is also the basis on which to allocate systems for fully automatic operation. The cockpit and its equipment must provide the pilot with maximum situation awareness. Otherwise no amount of sophisticated weaponry and aircraft agility and performance will guarantee superiority over the enemy. A lack of information can arise from a number of causes, one of which is inadequate sensors and an insufficient view of the world outside the cockpit. Conversely, there may be sufficient sensors and view of the real world, but the total information is presented in a confusing way.

A typical forward looking infra-red (FLIR) display which enhances both target acquisition and safety when operating at low level. *Smiths Group*

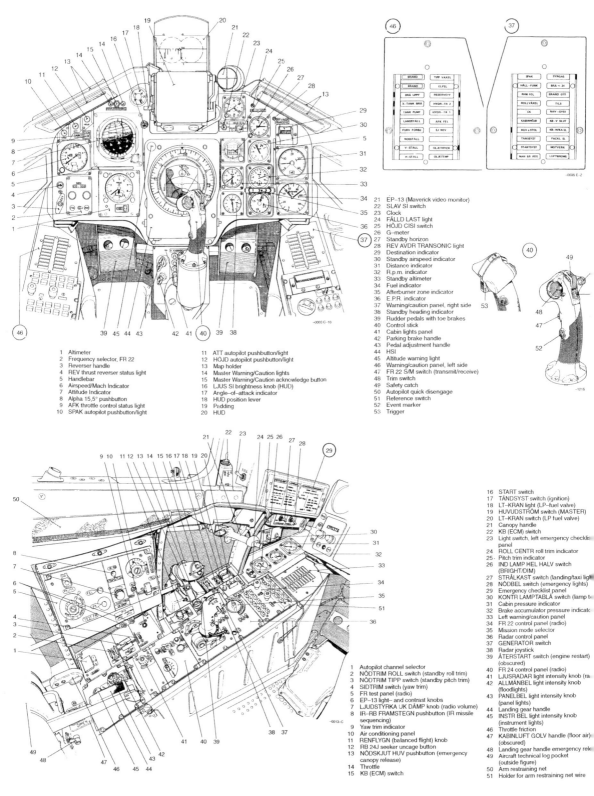

SaaB Vigen AJS-37: A complete guide to the cockpit. *SaaB AB*

21 EP–13 (Maverick video monitor)
22 SLAV SI switch
23 Clock
24 FÄLLD LAST light
25 HÖJD CISI switch
26 G–meter
27 Standby horizon
28 REV AVDR TRANSONIC light
29 Destination indicator
30 Standby airspeed indicator
31 Distance indicator
32 R.p.m. indicator
33 Standby altimeter
34 Fuel indicator
35 Afterburner zone indicator
36 E.P.R. indicator
37 Warning/caution panel, right side
38 Standby heading indicator
39 Rudder pedals with toe brakes
40 Control stick
41 Cabin lights panel
42 Parking brake handle
43 Pedal adjustment handle
44 HSI
45 Altitude warning light
46 Warning/caution panel, left side
47 FR 22 S/M switch (transmit/receive)
48 Trim switch
49 Safety catch
50 Autopilot quick disengage
51 Reference switch
52 Event marker
53 Trigger

1   Altimeter
2   Frequency selector, FR 22
3   Reverser handle
4   REV thrust reverser status light
5   Handlebar
6   Airspeed/Mach Indicator
7   Attitude Indicator
8   Alpha 15,5° pushbutton
9   AFK throttle control status light
10 SPAK autopilot pushbutton/light
11 ATT autopilot pushbutton/light
12 HÖJD autopilot pushbutton/light
13 Map holder
14 Master Warning/Caution lights
15 Master Warning/Caution acknowledge button
16 LJUS SI brightness knob (HUD)
17 Angle–of–attack indicator
18 HUD position lever
19 Pedding
20 HUD

16 START switch
17 TÄNDSYST switch (ignition)
18 LT–KRAN light (LP-fuel valve)
19 HUVUDSTRÖM switch (MASTER)
20 LT–KRAN switch (LP fuel valve)
21 Canopy handle
22 KB (ECM) switch
23 Light switch, left emergency checklist panel
24 ROLL CENTR roll trim indicator
25 Pitch trim indicator
26 IND LAMP HEL HALV switch (BRIGHT/DIM)
27 STRÅLKAST switch (landing/taxi light)
28 NÖDBEL switch (emergency lights)
29 Emergency checklist panel
30 KONTR LAMPTABLÅ switch (lamp test)
31 Cabin pressure indicator
32 Brake accumulator pressure indicator
33 Left warning/caution panel
34 FR 22 control panel (radio)
35 Mission mode selector
36 Radar control panel
37 GENERATOR switch
38 Radar joystick
39 ÅTERSTART switch (engine restart) (obscured)
40 FR 24 control panel (radio)
41 LJUSRADAR light intensity knob (radar)
42 ALLMÄNBEL light intensity knob (floodlights)
43 PANELBEL light intensity knob (panel lights)
44 Landing gear handle
45 INSTR BEL light intensity knob (instrument lights)
46 Throttle friction
47 KABINLUFT GOLV handle (floor air) (obscured)
48 Landing gear handle emergency release
49 Aircraft technical log pocket (outside figure)
50 Arm restraining net
51 Holder for arm restraining net wire

1   Autopilot channel selector
2   NÖDTRIM ROLL switch (standby roll trim)
3   NÖDTRIM TIPP switch (standby pitch trim)
4   SIDTRIM switch (yaw trim)
5   FR test panel (radio)
6   EP–13 light- and contrast knobs
7   LJUDSTYRKA UK DÄMP knob (radio volume)
8   IR–RB FRAMSTEGN pushbutton (IR missile sequencing)
9   Yaw trim indicator
10 Air conditioning panel
11 RENFLYGN (balanced flight) knob
12 RB 24J seeker uncage button
13 NÖDSKJUT HUV pushbutton (emergency canopy release)
14 Throttle
15 KB (ECM) switch

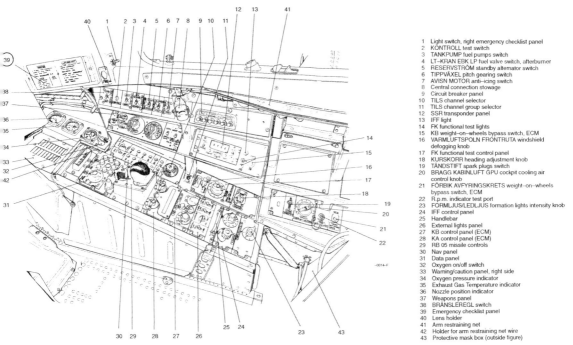

1. Light switch, right emergency checklist panel
2. KONTROLL test switch
3. TANKPUMP fuel pumps switch
4. LT–KRAN EBK LP fuel valve switch, afterburner
5. RESERVSTRÖM standby alternator switch
6. TIPPVÄXEL pitch gearing switch
7. AVISN MOTOR anti–icing switch
8. Central connection stowage
9. Circuit breaker panel
10. TILS channel selector
11. TILS channel group selector
12. SSR transponder panel
13. IFF light
14. FK functional test lights
15. KB weight-on-wheels bypass switch, ECM
16. VARMLUFTSPOLN FRONTRUTA windshield defogging knob
17. FK functional test control panel
18. KURSKORR heading adjustment knob
19. TÄNDSTIFT spark plugs switch
20. BRAGG KABINLUFT GPU cockpit cooling air control knob
21. FÖRBIK AVFYRINGSKRETS weight–on–wheels bypass switch, ECM
22. R.p.m. indicator test port
23. FORMLJUS/LEDLJUS formation lights intensity knob
24. IFF control panel
25. Handlebar
26. External lights panel
27. KB control panel (ECM)
28. KA control panel (ECM)
29. RB 05 missile controls
30. Nav panel
31. Data panel
32. Oxygen on/off switch
33. Warning/caution panel, right side
34. Oxygen pressure indicator
35. Exhaust Gas Temperature indicator
36. Nozzle position indicator
37. Weapons panel
38. BRÄNSLEREGL switch
39. Emergency checklist panel
40. Lens holder
41. Arm restraining net
42. Holder for arm restraining net wire
43. Protective mask box (outside figure)

The overloaded pilot

From the 1950s onwards more and more information was being provided to pilots. Instead of suffering, as the preceding generation had, from a lack of information, they were now being overloaded with electronically generated data. Each item of information on its own could be assimilated and acted upon. However, when the data started to multiply, the pilot had to keep one step ahead of the situation both inside and outside the aircraft. Part of the situation awareness problem in the 1950s and 1960s arose from inadequate methods of presenting radio, radar, weapon-aiming and aircraft-systems status. It took another thirty years to develop information and management systems that reduced the incidents of aircrews misreading or misunderstanding information inputs. By the end of the three decades there was also a better understanding of situation awareness. The cockpits of multi-function, multi-weapon aircraft in the 1970s were awash with instruments and controls. At the end of the 1970s and to some extent in the early 1980s, good ergonomics had to be compromised in order to fit in all the extra avionics that had been developed following advances made in digital and data bus technologies, particularly as new and more complex weapon and detection systems were added.

Since the advent of utilities and communications-management systems a pilot has been relieved of much of the sub-systems' management tasks. Among the systems developed to reduce workload and

The pilot's workload is reduced by many semi-automatic avionic systems. This is the selection panel for the missile management system in a Panavia Tornado. In older aircraft cockpits the pilot had to make time-consuming and complicated selection procedures using rows of switches. In the Tornado, the pilot with one touch can select Medium Range or Short Range air-to-air missiles or Gun. The weapons management system then arms the appropriate circuits and configures the aiming system to match the weapon characteristics. *Smiths Group*

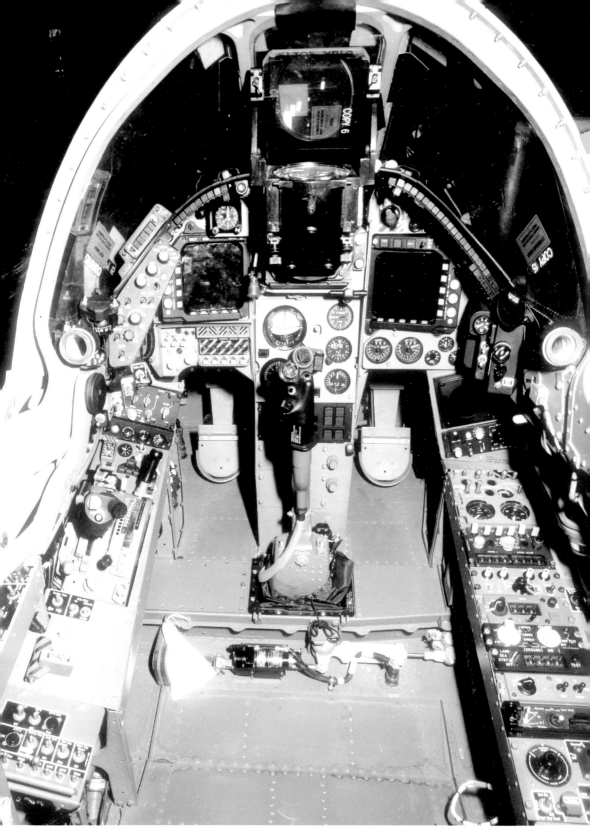

Harrier GR7. HOTAS and up-front control panel along with two large electronic multi-function displays improved the cockpit interface compared with that of the earlier versions of the Harrier. *British Aerospace*

improve navigation and target-finding accuracy is terrain profile matching. This matches radar altimeter height with the terrain profile stored in an onboard computer. It operates automatically from take-off to touch-down and is able to point an aircraft at a selected ground location. It can also include the ability to discriminate between a particular part of a target in order to avoid collateral damage. A complex sortie can be planned in advance and 'played back' on a TV so that the pilot can check the details and 'rehearse' the different stages of the flight. For both fixed and rotary-wing attack aircraft this type of system reduces workload, particularly when operating low down amid both man-made and natural objects, such as power lines, towers and cliffs and ridges.

The cockpit conflict

The primary aircraft control interface is made up of two essentially incompatible elements. These are the human pilot and the machine. Either would be happy without the other. Or, rather, the design of each would be less complex and less a matter of trade-offs were the other eliminated. Those responsible for cockpit design may wish that they did not have to make provision for a human pilot. The human body not only takes up space and volume, it demands a life-support system and above all requires an elaborate control interface. Although a seemingly simplistic observation, nevertheless there is some truth in the concept that the two elements of the man-machine interface are in conflict. The task of the designer is to eliminate it as far as possible.

Civil and military differences

Civil and military cockpits exhibit both common features and significant differences. Leaving aside air force transport aircraft, the shape and equipment of an air force cockpit, when compared with that of a civil aircraft, reflects the different operational role, the different level of acceptable risk taking and the often very different operating environment.

The 'shirt-sleeve' attire of the airline pilot contrasts with special survival and anti-G garments, the 'bone dome' and the numerous pipes and connections worn by the fighter/attack pilot. The modern information interface of the helmet-mounted display, which provides target acquisition and aiming, as well as a 'point and speak' function, integrates the aircraft with the human pilot. The military pilot's cockpit is equipped to enable the aircraft not only to detect threats but to lock onto and destroy them. In contrast the airline pilot needs a control interface equipped primarily to enable 'civil' threats, such as other air traffic and proximity to high ground, to be avoided. The civil interface is also equipped to enable the pilots to make the most effective or economical use of the aircraft; so that it departs and arrives on schedule and does not burn fuel at an uneconomic rate. Above all, the civil flight deck is designed to maximize safety of operation. In contrast the military cockpit is an integral part of a total weapon system for which risk taking is an accepted factor during a sortie. The technologies are similar but their applications differ.

Head Up Display with 'up-front' control panel used to command the aircraft's navigation and attack systems. The 489mm long main body is at an angle downward from the combining glass and control panel so as to fit into the converging lines of an aircraft's nose. *Smiths Group*

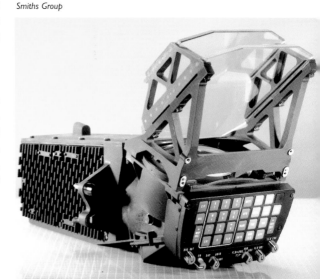

A good fit

It goes without saying that the cockpit must fit the human pilot and his or her visual and tactile interfaces. In other words, displays must be related to the pilot's eye reference point, and the control column, levers, buttons and switches must be within easy reach. This is all very obvious and you do not need a degree in ergonomics to appreciate the need to put things in the right places. The TLAR approach of sixty or more years ago is definitely not allowed. Those responsible for the cockpit design are given a maximum allowed volume in which to accommodate the human pilot, the controls, the instruments and the ejection seat.

In a critical path analysis of all the separate design tasks for a new aircraft the cockpit is a critical item. Aerodynamics, structures, electrical and utilities systems can take significantly less time to design and prove than the cockpit and its machine-human interface systems. From the beginning of the design process the demands on those responsible for 'writing' the software increase with each passing month. Proving the interface software becomes the major time and cost factor. Although this is a simplified description of a very complex operation nevertheless it emphasizes the fact that the avionics and associated software can dominate the design process from the 'back of an envelope' stage to the first test flight of a new aircraft.

The operational role of the aircraft affects everything related to the cockpit. However, the cost of a military aircraft, measured in millions of dollars, is so great that it often has to perform more than one operational task. With multi-role combat aircraft, as exemplified by the F-15, F-18, Tornado and Typhoon, the design of the cockpit was very much influenced by the overall 'multi-role' part of the specification. The different operational roles for a fighter/attack aircraft can include the following:

Air superiority

Air defence interception

Close support interdiction

Interdiction and strike

Close air support

Tactical reconnaissance

Anti-ship strike

Long-range ferrying.

A typical requirement, which acknowledges the very hostile air-to-ground war environment, is an 80-90 per cent probability of a successful strike against a target in one pass irrespective of weather and visibility. This and other requirements directly affect the cockpit design process.

Design team

A cockpit design group is responsible for the displays and controls as well as the weapon systems, and the integrated defence and ground-support systems as well as the crew escape, cockpit environment and life-support systems. It has to interface with many individual specialist design offices. During the evolution of a new aircraft the aerodynamicists and stealth specialists, along with the engine team, demand optimum shapes and volumes throughout the length of the fuselage, including the cockpit area. Therefore the cockpit group has to fight all the way for every inch and cubic inch.

The overall goal of the cockpit design team is to produce a control interface that will provide adequate interchange of information and commands during each of the operational roles for which the aircraft has been designed; ensure that the human pilot's abilities are used most effectively; and protect and ensure the pilot's safety and recovery in the event of disaster. Not many words, but they represent everything that the pilot will need. The time when the cockpit often took second or even third place in design resources has long gone. Also, the time has gone when specialists in different departments of a design centre worked away isolated from others, so that late, often very late, in the total aircraft design process they emerged to demand space and services in the cockpit for their particular system.

Pilot experience

As a cockpit design progresses, the flight operations and flight test teams become involved. Seventy years ago an operational pilot would rarely be afforded the chance to comment on the design of a new cockpit at the 'drawing board' stage. Sometimes the company's own test pilot had no say in what went where. As aircraft became more complex the test or experimental pilot had to take a more prominent role during the early stages of a new design. In more recent decades it has been accepted that those whose primary place of work will be the cockpit need to have a say in its design: not half-way through the process but from the beginning. Today, therefore, the aerodynamicists, structural and systems engineers, stress and propulsion specialists and the instrument and controls designers are joined not only by ergonomists but most importantly by operational aircrews with current experience of combat flying. The experience of air force pilots is now an essential contributor to the overall design process of a cockpit.

ERP

One of the first design stages for a cockpit are computer-generated images and arrangements of equipment against which the anthropometric factors can be tested. As with most areas and volumes in an aircraft, there has to be a datum. For the cockpit this datum is usually the pilot's eye reference point (ERP), or datum eye position. This datum is used when determining the required arcs of view needed by the pilot to see downwards over the nose, to the sides and aft. It is also used as the datum for viewing all instruments and controls, as well as for the optics of the HUD. An early example was the pinhole camera used when settling the major dimensions of the cockpit of the AFB 1 fighter of 1917.

Ideally the arcs of view required by the pilot, particularly for a fighter /attack aircraft, need to be as wide as possible throughout an imaginary sphere centred on the ERP. In most fighter/attack aircraft the cockpit is forward of the wings and therefore the pilot's view aft is restricted. Irrespective of the abilities of the avionics to find and aim weapons at targets, the pilot still needs to be able to see what is happening outside the cockpit. Spherical vision, that is the ability to see in all directions, is the ideal, but it is not always practicable. The pilot's ERP is raised above the upper surface of the fuselage as far as possible without compromising the aerodynamics. A large, one-piece bubble canopy, without framing, is the ideal, and is a feature of most late twentieth-century fighter/attack cockpits, such as the F-22 Raptor. With the F-16, General Dynamics went all the way and eliminated the traditional windscreen arch. The 20 mm thick, monolithic polycarbonate transparency combines windscreen and canopy in a one-piece moulding.

An F-15 was engaged in mock combat with another aircraft when they collided. The pilot of the F-15 managed to regain control and decided not to eject. He could not see the extent of the damage. Apart from indications that fuel was rapidly being lost, the aircraft was just about controllable, providing he did not try to fly it at low speed. He made a landing at twice the normal speed. On raising the canopy, undoing the seat harness and looking to the right, he could see, for the first time, that all the wing on that side was missing!

Interface Equipment

Keyboards

Increasingly in the early 1970s military cockpits were being equipped with interface units made up of arrays of alphanumeric keyboards. At the same time this type of interface was a typical part of non-aviation equipment. Domestic appliances, telephones, car park entrances and personal calculators were accessed through a keyboard or pad. As with other innovations, standardization took time to take effect. Some keypads had the numerals arranged left to right, top to bottom, starting with '1' top left. Others, particularly calculators, had '1' at bottom left, as with most computer keyboards. RAF aircrews were warned against mistakes induced by proficiency in using one arrangement of keys on ground equipment being applied to a different layout of keys in the cockpit.

As technology advanced over the decades, it came up with smaller, more versatile, more adequate and adaptable controls. But the human hand did not follow suit. It remained the size it always had been. Therefore the limit was reached below which there was no point in further miniaturizing selector keys and buttons if a particular one could not be selected without accidentally operating others, especially when wearing gloves. Also to be considered is the virtual2 impossibility of moving the hands off the throttle and stick when subjected to extremes of G: hence 'Hands On Throttle And Stick' (HOTAS), and now 'Voice Throttle And Stick' (VTAS). The 'touch' access screen, so common with

Sea Harrier FRS1. On the left of the seat are the thrust and vectoring-nozzle control levers. The latter is fully forward in the fore and aft zero degrees nozzle position. BAE

Cockpit of an F-16. The semi-reclining seat limits the instrument panel space above the pilot's feet. The HUD and its up-front control panel and the two CRT displays are an example of the move in the late 1960s away from conventional 'clock' type displays. The F-16 was one of the first fighters to have a side-stick control. Both the side-stick and the rudder pedals are of the force-sensing type requiring minimal movement of hand and feet. The reason why there is no windscreen frame visible is because the canopy is a one-piece, frameless, unit.

industrial and domestic equipment, simplifies the control interface. But the cockpit environment sometimes involves high G or severe vibration so that the pilot cannot move the arms and fingers or make precise adjustments of the controls.

Side-stick control

For aerodynamic reasons the military cockpit is of minimum area and volume. The pilot, the ejection seat and survival gear, the controls and instruments, including the target-detection and weapon-aiming systems, occupy a narrow space extending fore and aft. The aerodynamics will not tolerate any spreading sideways. A primary control stick mounted at the side of the pilot's seat is an alternative to the traditional control column set between the pilot's legs. A side-stick was evaluated in an F-4 in 1972.

Modern examples of side-stick-control aircraft are the F-16 and F-22. The Bell AH-1 Cobra and T-50/A-50 (advanced trainer and light combat aircraft) are other side-stick examples. The MiG-29, on the other hand, both the production A/B/C marks and the MiG-29M, have a conventional stick, as do the F-15E Strike Eagle, F/A-18 and EF2000/ Typhoon.

The miniature side-stick in the F-16 allows the pilot to fly the aircraft by moving his wrist only, thereby increasing control precision. The original decision to use a side-stick engendered much opposition. For one thing the side-stick and its mounting took up cockpit 'real estate' in a position usually dedicated to controls for communication and secondary systems. Another objection related to battle damage; particularly if the pilot lost the use of the right arm. The counter to that 'if' argued that in those circumstances the pilot would have no option other than to

Hawk 200. Once the weapon-aiming system sequence and symbology has been selected, using the up-front control panel at the base of the HUD, the pilot uses HOTAS (Hands On Throttle And Stick) control.
British Aerospace

eject. With the side-stick clear of the main instrument panel there is room for more instruments mounted directly in front of the pilot.

When the side-stick was first mooted there were two opposing techniques for sensing the pilot's hand movements. With one system the stick was fixed. When pressure was applied sensors converted it into digital signals to the flight-control system. With the other system the stick was given about 8 mm of movement, and this was the method selected for the F-16.

HOTAS

It was realized that a fighter/attack pilot, when concentrating on target acquisition and aiming, did not have time in which to even glance down at the controls or instruments. Aircraft had been lost because the pilot had been so occupied, 'head down', with reading or adjusting instruments and controls that on looking up he had become disorientated. The pilot's situation awareness has to be kept at the highest level. To use a crude example, the pilot sees the target ahead; arms the weapon system and follows the commands of the aiming system. All is set to press the 'fire' button or say 'Shoot'. Instant blackness and the aircraft and its pilot are destroyed. What happened? The answer might be a complete lack of situation awareness. The only thing with which the pilot was concerned was the target. He did not see the enemy aircraft or react to the missile-warning note. Extending this example further, an attack aircraft pilot attempting to navigate to a target that is surrounded by high ground in poor visibility may not be fully aware of what is happening.

Without adequate sensors, such as ground proximity warning, as well as ECM systems to warn of and protect from enemy threats, the attack is unlikely to succeed. Fixating on the HUD can be fatal. Awareness of the complete situation outside and inside the cockpit is essential. Therefore the cockpit and

its equipment must at all times ensure that the pilot is aware of what is happening and what will happen. A first step towards improving the interface in these circumstances was the Up Front control panel positioned immediately under the HUD combining glass. This keyboard enabled the plot to make all function selections associated with using the HUD at one location and without having to look and reach for indicators and controls located down in the cockpit.

The F-4 Phantom was intended originally to be a high-altitude interceptor of Soviet bombers penetrating American airspace. In the Vietnam War it was called upon to perform a number of different tasks, including intercepting enemy fighters and attacking them with missiles. But the F-4 was not intended to be a 'dogfighter', and so in 1965 the USAF had to start a massive development programme in order to meet a different type of air warfare. The result was the McDD F-15 Eagle, whicht entered squadron service in 1974 and was capable of a wide range of operational tasks. Its importance to the history of the cockpit is that it introduced the concept of Hands On Throttle And Stick (HOTAS).

With HOTAS all the essential selector buttons and switches are located on the throttle(s) or on the control column. For example, a throttle lever could include: radio transmit switch, weapon range-setting knob, speed brake button, radar antennae elevation control, and radar display-cursor control. The top of the control column can have, in addition to the conventional camera/gun/missile trigger for the pilot's index finger, a step button for nosewheel steering select/radar discrimination/missile select, trim control, weapon release, and target designation.

Voice command

In the twentieth century, research started on the vocal interface. The presentation to the pilot of voice messages and warnings posed few audio problems other than which type of voice to use: male or female, soothing, nagging or authoritative? However, when it came to using the pilot's voice to command and question the aircraft the wide variations in human voice characteristics took some sorting out. To prevent inadvertent, dangerous or unwanted vocal noises being acted upon by the aircraft's systems, individual pilots are trained to make acceptably framed commands and questions, and their voice 'prints' are fed into the speech-recognition software of the vocal interface. A number of word protocols have to be used to avoid ambiguities. For example, if the pilot says 'Fuel', the direct voice input (DVI) system selects an appropriate subset in anticipation that the next word will specify that information about the fuel system should be displayed or the pilot be given a verbal warning about the fuel state. The need for a high level of discrimination on the part of a DVI system is emphasized if we listen to other words that under the stress of combat and in high noise environment might sound like 'fuel'. Obviously any voice command system must be programmed to reject foolish and potentially dangerous commands.

The vocal interface is of particular importance in the military cockpit because it provides an essential element in the 'look, point and fire' sequence. Weapon selection, arming and release are commanded by voice in far less time than it takes to reach and touch selector controls. As with HUD and a helmet-mounted display (HMD), a vocal interface enables the pilot of a military aircraft to fly 'head up', look out and keep the hands on the primary controls at all times.

Under the heading of the acronym DVI there are a number of different speech-recognition techniques. These include speaker-dependent and speaker-independent, as well as the recognition of isolated words, connected words and continuous speech. A speaker-dependent system has to be programmed to recognize an individual voice. In other words it has to be trained by listening to a vocabulary repeated many times until it has built into its memory a template for every word. To interface with the DVI system a pilot's voice is analysed at a ground-based computer station in advance of each flight. The system is able to recognize a pilot's individual voice pattern at all times, and in flight can cope with the physical strains placed on the vocal chords by G forces and other stresses imposed on the pilot during combat. When the pilot speaks, the DVI system scans its memory, in microseconds, of course, so as to match what it hears with one of the word templates.

A typical DVI system for a fighter/attack aircraft can handle up to twenty-five different functions based on a 200-word vocabulary. These can include calling up specific displays on the electronic screens, and selecting radio channels and frequencies. DVI and the cockpit aural system, together with the visor or retinal imaging displays, took the HOTAS concept of the 1970s many stages further on in cockpit evolution. In doing so it introduced the acronym VTAS for Voice, Throttle and Stick. Today the cockpit interface during critical phases of flight is concentrated directly in the pilot's eyes. The tactile interface functions are reduced significantly because some of the pilot's control actions are conveyed by DVI.

Expanding the visual interface
There a number of techniques for enhancing the visual interface, particularly when the target is beyond visual range (BVR) or is obscured by environmental conditions. Examples are forward-looking infra-red (FLIR) and low-light TV (LLTV). FLIR with a laser target designating system, such as thermal imaging airborne laser designator (TIALD), provides an real-world display either on the HUD or on the HMD combined

with night-vision goggles (NVG). A typical FLIR can be in the 'boresight' mode, that is fixed as if it were a gun, or it can be aimed and locked on to a particular target by the pilot. The control can either be a small joystick or a thumb button on the top of the control column. This is sometimes one of the control functions at the centre of decisions on whether to design for a single-cockpit fighter/attack aircraft or have tandem cockpits with the workload divided between the pilot and a specialist weapons officer.

A TIALD system interfaces with the aircraft's navigation and mission-planning computer. Global positioning coordinates are used to locate a programmed target automatically. The target is displayed on one of the cockpit displays. Once it is confirmed by the pilot, it is locked onto the target and the bomb is guided by the laser beam.

Because a target designator system may not be pointing directly along the aircraft's flight path an additional display on the HUD or HMD is needed to show the pilot the relative bearing of the target.

In the eye

There are different methods for presenting information to the pilot's eyes as alternatives to head-down instruments and the HUD. Helmet-mounted displays (HMDs) and retinal imaging systems (RISs) are examples. Irrespective of the technology used, the essential requirements are freedom of head movement and low weight. The conventional 'bone dome' is a heavy load on the pilot's neck muscles, particularly when subjected to high G effects. Whatever form an HMD takes it must help to maintain the wearer's consciousness, clarity of speech, acuity of

The pilot of this F-18 is wearing night vision goggles (NVG). These have to be compatible with scanning the instrument panels and when looking through the HUD. *Boeing*

hearing and vision during the violent manoeuvres of an agile 'point in any direction' fighter. The HMD provides the primary visual interface in the majority of modern fighter/attack cockpits. An important requirement for any HMD is the ability to accommodate different eye spacing.

The HMD is used in conjunction with the HUD, or, for some applications, replaces it. There are various types of helmet-mounted displays: some project HUD-type symbology and alphanumerics onto the helmet visor, others have a miniature equivalent of the HUD combining glass set close against the pilot's eyes. An HMD can provide a lightweight binocular visor-projected display, with the visor on the helmet combining and reflecting video, symbology and alphanumerics into the pilot's line-of-sight, along with a real-world view enhanced by night-vision goggles (NVG). The optical design allows the use of a standard spherical curved visor. This has a neutral density, partly reflecting, combiner coating. The coating ensures high display brightness, which at the same time does not distort or attenuate the view of the real world. As the visor is spherical to the pilot's centre of vision, display accuracy is not affected by visor movement. For example, the visor can be partly raised without distorting the display. An HMD can also display simple directional arrows that can be used for steering a TIALD and for off-boresight aiming of missiles.

A target-designator system must not overload the pilot during critical phases of flight, such as when attacking a heavily defended ground target. As mentioned, it is also

The DASH helmet-mounted targeting and display system worn by the pilot of an F/A-18. Tactical, attack and flight information is projected onto the visor of the helmet and focused at infinity. *Boeing*

The lightweight (150 gms) monocular helmet-mounted ALPHA sight. *GEC-Marconi*

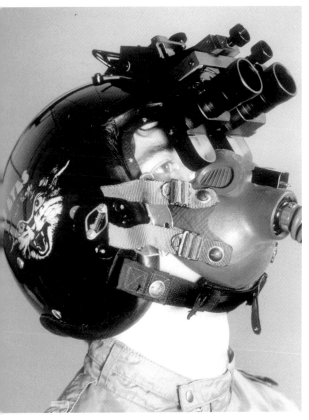

'Cat's Eyes' night vision goggles (NVGs) which give the pilot the ability to see outside the cockpit in the dark as well as able to see FLIR images, graphics and alphanumerics displayed on the HUD. *GEC Avionics*

control, say 'Shoot'. The 'head-free' design concept also relates to the ability of modern avionic systems to warn the pilot of threats, such as SAMs, and to engage targets anywhere within a sphere surrounding the aircraft; including dead astern and directly below: in other words, full 'spherical vision and awareness'.

To see at night

Night-vision goggles have an image-intensifier tube (IIT) that captures red and infra-red light emitted by celestial bodies, engine exhaust, humans and artificial light sources. The electro-optical system presents a green monochromatic image to the wearer's eyes. With NVG a pilot can fly in formation, distinguish ground targets and visually 'lock on' to enemy aircraft. Although the principle of IR detection had been experimented with in the Second World War, it was not until the late 1970s that a production standard NVG was available. The US Army encouraged NVG development because it was seen as being essential for helicopter night operations.

As with the collimated HUD and HMD, an NVG is focused at infinity. Therefore the pilot has to change eye focus when looking down at the in-cockpit displays. This is why the NVG is mounted about one inch away from the pilot's eyes so as to allow direct vision downwards into the cockpit. An NVG is very effective at processing light sources at a great distance. This means that all extraneous in-cockpit light sources have to be removed, otherwise the head-down instruments might be difficult to read. In other words, all cockpit instruments and lighting must be NVG compatible.

The NVG is a bulky and weight-imposing addition to the 'bone dome'. In the 1980s lighter and neater helmets were developed that integrated HUD and NVG. Dual-purpose combining glasses (objectives) in front of the pilot's eyes allow direct vision of the cockpit

important to prevent the pilot 'fixating' on the target display, thereby allowing the aircraft to depart from the required trajectory or get too close to the ground; or even ignoring the ground proximity warning system.

Irrespective of the method of presenting information, an HMD enables the pilot to turn the head away from looking directly forward; rather than having to position the target within the field of view of the HUD. It gives head freedom and the ability to look directly at a target by placing an aiming mark over it, and then, if the aircraft and its weapon systems are equipped with voice instruments. The pilot can also scan on either side of the combiner glasses.

Look and shoot

The speed of air-to-air combat or the limited time available when attacking a ground target requires that as much as possible of the information needed by the pilot must be fed through the helmet to the eyes and ears. Head up, along with VTAS, continues to be the principal element in the interface between pilot and aircraft. However, the HUD information is projected against the point in space or on the ground at which the aircraft is pointing. The pilot needs to be able to see and point at targets outside the normal forward line of sight. The ability to look in all possible directions is essential, both in avoiding hostile devices and for aiming weapons that in themselves do not depend on being launched when the aircraft is actually pointed at the target.

Cockpits for Combat

The machine has control

With the F-16 of 1974 came the concept of the unstable aircraft. In order to maximize performance and agility, combat aircraft are deliberately designed to be unstable. The majority of modern fighter/attack aircraft have to be flown 'hands on' all the time by computers, because a human pilot does not have the required ability. However, the FBW computer control systems provide the pilot with virtually unlimited freedom to hurl the aircraft around the sky without exceeding its aerodynamic and structural limits.

F-117

The F-117's stealth shape directly affected the shape of its cockpit. The combination of a windscreen and canopy shaped to provide the pilot with the necessary undistorted fields of view and at the same time minimize any contribution to total airframe drag can also compromise stealth characteristics. The strength and characteristics of an aircraft's radar signature depend very much on its curves and discontinuities. A stealth aircraft design has to avoid openings and small projections and discontinuities of the surface. At the same time the major elements of the surface have to be set at angles that deliberately attenuate and reflect incident energy in different directions. The nose and cockpit canopy of the F-117 are formed into a quasi-pyramid shape by straight lines in both elevation and plan. The result is an external cockpit shape unique to this aircraft. However, the pilot's arcs of view, particularly when banking, are restricted. The direct view astern is also restricted. The restricted view on each beam prevents F-117s being flown in formation other than line astern.

F-22 Raptor

The cockpit of the F-22 is equipped to enable this thrust-vectoring agile aircraft to perform air-superiority operations over hostile territory. A combination of stealth, supersonic cruise and integrated avionics enable it to penetrate the enemy's defences and avoid air-to-air and surface-to-air missiles. In a typical sortie the pilot's workload is kept to an acceptable level by an advanced information and control interface. This might have been achieved with a two-seater design, but the USAF decided that a single-seater had both cost and operating advantages. The avionics are integrated so as to maximize the pilot's situational awareness. A major contributor to this is an extensive and sophisticated datalink to ground-based and airborne information centres that together reduce the reliance on visual information. Essentially this means that the pilot of an F-22 does not just have to rely on the aircraft's stealth characteristics to avoid detection, because there is a constant inflow of information relating to all aspects of the operating environment: the position of

F-22 Raptor with one piece moulded canopy having no view-obstructing frames. *Philip Jarrett*

friendly elements in the air and on the surface; the position and potential actions of hostile elements; and at all times an overview of the tactical situation. A key factor is the option for 'silent running', when the aircraft is configured so as to emit no electronic signals. In that condition the pilot relies on data received from other aircraft, such as an AWACS, for information; which otherwise would have been provided by the F-22's own navigation systems, radar, laser and IR sensors.

JAS-39 Gripen

The JAS-39 Gripen provides a good example of the level of cockpit technology reached in the late twentieth century. Aesthetics in themselves do not win battles, but they can contribute in a small way to good ergonomics. The Gripen cockpit has an uncluttered appearance. It also emphasizes the way in which the designers integrated a number of systems, including the EP-17 displays, the four double-redundant multiplexed data buses, the head-up display and three 6 in x 8 in colour head-down displays.

The three electronic displays in the JAS-39 are:

A flight data display of alphanumerics and symbology providing attitude and performance

A horizontal situation display with a digital electronic map overlaid with tactical data and symbology

A multi-sensor display for air-to-air and air-to-surface radar, FLIR and the status and position of reconnaissance pods and external stores and weapons.

In the JAS-39, as with most of its contemporaries, data that have been initially loaded into the sortie computer can then be transferred or updated to a number of different destinations within the cockpit and to other aircraft, such as an AWAC, and to tactical command stations on the ground or at sea. Current tactical data are made available to the pilot immediately by being presented on one of the multi-function displays. The efficiency of the Gripen's integrated cockpit interface is also enhanced by inertial navigation, terrain-based navigation and global positioning systems. The integrated landing system takes data from these systems to provide the pilot with an accurate glide-slope for night and low-visibility landings.

By the end of the twentieth century cockpit technology had advanced out of all recognition from the days when the pilot had to depend on instructions from the ground and a mixture of luck and skill to get back and land safely, with only minimal help from terrain features, such as lighting. The latest version of the Gripen cockpit has three multi-purpose colour displays (MPCDs). These are

SaaB JAS-39 Gripen. By the 1980s the increasing reliability and versatility of electronic displays relegated electromechanical instruments to a standby role. *SaaB AB*

50 per cent larger than the first series, and present their information using a special set of pastel colours intended to improve readability when exposed directly to sunlight and when viewed through NVGs.

Russian cockpits

Russian high-performance aircraft, such as the Su-27 and the MiG 29, were developed in the late 1960s and early 1970s. Their aerodynamics and control systems were equal in performance to their contemporaries in the West. However, the technologies applied to the cockpits of both aircraft were a generation behind those of the Americans and Europeans. Pointer-on-dial electro-mechanical instruments predominated and remained the standard well after electronic displays had become the norm for Western fighter/attack aircraft. Not until late in the lives of the Su-27 and the MiG-29 were cockpit displays installed comparable with what had become the standard in other countries. Behind the decision to upgrade both aircraft was the need for Russia to export its aviation products. If Russian aircraft were to compete successfully in the world market their avionics, and in turn their cockpits, had to match or be better than the opposition.

Su-27

The cockpit is pressurized and has a large two-section teardrop canopy. The pilot is afforded large arcs of view, including a 14° downward view over the nose. In an emergency the canopy can be jettisoned and the zero-zero ejection seat fired. In addition to a HUD the pilot can use an HMD for aiming short-range air-to-air missiles in a 'point and shoot' mode. The arrangement and function of the principal controls and instruments is to the HOTAS format. In its most advanced version the Su-27 cockpit might be mistaken, if it were not for the

Cyrillic captions, for that of an American fighter/attack aircraft.

MiG-29

One in a long line of successful fighter and fighter/attack aircraft that at times caused potential enemies potential problems, the MiG-29 Fulcrum is an air-superiority weapon. The early versions had a cockpit equipped to the then current Russian state-of-the-technology, which was not up the same standard as that of the West. As with the Su-27, the avionics and in turn the cockpit interface had to be upgraded; particularly for the export versions of the MiG-29. Luftwaffe pilots had become used to flying American and British aircraft and to their systems and associated instruments and displays. When MiG-29s of the onetime DDR air force were absorbed into that of the unified Germany, their cockpits had to be upgraded. Performance and navigation data and displays were converted to American/British units, such as knots, feet and nautical miles. Pilots cost just as much to train in Russia as in any other country, so a zero-zero ejection seat is an important part of the cockpit.

The elevated position of the pressurized cockpit and the bubble canopy with one-piece windscreen and triple rear-view mirrors give the pilot wide all-round visibility. The curved windscreen is made of electrically de-iced glass and has a magnesium alloy frame. The canopy is hinged at the back and when closed is secured by four locks. It is pneumatically actuated and has three positions, including partly open for taxiing. A warning light and a voice information system are triggered if the canopy is not fully closed. In an emergency the canopy can be jettisoned manually or is jettisoned automatically as part of the ejection sequence.

In its later versions the MiG-29 pilots

were given the combat benefit of an HMD for point-and-shoot release of air-to-air missiles. The Luftwaffe pilots were able to use the Russian HMD during mock combat with F-16s and F/A-18s. It was noted that Mig-29 pilots had to pay far more attention to their instruments during a fight because there was far less automation of systems compared with those of the F-16s and F/A-18s. For example, the thrust and flight control systems of the F-16 automatically prevented the aircraft going outside its safe flight

VTAS (Voice Throttle And Stick). Fifteen function buttons, switches and 'thumb' controls mounted on the throttle and the stick. *Author*

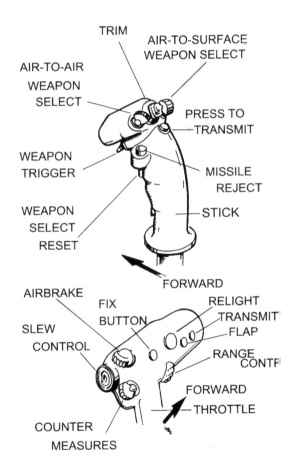

envelope, whereas the MIG-29 pilot had to keep 'one eye out' on the instruments so as not exceed the design limits. In doing so the target could be momentarily lost to sight. The Luftwaffe MiG-29s provide a good example of modern weapon system control. The IR target-seeking and attack system can lock automatically onto a target as soon as it enters the system's acquisition envelope. The target position and status is displayed on the HUD and the pilot's HMD. Because the pilot can 'point and shoot' using the HMD the aircraft does not have to be directly pointed at the target.

A cockpit for Europe

Typhoon

The Eurofighter Typhoon is expected to serve as a first-line aircraft for at least the next twenty years. Therefore it is equipped with the most advanced technologies available. When subjected to high levels of G the pilot must not be deprived of consciousness, of information or of the ability to control the aircraft. Therefore the cockpit and its information systems, such as visual displays and voice systems, were designed to ensure that the pilot is not deprived of both information and the ability to react to the rapidly changing environment, both inside and outside the cockpit.

The attention given to the ergonomic factors was far greater than that applied to previous European fighter/attack aircraft. The reduction of pilot workload and ensuring safety were major design targets. Safety and survivability, and therefore certainty of completing a sortie and recovering to base, is enhanced by the twin-engined configuration and the quadruplex control system, which conveys the pilot's flight control inputs to the control surfaces. This system also leaves the pilot free to concentrate on using the aircraft as a weapon system without fear of stalling or over-stressing it. Also

contributing to workload reduction is the provision of an intelligent ground proximity warning system.

Those responsible for the cockpit design of the Typhoon were faced with the following major requirements: the aircraft's primary role as a single-seater, low-weight, highly-agile, air-superiority fighter: a cockpit interface matched to a weapon system for both 'beyond visual range' and 'close-in' combat situations.

To meet these criteria, within a cockpit envelope restricted by the comparatively small size of the aircraft, three fundamental concepts were adopted. These were: a central 'conventional' control column, rather than a side-stick; three head-down multi-function colour electronic displays and a head-up display. The complete interface design is based on the VTAS concept. The centrally mounted control column has up to twelve switches as well as an X/Y cursor control used to manipulate information on any of the three multi-function display screens. Altogether VTAS can be used to access about fifty different functions. With the Typhoon and its contempories one of the most important stick-mounted controls is for the FLIR system. This can be used in the 'boresight' mode, or it can be slewed onto a target. Once 'locked on', the FLIR image, on the HUD, HMD or an HDD, stays on the target irrespective of how the aircraft is manoeuvred. Another function control on the stick is for changing the elevation angle of the search radar.

Situational awareness is maximized by the three types of visual display – three HDDs, a HUD and an HMD. There are few 'pointer-on-dial' instruments in front of the Typhoon pilot. In the event of a major failure of the electronic display systems there are 'standby' instruments that are independent of the main display systems. These are to the side of the main panel and provide the pilot with heading, airspeed, altitude and vertical speed to enable the aircraft to be recovered to its base.

The head-down displays can be used to present aircraft navigation, sensor, weapons, engine or systems information. The 'soft' keys mounted around each screen enable the pilot to select a particular set of information on any one of the three displays. Weapon aiming in the Typhoon is concentrated at the 'point and shoot' HMD, with its integrated NVG. This allows the pilot to engage targets that are not necessarily directly ahead of the aircraft. The HMD is used in conjunction with the HUD (30°in azimuth and 25°in elevation field of view) and with the three HDDs.

The aircraft's computer system provides flight and target information and weapon-aiming data that are projected electronically on the helmet's visor. During air-to-air combat, or when attacking a ground target, the pilot moves the head to bring an aiming mark, displayed on the visor, over the target. When detected, each target is automatically allocated an alphanumeric label that can be used to designate that target for attack, using the DVI system. The pilot speaks the appropriate DVI command, and microseconds later the target appears in the list of current targets on one of the multi-function head-down displays. The pilot may then allocate one or more weapons to that target using the fast reaction VTAS controls. When the target comes within a specified range a visual 'SHOOT' cue flashes up on the HMD, and the pilot can then use VTAS to release the weapon. The DVI system may still be used in this way, even if the

Eurofighter/Typhoon. HUD combining glass with minimal support so as to maximize the view ahead. Conventional position for the control column. *BAE*

target is beyond visual range (BVR).

When Typhoon cockpit studies started, an appropriate computer-aided-design (CAD) implementation was not available. Wooden mock-ups and anthropometric dummies and models had to be used to verify all decisions concerning dimensions and relative locations of cockpit elements and equipment. BAE's active cockpit simulator contributed to the design process and was of particular value when one of the Typhoon's customer air forces demanded a change.

As noted above, the layout of the cockpit controls and displays concentrates all the important switches used during air combat or ground attack on the throttle levers and the central control column (VTAS). As with other aircraft, such as the JAS-39, F-22 and JSF, the pilot does not have to 'scan' displays relating to such systems as electrics and fuel to ensure their correct functioning. These tasks are looked after by the aircraft's mission and vehicle-management systems. These will only make their presence felt in the event that something has gone, or is about to go, wrong and needs some action on the part of the pilot; thereby keeping workload at an acceptable level. In the

Typhoon the communications sub-system, in conjunction with a dedicated warnings panel, provides a wide range of voice warnings that alert the pilot to the failure of any of the aircraft systems. It also provides procedural instructions on how to deal with a particular failure. This goes some way towards the pilot associate concept based on artificial intelligence (AI).

Panic button

With most modern fighter/attack aircraft the pilot can select automatic flight control, A typical system also provides yaw, roll and pitch damping, which is very important at high angles of attack (alpha). Should the pilot become disorientated, following violent

Eurofighter/Typhoon. Three primary electronic displays under the HUD and with stand-by flight instruments grouped lower right. *Smiths Group*

manoeuvring, the 'panic button' can be pressed. The aircraft is then stabilized in straight and level flight. In the MiG-29, as an example, the panic button can be used to initiate automatic climb-out from a dangerously low altitude. In the cockpit of the Typhoon there is a 'when all else has failed' button. When pressed, this automatically returns the aircraft to a wings-level, nose-up attitude with the engines at an intermediate thrust setting. An ancestor of this system was used in the Douglas F3D-2 of 1950.

Upgrading

The first cost of modern high-performance aircraft is so high compared with earlier generations that their useful lives have to be extended by upgrading their systems. The avionics are usually the subject of upgrading in order to enable an aircraft to remain an effective weapon in the face of changes to the total air war environment. Better target acquisition and aiming systems demand corresponding changes and additions to the cockpit controls and displays.

The F/A-18E/F Hornet has an upgraded flight-control system that enables the aircraft better to resist damage to the control surfaces, which in turn gives the pilot more options when considering whether or not to eject. Changes to the cockpit were incorporated, which improve the pilot's situational awareness. The keypad below the HUD was replaced by an up-front liquid crystal control and display unit. This is touch-sensitive and is activated at the initial touch. This CDU can also be used to show IR and radar. Along with the HUD and the three existing HDDs, this provides the pilot with five principal electronic displays. There is also an LCD dedicated to engine and fuel systems information.

In their later years the Harriers received upgraded avionics along with a better HUD

and two multi-purpose multi-colour displays. The new electronic displays with their 'soft' keys on the periphery of the screen could be used by the pilot to select from a range of information. In the built-in-test mode the health of all major aircraft systems could be verified step by step.

Safety, Survival and Comfort

The modern fighter/attack aircraft cockpit is not a 'shirt-sleeve' environment. The pilot needs protective clothing and body-mounted equipment in order to survive. John Farley, an experienced RAF and test pilot, provided a succinct summary of the protective clothing and safety equipment required by the pilot of a high performance aircraft:

This can incur a significant performance penalty. It can cost the view from the cockpit, if the windscreen-support design requires birdstrike resistance; it can cost the view from the cockpit if the design case for aircrew headgear is crash or ejection protection. It can cost volume in the cockpit, taking up space badly needed during normal flight. Aircrew safety has to be paid for in complexity, training requirements, and servicing. It requires checks, and so costs time.

The helmet has to provide protection of the head and a mounting for communication systems, oxygen mask, unwanted noise-attenuation and target-seeking and weapon-aiming displays. In earlier times a leather helmet with integral earphones and a detachable oxygen mask sufficed, the heaviest item being the oxygen mask. But modern, high-performance, agile aircraft can impose 8 G, or even higher, loads on the airframe and in turn on the frame of the pilot. Pulling into an 8 G manoeuvre increases the static 30-40 lb helmet load on the pilot's neck to over 240 lb. The helmet is not only heavy, it restricts the pilot's ability to make a wide-angle visual scan; essential when 'bounced' by an enemy fighter or threatening missiles.

In the past the pilot's 'bone dome' was designed just as a protection and communications carapace to the head. Subsequently provision has had to be made for NVGs and HMDs. This bit-by-bit progress has resulted in pilots having to wear bulky and heavy helmets. The helmet visor has to be a multi-role device so as to accommodate both in-cockpit and external vision in a wide range of ambient light, from darkest night to looking directly at the sun when at extreme altitudes. It also has to be compatible with and provide the optical base for an HMD or RIS.

Fighting G

Just a normal coordinated turn at 600 knots on a radius of 6,000 ft will impose 4 G on the aircraft and therefore on the pilot's body. The modern G-suit has inflatable bladders around the pilot's abdomen, legs and feet. These are inflated automatically when the acceleration along the vertical axis exceeds 2-3 G so as to prevent the blood surging away from the head and heart. However, modern high-performance 'agile' aircraft can also

impose high G levels in other directions on the body. These can be countered to some extent by a prone or supine position. But these postures introduce problems with operating controls, scanning instruments and 'looking over the shoulder'.

Ejecting

Modern ejection seats have saved many pilots, even when an aircraft has gone out of control close to the ground. A Russian pilot ejected safely from his MIG-29 when it was vertical and within 200 feet of the ground at the 1989 Paris Air Show, thereby giving a very public display and advertisement for the effectiveness of the zero-zero ejection seat. In the late 1990s some air forces studied the requirements for extending the range of body sizes and weights to which ejection seats were designed. One of the values used for calculating seat performance is the 'naked' weight of a subject. Extending the weight range down to about 100 lb and upward to

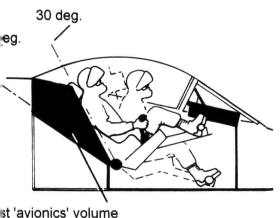

Reclining the seat to combat G requires HUD optics compatible with two different eye reference points (ERPs) and a loss of space in which to house avionics. *Author*

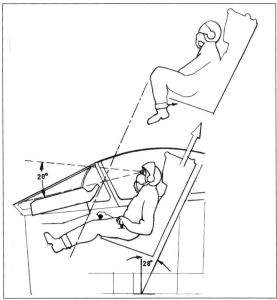

Inboard profile of pilot in the cockpit of the SaaB JAS-39 Gripen indicating the seat inclination and the view ahead in the vertical plane. This drawing emphasizes the need to pull the pilot's legs back automatically against the seat during the ejection sequence. *Author*

Ejection seat showing the straps which pull the pilot's legs back as part of the ejection sequence. *Martin Baker*

200 lb became the design requirement.

Although body weight became important in relation to seat dynamics, such as accelerations imposed on the pilot, it happened that during the 1980s and 1990s more equipment was being strapped on to the pilot. So much so that the lighter weight of some aircrews was compensated for by the increase in protective clothing and helmets with NVG and HMD, and other body-mounted systems. However, the main problem came with those aircrews who were at the upper end of the weight limit range. Here the heavier equipment weight came close to or exceeded that for which the escape system had been originally designed. The Martin Baker ejection seats for the US Navy and the Typhoon, for example, compensate for variations in 'naked' pilot weight so that the lighter crew, such as females, are not subjected to excessive acceleration. At the other end of the weight scale these seats

produce greater ejection thrust. Of course it is not only the ejection thrust that can adversely affect the human body; there is the severe deceleration as the drogue parachute deploys. This may result in severe whiplash injuries to the smaller and lighter aircrews.

The modern fighter/attack cockpit can be defined in respect of five principal elements: the human pilot. the AI pilot associate, HOTAS and HUD/HMD and the ejection seat. Some of the functions of HOTAS are being passed to DVI, and in the future HMD may give way to retinal imaging systems (RIS). Interactive touch-screen displays are now available for interface functions, not allocated to DVI, which can be used in high-vibration and high-G conditions.

The Helicopter Cockpit

Right-hand preference
Civil helicopter technologies are combined in this chapter with those of the military. The pilot's (or pilots') position is similar, as are the primary controls and instrumentation. Right-hand preference (RHP) continues to influence the arrangement of the primary controls: left hand on collective pitch lever, right hand on the cyclic pitch control. Therefore, in the majority of types the principal pilot sits on the right and not on the left, as in a fixed-wing aircraft. Peculiar to the helicopter, as an aerial vehicle, is the hoist on the starboard side of those types used by navies, air forces, armies and civilian rescue and utility services. The military cockpits, compared with the civil, have more instrumentation and controls for searching, sensing threats and weapon aiming.

One instrument in particular is peculiar to the helicopter. This is the hover indicator used when close to the ground that shows along-heading speed and vertical speed. A typical example indicates along-heading speed over a range from minus 10 knots to

Sea King search and rescue helicopter with main door and winch on the starboard side as with the majority of rotary wing utility aircraft.

Cockpit of Merlin helicopter. Apart from having the principal pilot on the right, the layout and displays are little different from those of a fixed wing aircraft. Together the six AMLCDs on the main panel and the Flight Management System display control units on the central pedestal provide attitude and performance, navigation and engine and systems control and information. *Westland*

Sea King helicopter. Principal pilot in right-hand seat. Left hand on collective pitch lever. Right-hand on cyclic pitch stick. *Thales.*

plus 20 knots and vertical speed over plus/minus 500 ft/min. The armoured cockpits of the battlefield helicopters, such as the Tiger and Apache, are more akin to those of a fixed-wing fighter/attack aircraft. They are also completely integrated with the battlefield command and control systems. Landing a helicopter on a ship at night or poor visibility and with the deck rolling and pitching requires both a special skill and the help of visual aids. One system provides a visual display of glide slope and horizon continuously projected at the helicopter by a gyro-stabilized searchlight. The pilot sees the yellow, green and red slope indications similar to those at a runway. The other element of the display projects a horizon bar and ship's deck bar, so that the pilot can select the right moment at which to touch down.

Throughout the last three decades of the twentieth century, helicopter technology made significant advances in safety and reliability. This included the cockpit and its equipment. Today pilot workload is kept within limits by automatic control systems, particularly when operating close to the ground, off a ship's deck and when executing precise manoeuvres or using the hoist. Contributing to reducing workload are the full-authority digital engine-control systems, such as FADEC, and large-screen electronic displays of aircraft attitude, trajectory and performance; as well as navigation and tactical information and graphics. These, along with more accurate navigational aids, such as GPS, greatly improve the helicopter pilot's interface with the machine. Systems based on GPS and terrain-mapped databases are just as important to helicopter operations as to fixed-wing aircraft flying, particularly for 'nap of the earth' sorties. One particular use of helicopters is with police forces. The apprehension of criminals, especially those fleeing in cars, is helped by the use of FLIR

and TV images, both of which can be displayed in the cockpit. A feature of police and utility helicopter cockpits, such as the Eurocopter, is the wide fields of view provided forwards and downwards.

Auditory warning systems

Military interest in more sophisticated auditory warnings stems from the need for pilots (often working single-handed) to identify problems quickly. Helicopters in general are associated with the need for a pilot to react quickly to problems such as rotor-speed decay, loss of blade-control servo-pressure, or gearbox chip-detector warning. Speed of reaction to failures is even more important when sorties involve much low flying; a situation in which pilots must also be alerted to wire-strike hazards. In helicopters, gear and transmission noise is important as a source of sound that can swamp essential sound inputs to the pilot. In the military helicopter this can be attenuated by carefully designed helmets and by using auditory warnings fed through the earphones. Attachments to helmets, such as night-vision goggles, make it difficult to view a central warning panel at the lower level of the instrument panel. Auditory warning systems are one of the alternative means of overcoming this problem.

Helicopter fenestration

Some of the design decisions taken for the McDD Explorer were representative of helicopter cockpits in general. They included good all-round arcs of vision; not always achieved, and the use of canopy framing configured so as to resolve the conflict between the need for structural strength and the pilot's demand for an all-round view. An all-round view is particularly important for the helicopter pilot because of the need sometimes to set down into confined spaces. In the Explorer the horizontal frames were set low down and well below the plane of the pilot's ERP. The cyclic pitch-control lever had a pistol-type grip and was positioned so that the pilot could use a natural wrist-on-thigh position when flying.

Seats

The vibration levels and frequencies in a helicopter are different from those experienced by the crew of a fixed-wing aircraft. Seats specifically designed for the helicopter cockpit significantly damp out vibration. They also provide crash attenuation, and, importantly for those helicopters flown into 'harm's way', the seats, e.g. Martin Baker type S-92, are armoured. The Sikorsky S-92 crash-resistant seat from Meggit partly encloses the pilot in armour. Protection from frontal attack is provided by the cockpit structure and the armoured transparencies.

A comment on the report of an inquiry into the loss of an RAF Chinook emphasized the severe vibrations sometimes experienced by helicopter pilots:

The collective lever would have been well up under his left armpit as he tried to control Nr. The engine and flight instruments would have been very difficult to read because of the acute vibration. This is something that cannot be simulated and can only be experienced during high Nr autorotation on the real aircraft; even this is nothing like the vibration which occurs during high Nr with power on.

The Chinook has massive self-tuning vibration absorbers under each pilot's seat and behind the instrument panel to absorb the naturally large vibration experienced by Chinooks. The absorbers utilize spring, variable-lever arms and weights. If they go outside the normal Nr range of 96-102 per cent, not only do they not absorb vibration, but they will work in pro-phase, as opposed to anti-phase, and dramatically increase vibration under the pilot's seats and of the instrument panel.

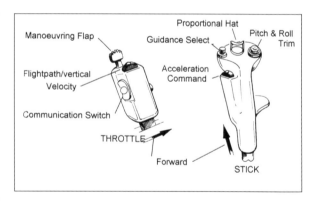

Extra controls added to the throttle and stick of the AMES YAV-8B ASTOVL of 1995 for more precise control during the hover and landing modes with nozzle angle controlled automatically. *Author*

CHAPTER TWELVE

Simulated Cockpits

Entertainment

A dramatic scene in a book or film often has a vehicle as a background. There are two basic stories in drama: unremarkable people in unusual and dramatic circumstances; or unusual or remarkable characters in non-dramatic or ordinary circumstances. The bridge of a ship, the cab of a locomotive or the back of a horse can provide an author with a dramatic background to a story. The aircraft cockpit is often used as the setting for a drama involving both unremarkable and remarkable people.

One of the foundation stones when writing a drama involving vehicles, be it book or film, is the adage, 'Never let the facts spoil a good story.' For ninety or more years the aircraft cockpit has featured in fictional writing and in films. However, its equipment is usually ignored. Or, if included, it is rarely accurately representative of the real thing. In the typical aviation novel the pilot, more often than not, leaps into the cockpit and within a few lines the aircraft is up among the clouds. Attendant mechanics and the need, even in a First World War fighter, for some manipulation of the engine controls and fuel system are ignored. Engine starting has rarely been a 'leap into the cockpit and press a button' type of exercise. It has usually required some deliberate sequence of actions and some time. This is of course anathema to the thriller writer or film maker. Just as in railway and automobile fiction and film, the reality of safety devices and operating

procedures have been ignored lest the facts spoilt or slowed up the action.

During the 1920s and 1930s there were a number of classic aviation films. Howard Hawks's Hells Angels used real First World War aircraft rather than models and included in-cockpit cameras. Other 'blockbusters' appeared along the same lines, such as Dawn Patrol. However, shots of instruments and controls were rare. During a dogfight sequence the studio placed a camera face onto the nose of an aircraft so that the audience could observe the actor pilot's facial emotions as he fired long bursts of machine-gun ammunition. Of course the 'film' aircraft were allowed seemingly unlimited supplies of ammunition.

When First World War flying films, such as The Blue Max, were made in the 1960s, the director and aviation adviser decided that the audience had to be able see the triggers being pulled. As they were on the control column and virtually out of sight then the 'pilots' used the gun-arming (cocking) levers on the breeches of the guns.

The Second World War generated millions of words and feet of film on aviation subjects. Korda's The Lion Has Wings of late 1939 is among a host of aviation films in which the producer and director never let the facts get in the way of the story. Korda's film, when seen today, is, as was intended, 100 per cent propaganda. The RAF pilots and aircrew wear white or light-coloured flying clothing. The Luftwaffe crews are in all-over black, including their scowls. The cockpit shots in an RAF Wellington are reasonably accurate. However, when the same cockpit serves for that of a Luftwaffe bomber the film is reversed so as to position the pilot on the right.

One of the most obvious changes made to facilitate filming occurred among American fighter cockpits. These were usually depicted as being extraordinarily roomy. Although the cockpits of American fighters were larger than those of other nations they were nowhere as large as those of the Hollywood mock-ups. Hollywood had an advantage over other film centres in that American pilots usually used a throat microphone and therefore the star's features were not hidden by a face-mask microphone. Throat microphones were also used in the Luftwaffe.

Simulating

The aircraft in its three-dimensional environment is a far more difficult machine to control than those that manoeuvre in fewer dimensions, such as surface vehicles

and ships. From the earliest days of powered heavier-than-air flight the ability to change or correct aircraft attitude was only mastered quickly by a few. The majority needed between eight and ten hours in a dual-control trainer aircraft before they could be let loose on their own. Advertisements of the 1900s sometimes referred to the liability of pupil pilots for 'breakages'. Therefore thought was given to the use of ground-based training devices by which pupils might acquire the skills of control coordination without leaving the ground and without incurring 'breakages'.

The word simulation is defined in the OED as the action or practice of simulating, with intent to deceive. In the context of the modern simulator the word deceive is still applicable in a non-pejorative sense, because pilots are deceived as far as possible into believing they are in a real aircraft. 'As far as possible' is not a quantitative measure. It is very much qualitative in that users of a simulator will have varying expectations depending on their experience. Furthermore there can be variations in the extent to which a simulator accurately replicates the real world. In some the effects of motion may be minimal or non existent; in others the real-world scene might be limited in the extent to which it replicates ground features. Much depends on the purpose and the cost. If money is no object, then a six-degrees-of-freedom-of-movement system with an extremely realistic view of the world outside the cockpit windows can be had.

In the *ab initio* stage of a pupil pilot's progress a simulator provides freedom from the limitations of flight in poor visibility. Even in a real aircraft there are practical limitations to the extent to which

Airbus A 320 simulated cockpit. Pilot's left hand on side-stick control, right-hand on thrust levers as the aircraft is being aligned for take-off.
Thales

pupil pilots can experience the control effects and aircraft responses at the boundaries of the flight envelope. Apart from cost, compared with flying the real aircraft, there is the overall need for safety that makes the simulator a useful alternative to actual flight. At the other end of the pilot scale a simulator enables the experienced pilot to complete an Instrument Rating check or gain a new aircraft type in his or her licence without the need to burn thousands of litres of fuel flying a real aircraft at a time when it should be earning money for the airline. The modern simulator enables the military pilot to acquire the skills needed to make the most effective use of the aircraft as a weapon system, particularly when new weapons and systems are introduced into service. It also enables extreme manoeuvres to be demonstrated which in a real aircraft might exceed the design stress limitation.

Early days

Early examples of flight simulators included the simple arrangement of a seat on a flexible mounting on which a pupil sat and endeavoured to keep the seat upright by coordinating the aileron and elevator controls. The task was made more difficult by the instructor, who could prod the system to make it unstable. The Sanders Teacher of 1910 had wings and was slightly more realistic in that it could be turned into the wind in order to generate lift. Other early 'simulator names' are Anderson, Billing, Gabardini, Ruggles and Walters. Some early flight simulators were specific to a particular type of aircraft. Learning to fly the French Antoinette monoplane of 1909 anticipated the time when modern simulators emulate the flight characteristics of a particular type of aircraft.

One method of ab initio training used aircraft which had their wings reduced in span. Pupils could taxi at speed but could not

The Link Trainer, developed in 1929, that could roll, pitch and yaw. It was a major contributor to instrument flight training and the precursor of the modern far more realistic simulators. *Link*

take off. It may be stretching the definition of simulator to class these 'penguins' as simulators. In the early 1930s there were numerous patents applied for relating to machines that attempted to emulate flight. Some were cockpits mounted on the end of a long arm that could move in a vertical plane, and others were similar to the whirling-arm devices of a fairground. One in particular, the Whiting, anticipated the modern dome-type simulators. The cockpit was fixed at the centre of the dome. The dome moved in response to the pilot's control actions and was painted with a horizon dividing scenery from sky.

Despite the tremendous increase in the number of pilots to be trained in the First World War the majority of training aids were aptitude testers, such as the Ruggles Orientor. This may have been the first to make use of electric motors to effect attitude changes in the replica aircraft. Another early simulator, of the effects of aileron, rudder and elevator movements, consisted of a model aircraft suspended in a glass wind tunnel. This provided much entertainment at exhibitions. The concept of the three-axis flight simulator was described in a patent of

Leander & Heidelberg granted in 1917. This was operated by compressed air, and anticipated Link's practical system. In the 1920s inventors tried to develop a means of projecting a visual display, but none was to an acceptable standard of realism.

In the 1920-30s, Rougerie, Reid, and others developed more elaborate devices for assessing a pupil's latent control ability. However, these had no or limited movement, and were primarily used to check response times to changes in control position and instrument indications. In 1933 the RAF started to use the Reid reaction-testing device. Its primary purpose was to eliminate, at an early stage, pupils who were likely to prove bad pilots. It also pre-selected those who were more fitted by temperament to make good fighter pilots. The Reid apparatus tested the speed of reaction in making restoring movements of the controls.

Cockpit simulators started to be used for research in the 1940s. A notable example was the Cambridge Spitfire Cockpit, used to assess pilot speed and accuracy of response to control demands in a stressful situation and over a long period. From the 1950s onwards, increasing use was made of training simulators as research tools. A simulated aircraft can be commanded to perform extreme and hazardous manoeuvres that would be unacceptable with the real aircraft. A simulator reduces the risks involved in flight testing, particularly of a prototype. At the same time it reduces the cost of aircraft development by enabling sufficient statistical samples of particular aspects of performance to be obtained without the need for time-consuming flight testing.

The essential Link

Link is the name most readily associated with simulators. Although it was not the first, it was undoubtedly the first mass-produced, all-purpose, affordable, flight-training aid. It was also a moving-base device that provided some of the sensations experienced when applying bank, pitch and yaw. But the early Link Trainers could not be used to simulate extreme flight conditions, even though they could be stalled and spun.

The movement of the small fuselage, with its single-seat cockpit, was effected by air motors whose design owed much to the church and theatre organs made by the Link family business. For example, the training motor for turning the cockpit about its vertical axis, in response to aileron and rudder control demands, consisted of a number of bellows connected to a multi-throw crankshaft. Similar technology was used for aileron and elevator. It was all very simple and could be mended by unskilled personnel using simple tools.

The potential value as a training aid of Edwin Link's 'Blue Box' of 1929 was not immediately recognized by the aviation world. It became an amusement arcade attraction, and Link even added a coin-in-the-slot feature; as described in UK Patent 370,128. In some ways this turn of events anticipated the present-day 'desktop' PC flight simulators that are neither a toy nor a completely realistic training device. The blue-painted 'Blue Box' or 'Pilot Maker' Trainer arrived on the aviation scene just at the right time. Aviation in general was expanding and figuratively pushing against the 'visibility barrier'. If pilots inadvertently or foolishly attempted to fly in cloud for more than a few minutes, they usually ended up in a 'graveyard spiral', striving to recover the aircraft from a dangerous situation. The Link Trainer with the hood down taught the basic rule: 'Believe and follow what the instruments tell you. Ignore the sensations of apparent movement and do not try to fly by the seat of your pants.'

A significant milestone in simulator history was the decision in 1930 by the Pioneer Instrument Co. to use a Link Trainer to demonstrate the importance of their instruments in helping a pilot to avoid loss of control in cloud. It is important to note that Link did not advertise his invention as a 'simulator'; in fact the word is hard to find among the literature of the time. It was an Aviation Trainer. Not until after the Second World War did 'simulator' become common usage. Although not of great importance, it may be of interest to note that some might argue that you should not call a training device a 'flight' simulator unless it at least moves around the three axes of roll, pitch and yaw.

In 1934 the US Army was persuaded to buy six of Link's Pilot Makers. This was the year in which the Air Corps had lost eight aircraft, with five pilots killed and six injured in crashes while attempting to carry the US Mail. The pilot's lack of training in flying on instruments when confronted by poor visibility and turbulence was the major cause of the disasters. At about this time Link tried to interest the US Navy in his Aqua Trainer. This sat in the water and was powered by a small petrol engine driving a propeller. The Aqua Trainer could rise off the surface and respond to the pilot's control inputs. It provided a pupil pilot with the essential 'feel' of a seaplane during the critical flight phases of take-off and touch-down on water. It was an innovative idea but failed to interest enough potential customers. By 1936 Link had added an instructor's table to the Pilot Maker. This was equipped with duplicate instruments and an electromechanical device that moved a 'crab' carrying a marker pen across the chart on the instructor's table.

Once under the hood in the Link, the pilot was isolated from the world. It was used by the airlines and training schools for navigation, let-down procedures and approaches to a landing. It became recognized as a way of teaching pilots in 'flying the range': in other words, navigating

across the USA among the directional and non-directional radio beacons, and following the aural and visual indications of the radio ranges. It is important to note that there has always been a strong aversion to using a flight simulator as the only means of teaching someone how to control an aircraft. It was argued that the basic skills of controlling an aircraft should first and foremost be taught in a real aircraft. But on those days when even the birds were grounded the 'Link' could still fly.

To meet the demand for greater realism, Link trainers became increasingly more sophisticated. Later models were no longer 'general purpose'. Type-specific models were built. Their 'flight' characteristics were arranged to emulate those of a specific aircraft type, such as the AT-6 Harvard trainer. As the Second World War progressed there was an increase in the number and range of overwater flights, such as the transatlantic ferry service. In the absence of long-range radio navigational aids crews had to rely on astro-navigation. Link, in association with Captain Weems, USN, an authority on celestial navigation, developed the Celestial Navigation Trainer (CNT). The 'fuselage' of the CNT was suspended within a dome onto which were projected lights representing the stars. A bomber crew could complete a long-range flight, navigating by sextant shots of the artificial stars. A reproduction of the terrain was projected below so that the bomb aimer could use the bombsight. The RAF calculated that by the end of the war it had saved 50 per cent of its training time and costs by using the CNT. The importance of the CNT to the history of this subject is that it was the first production-standard, moving-base simulator with positions for more than just a 'solo' pilot.

Developed in parallel with Link's Pilot Maker were examples of the more basic types of simulator that were used to test the visual, tactile and control coordination and responses. Link trainers were also used by the RAF in the Second World War for the aptitude assessment of potential pupil pilots. The Second World War required a massive increase in the production of Link Trainers. At the end of the war units were coming off the assembly line every forty-five minutes.

Other than the Link Trainer and the Link Celestial Navigation Trainer, the US air services and the RAF had few moving-base simulators during the Second World War. There were about thirty types of synthetic training devices used by the RAF in the 1940s. They included a fixed-base, bomb-aiming, training device for both pilots and bomb aimers that used a moving-map display to simulate the movement of an aircraft relative to target; a complete fuselage of a bomber in which pilots, navigators and flight engineers, but not air gunners, could make a simulated sortie during which their skills were monitored by an instructor who could inject faults and errors into the different systems (the Silloth Trainer).

A fixed-base Spitfire cockpit was used for teaching the correct techniques for identifying and intercepting target aircraft in different visibility conditions; the 'targets' were model aircraft suspended from an overhead moving chain that simulated different ranging situations. A dome was used by the Royal Aircraft Establishment in the late 1940s for its air combat simulator. This used a Spitfire cockpit and optical projection of an enemy aircraft onto the surface of the dome. In 1973 the RAF made a 'homemade' fixed-base simulator for one of its Shackleton squadrons. This particular example met the need during peacetime for realistic training in searching and attacking when there were not enough real targets to represent wartime conditions.

UK simulator builders also based their technology on that of the pneumatic organ. As an example, the Automatic Player Piano Company, which made training devices for the RAF, was already familiar with the levers, linkages and bellows that made up so much of the simulator technology of the time. The 'organ and piano builder' simulators contributed significantly to training in the 1940s, but their mechanisms were adversely affected by climatic conditions and mechanical problems. This encouraged the development of simulators based on the electronic computer. Bell delivered the first production operational electronic simulator in 1944.

Radar training

The increasing use of airborne radar systems in the RAF encouraged the development of training methods under the general heading of synthetic devices, which simulated the procedures and techniques to be used in flight. At first a Link Trainer was modified for use as an AI radar training device. However, the Link's 'flying' characteristics proved unsuitable for the purpose. The next step was to build a mock-up of the cockpit of a night-fighter equipped with controls and instruments, radar units and a reflector gunsight. The cockpit was at the focal point of a cyclorama screen on which was projected the image of an enemy aircraft. All systems used for flight, navigation, interception, aiming and firing the guns were included. Simulators were also developed in the Second World War for training aircrews in the use of GEE and Oboe, ASV and H2S. These saved two million actual flying hours and 250 million gallons of fuel.

The importance of training

Many new problems arrived with the upsurge in civil aviation after the Second World War. The basic training method of acquiring experience by sitting in the right-hand seat of an airliner was no longer sufficient to ensure a safe standard of competence. It was soon realized that the new generation of civil aircraft needed comprehensive training equipment for the flight crews. In 1948 Curtiss Wright developed a flight simulator for the Stratocruisers of Pan Am. This was the first full aircraft simulator to be owned by an airline. However, there was no motion or simulation of the real world. The British company Rediffusion is credited with the first electronic simulator for airline use. This was used by Stratocruiser pilots of BOAC.

Jet Training

The jet airliners that entered service in the late 1950s, such as the Boeing 707, required an accurate landing approach path and needed to be established on the extended runway centre-line and the descent path at least five miles out from the touch-down point. If they were well off the required approach path and within the last mile out from the runway threshold they could not be brought back easily and safely onto the glide slope and localizer.

Adding to the difficulties for the pilot was the slow response, compared with piston-propeller power, to a sudden demand for more thrust. The high approach and landing speeds, compared with earlier years, of the post-war generation of civil airliners encouraged the development of new approach-light patterns. The Calvert systems, developed at the Royal Aircraft Establishment, Farnborough, were evaluated on a simulator consisting of a wide belt on which were small lights to represent the approach pattern. These were viewed from a fixed eyepoint. Compared with modern simulators these fixed-base and fixed-eyepoint training and research devices were extremely crude. Therefore, simulators had to be developed that could replicate all phases of flight and aircraft attitude. However, in the early years of the 707 only fixed-base

simulators were available, and even as late as 1958, in jet transport development terms, the Comet IV simulator only had motion in pitch.

In the 1960s some simulators relied on a small CCTV camera that was 'flown' over a detailed model of terrain. The resulting image was then presented on a large TV monitor mounted in front of the cockpit windows. Compared with modern visual displays, the field of view was limited to about 50° in azimuth and 30° in elevation. At the time this technology, even with its limitations, was viewed with wonder.

Simulating trouble

Fifty years ago or more, aircraft were more prone to failures of engines and systems. Pilots were always on the alert for sudden failures, and in consequence 'on-the-job' training had often to be very realistic and demanding. Today there is far more redundancy designed into systems, so that failures are less frequent, and because of extensive monitoring systems they can sometimes be anticipated. Therefore one of the functions of the modern flight simulators is to provide realistic problem situations. Coping with some problems cannot be rehearsed safely in a real aircraft. For example, completely and suddenly shutting down an engine during take-off is never attempted in the real situation. But it can be demonstrated in a simulator.

Even as late as 1970 airlines were using their expensive aircraft for instructing pilots in the correct procedures for handling engine and system failures. This included engine failures at or after the V1 decision speed. The number of fatal accidents, particularly those resulting from deliberate failing an engine, in the USA between 1962 and 1972 involved eight aircraft written off and forty-one deaths. These accidents, plus the fact that six FAA inspectors died in the accidents, prompted investigation into far less hazardous methods of training to cope with emergencies. To the attribute of safer flight training by using a simulator was added the benifits of reduced training costs.

Simulators can provide repetitive practice but do not always give a direct interaction between instructor and pupil. A simulator is not good at interacting in an interpersonal way when compared with a human flight instructor. Although a simulator can be used to assess the performance of a pilot, particularly when used as a training aid, it cannot necessarily teach aircraft-handling technique or provide advice based on experience in the same way as can a human instructor.

An airline training flight in a simulator is far more than the crew turning up as if it were a classroom. The crew has to attend a normal briefing session, flight planning routines must be gone through in detail and at the end of the flight there is debriefing. An air force crew goes through a similar and rigorous programme that replicates all aspects of a sortie, from briefing to debriefing.

Zero Flight Time training

In 1970 a CAE four-axes Boeing 747 simulator was developed for British Airways. A second in 1975 had the Singer Link-Miles Night-Vision System. The night-vision system was generated by a computer and therefore was an important technological advance away from the CCTV systems. All potential hazards, including engine failure on take-off at a critical speed, could be demonstrated and crews trained in the correct recovery actions. By the mid-1980s the FAA in the USA,

the CAA in the UK and the European Joint Aviation Authority had agreed Zero Flight Time (ZFT) for recurrent crew training and type conversion. This is a milestone in the history of the cockpit. Under the new rules a simulator could be used as an alternative to actually flying in an aircraft. Obviously the authorities concerned with flight safety demand a minimum acceptable set of standards for a simulator. These define what is termed the Level D. With the addition of specialized software programs, a Level D simulator can be used by an air force for training in low-level flying, in-flight refuelling, combat sorties and those tasks specific to the helicopter, such as oper-ating into confined spaces and lifting and lowering stores.

The cost of realism

Today the digital computer and associated systems can replicate or emulate with a high degree of accuracy most of the environments in which mankind has to exercise control over machines, of which the simulated aircraft cockpit is an outstanding and important example. At all stages of pilot training, from ab initio to gaining a supersonic rating, a simulator is now an essential aid. The optimum design solutions and the eventual operational effectiveness of a new aircraft type depend very much on modelling and simulation.

Boeing 747-400 simulator. The wide, 150° view provides a realistic representation of the real world. This is an example of an approach to a landing being made at night. *Thales.*

The modern simulator is a combination of a big-memory digital computer, electro-mechanical or electrohydraulic motion system and 'real world' image generator. The last displays a visual representation of the real world along with apparent movement that responds smoothly to control inputs. The question that sometimes has to be answered in the world of simulators relates to the required degree of realism. The degree of realism required will depend on a number of factors; such as cost and the training and familiarization roles required by the user. If cost is not the limiting factor, then you can virtually have any function or situation and any effect simulated in full colour and with realistic motion and movement of both the user's cockpit and the 'real world'.

Even though a simulator can provide a less costly alternative to training and research in an actual aircraft and, of course, provide no-risk flight, it is still an expensive item of capital equipment that has to earn its way. The first cost could be about 45 per cent of the simulated aircraft. A typical comparison of operating costs between those of a modern flight simulator and using a real aircraft for training is in the order of 1 to 8 for a Boeing 747, 1 to 3.5 for a 757 and 1 to 2.5 for a 737, to which advantage the elimination of 'breakages' is an important factor. A comparison of operating costs can also indicate the point in a training programme at which a trade-off has to be made between the capital and operating costs of a simulator and the costs of 'real' flight training. The operating cost ratio is in proportion to the size and complexity of the aircraft being simulated. For example, the capital and operating costs of a simulator for business and feeder aircraft may show little advantage to the simulator. With small and simple aircraft the ratio goes right against the simulator.

The step upwards to the moving-base simulator so as to provide inputs of acceleration, motion and attitude is a big one and involves anything up to $1 million or more. A six-degrees-of-freedom simulator for a Boeing 747, for example, will set you back a fortune. If you cannot afford your own then you have to buy time at $2,000 plus/hour on someone else's simulator.

One aspect of flight simulator economics is the ability to repeat and analyse critical and important phases of flight. With civil and military transport aircraft, take-off techniques, coping with engine and system failures, departure and approach patterns and landing phases take precedence over en route simulated flight. For long-range navigation and fuel-management exercises a fixed-base, less costly simulator may be acceptable. A simple fixed-base procedures trainer may meet a particular training programme in which the instruments and controls are nothing more than illustrations positioned correctly on representations of the main instrument and controls panels of a cockpit. Professor John Rolfe summarizes the design criteria for a simulator as:

It must take account of the input/output characteristics of the human operator

The degree of realism and content must be related to the user's needs. If the quality of the simulation is either too simple or too complex it will result in dissatisfaction and criticism

The value of the simulation must be based upon its ability to bring about the intended changes to behaviour, i.e. that training has been achieved.

PC simulators

For those who have neither the qualifications nor the money to fly as P1 or P2 in a Boeing 747, or as a fighter pilot in a MiG-29, the PC-based simulator is the answer. For the historian needing to bring life to descriptions of the pilot's environment and experiences in aircraft of past eras, the PC simulator is in many ways far better than watching old films.

The boundaries between the PC simulator, the fixed-base training aids and motion-platform systems are becoming blurred. In about 1980, a flight simulator program for use with a PC had a limited and not very realistic response to 'pilot' control inputs, a slow refresh rate for the visual scene and few aircraft types and airfields. En route flight had to be IFR because there was no scenery database from which to ascertain your position. Although the ubiquitous personal computer can provide a 'fixed-base' simulator of the instruments and sounds of an aircraft, along with an albeit limited representation of the 'real' aircraft, there is very limited feedback to the user's senses; particularly of motion and acceleration effects. But despite its limitations, the PC-based simulator has a number of advantages. It can be easily moved and in its laptop form provide a training and familiarization aid that can be accessed at any time. Furthermore, its simulated instruments and controls are not necessarily dedicated to just one type of aircraft. Laptop computers are being used to emulate a complete flight-management system. Pilots can use them when qualifying for a new aircraft type as an initial part of a training programme.

PC-based simulators can be used for introducing, explaining and demonstrating the operations of an aircraft and its associated equipment. Animations of instrument responses, the dynamics of mechanical systems and the flow paths of electrical and fluid systems provide familiarization and training for both air and ground crews. This type of training aid teaches equipment operating practices and diagnostic procedures such as engine run-up and fault-detection sequences, inputting navigation key data, such as waypoints, and selecting flight-management computer operations.

Today there is a range of software and hardware on the market with which to equip and 'fly' a home-built simulated cockpit. The PC-simulator packages on the market can provide both an aid to training and hours of interest to those who have no access to a real cockpit. The degree of realism of both the interior of the cockpit and the visual scene outside continues to be improved year by year. By combining film of terrain and specific locations with computer-generated imaging the external view can be astoundingly realistic. Only a brief scan through the publications devoted to PC simulators is needed to reveal a wealth of systems and equipment covering military and civil fixed-wing and helicopters; along with a range of airports and different types of terrain. The only limiting factor is the user's budget.

The PC-simulator provides a useful tool not just for training and entertainment but for experiments with different control interface arrangements, and all at an acceptable cost. Eventually the literature may include reports on the psychological and physiological effects imposed on PC simulator pilots. In the past twenty years the PC simulator, as well as all other types, have had the quality of replication of the scene outside the cockpit advanced far beyond the early days. Today the 'pilot' of a PC simulator is presented with a virtual view of the cockpit and a multi-screen view of the world. The hardware available now includes complete full-size replicas of the primary flight controls, and not just, as in the past, a desktop joystick.

Turbulence and noise

An example of the way in which a sophisticated flight simulator can advance both safety and reduce training costs is by simulating turbulence, downbursts and windshear effects. These conditions can be elusive, and so searching for them in a real aircraft is an expensive and unproductive way of training pilots. By simulating them on the weather radar and through the motion system, pilots can be trained in the correct operating procedures. Flight simulators can improve an air force's community relations. The public in general, except in time of war, not only resent paying for an air force but object strongly to being kept awake at night or having their peace and quiet shattered by low-flying aircraft. Night and low-flying training can be simulated to the benefit of both parties.

Hostile environments

The majority of the world's principal air forces acquire sophisticated simulators as part of a defence package. They depend on simulators for type training, system upgrade familiarization and for simulating combat without risk. Those air forces with deep pockets can acquire fighter/attack simulators that enable two or more 'aircraft' to be flown simultaneously so that each pilot can format with other 'aircraft' or engage in air-to-air combat and ground attack.

The modern simulators are an essential part of the preparation for a sortie. The simulator can be used to expose pilots to a wide range of possible events so as to improve their ability to survive and to complete the operational tasks effectively. For example, the Link F-16 Simulation and Training System for the USAF allows the pilots of different aircraft types to train in virtual formation. By combining satellite imagery with computer mapping, aircrews are presented with a visual perspective view of a target. Different directions of approach can be rehearsed. The release and control of ordnance can be replicated to determine their probable effectiveness. Even the hostile reaction of the target can be simulated. The simulator of the cockpit of the B-2 stealth bomber is on a six-degrees-of-motion platform. The visual system provides a wide-angle view outside the cockpit. This is an example of a simulator based on the civil FAA/JAA Level D standard to which additional functions have been added to match the operational role of the B-2. For example, there is full simulation of the weapons system and the deployment of ordnance, as well as the important simulation of air refuelling.

Upgrade simulators

The constant search for ways to reduce costs in a world of ever more restrictive civil and defence budgets is often met by upgrades to existing aircraft types. Certification for airworthiness requirements and the training of aircrews for an upgrade can be helped by

Modern flight simulation for a fighter/attack aircraft equipped with a HUD and up-front control panel for flying HOTAS (Hands On Throttle And Stick).

Tornado simulator cockpit despite the 'Phantom II' shoulder badge. *BAE*

the use of simulators. Changes to the aerodynamic characteristics of an aircraft consequent on reconfiguration can be simulated without the costs and safety implications of flying an actual aircraft. The simulator's role can be advanced from aircraft handling, performance and navigation to take in the extended environment in which the aircraft is assumed to be flying. Tactical situations can be tried out in a military simulator cockpit, and in transport-type cockpits ATC situations can be simulated, including mid-air collision threats.

Simulation demand

The demand for all degrees of simulation continues for airliners, corporate and business jets, regional jets and turboprops, as well as helicopters. In one year more than thirty civil full-flight simulators were on order from the principal manufacturers for these types of aircraft. Training centres have been established by the simulator manufacturers that are available to all airlines whose

accountants welcome the opportunity to avoid large capital expenditure. A typical simulator is the CAE full-motion Airbus A330-200 for Emirates airline at its Dubai training centre. This is fitted with the Evans & Sutherland ESIG 3350GT image-generating system for reproducing images of all destination airports on its routes as well as all expected visibility conditions, including fog and sandstorms. The airline also has CAE full-motion simulators for its A310/A300 and Boeing 777 aircraft and a fixed-base system for its A310 training unit.

Behind the scenes

When reading about the controls and instruments of a particular aircraft, the reader expects to be given some information

F-22 simulator cockpit for training pilots in the use of the four electronic colour displays and the integrated control panel. Also visible are (left) the throttle levers and (right) the side mounted control column. The defence display on the left provides a plan view of air and ground threats. In the middle is the primary situation display showing tactical information, tracks, ground positions and aircraft's sensor search volume. Shape and colour of target icons depict threat identity, track quality and priority. On the right is the secondary attack display giving a plan view of air threats with their altitudes, missile launch-envelopes, weapon steering cues and missile-fly-out paths. The lower display covers stores management, engine and systems information and functions.

The integrated control panel at the top is the interface for the HUD. Two other electronic displays not included in the simulator are (left) for communication and navigation functions and (right) for standby flight instrumentation display. *Boeing*

A Boeing 747-400 full flight simulator for British Airways. *Thales*

simulator is designed to replicate as closely as possible the performance characteristics of a particular aircraft type. Analysis of the in-flight performance data of the real aircraft by a powerful digital computer provides the basis for a software program. Writing the programs that translate real flight data into simulated data is a major task. The number of parameters that have to be analysed and correlated runs into thousands. It is obviously not as simple as just arranging the software so that if the pilot advances the throttles the airspeed will increase and the airspeed indicator will show the increase. For example, the fuel flow rate will also increase, the fuel contents will decrease and many other instruments will also alter their indications, and each system will adopt a new datum. It is difficult to think of an element in an aircraft that ignores changes in others. A modern aircraft is a 'living' thing made up of many data systems and operating systems, each of which 'talks' in the electronic sense to each of the others. The software program can also integrate a simulator into a simulated air traffic control or air/ground war situation.

The moving base or platform has to be given six degrees of freedom of movement in order to simulate the effects of roll, pitch, yaw, fore-and-aft surge and heave. As much as possible, it has to impart attitudes and accelerations to the human senses that are interpreted in such a way that the pilot believes it is a real aircraft. The software provides the commands that make the simulator move in response to changes made either by the pilot or the flight-management

about the aircraft's configuration and essential features: for example, the type and number of engines and any interesting or unusual handling characteristics. In the case of the simulated cockpit, the reader will want to know something about the mechanism that plays the part of the real aircraft and how it is made to 'fly' in an artificial three-dimensional environment.

The descriptions of the techno-logy of civil and military-type flight simulators may be dealt with together. Essentially the moving-platform mechanisms and the image-generating technologies are similar. A flight

Airbus 320 simulated cockpit. All displays and controls are   represented. The apparent movement of the external scene and the flight deck provide a close replication of both the changes in the   visual scene and the motion sensations experienced in the real aircraft.   *Thales*

Compared with the Link trainer of 1929, a modern six-degrees of freedom of movement simulator is a massive machine. *Thales*

system to the control surfaces. The digital signals are converted to analogue electrical signals, which in turn are translated into movements of the hydraulic rams or electric-motor-driven legs that support the cockpit platform. The usual arrangement of 'legs' consists of six hydraulic rams arranged as three pairs, each forming a triangle whose apex carries the simulator platform. All six rams work together to make the platform roll, pitch, yaw, sway, surge or heave, or any combination of these.

Sounds, vibrations, and a real-world projection system are added to the moving-base structure containing a replica of the aircraft cockpit. The cockpit and its controls are often the 'real' thing and are readily available, whereas the signals that drive the instruments and the platform motion, and also provide feedback and 'feel' through the controls, have to be generated by software for the flight simulator's computer. One way of comparing the quality of different computers is to check the time taken to respond to a demand for a change in 'aircraft' attitude. The modern design goal is 100 milliseconds or less. A very important requirement for a simulator is that the visual scene representing a real world must not lag. In other words the subtle changes in the scene required must take place in less than 100 milliseconds. For the simulation of an extremely agile aircraft the lag must be even less.

No system is perfect and no human pilot is perfect. The flight simulator designer has to reconcile the two. Experienced pilots will comment that a particular simulator 'does not feel like the real thing', or 'the real aircraft does not fly the way the simulator indicated it would'.

Human senses

A particularly important relationship that must be correct in order to achieve maximum realism is that between the movement of the platform and the human senses. The non-visual human senses that detect movement respond to accelerations. The sensations of movement, or rather accelerations, induced by a simulator must be matched by the simulated display of the outside world. It so happens that the body usually detects movement before the eyes perceive changes to the world. The simulator must be designed so that the relationship between the pilot's physical and visual senses is accurately coordinated. Otherwise the illusion is shattered. In some of the earlier flight simulators the ideal coordination was not achieved and could induce nausea.

Acceleration

A motion platform can reproduce the initial accelerations of the real aircraft in all six degrees of freedom. But it cannot roll or loop through 360° or impose high and continuous G forces on the pilot. However, this limitation is overcome because a motion platform is essentially an acceleration device that produces only an initial acceleration (a 'kick') along a particular axis of motion. Once the kick has been imparted then the jack motion is 'washed out', that is slowed, and then reversed so as to reset the platform back to its neutral position ready for the next control action. This is done at a rate which is below that at which the pilot's vestibular apparatus responds to accelerations. This use of an onset acceleration input corresponds to the short-term effects experienced by the pilot when flying a real aircraft.

Platform pitch angles can be used to give pressure on the back to simulate acceleration or to give the sensation of being pressed forward into the harness during deceleration. These effects are obtained by driving the visual scene to the same pitch angle as the platform. For example, during take-off the platform could be pitched to, say,

20 degrees at a rate that remains undetected by the pilot's senses. At the same time the visual horizon is pitched up at the same rate. Because the seat is leaning back there is a continuous force on the pilot's back. As the visual scene has also moved in concert this force is sensed as a sustained longitudinal acceleration.

Visual simulation

As mentioned, the visual projection of the outside world is coordinated with the movements of the simulator platform. Under certain conditions of flight the visual scene does not follow the platform. If the simulator platform were left in the banked position the pilot would feel uncomfortable, as no centrifugal force would be keeping the body upright in the seat. Therefore the platform is levelled off, but the attitude displays and the image of the outside scene continues to show that the aircraft is still in a banked turn. If the physical effects of side slip are to be induced then the platform is tilted further to one side. However, the visual scene does not show the increased bank angle. In other words the system deliberately gives false information in order to simulate correctly.

In addition to inducing sensations of movement by altering the angles and attitudes of the platform, motion-sensation-inducing seats can be used. These have inflatable pads for applying pressure to the body. For example, inflating the pad against the pilot's back gives the sensation of acceleration. The harness can be tightened, thereby forcing the pilot downwards as if being subjected to positive G. There are many and 'devious' ways in which the simulator people can deceive.

A realistic image

The requirements for simulators intended for training pilots and other aircrew who operate fixed-wing or rotary-wing attack aircraft specify maximum arcs of view: 200° of simulated 'world' from left round to right simulate the 'over-the-shoulder' scanning pattern needed when searching for and attacking ground targets. Compared with early visual systems the current visual displays of the external scene are virtually seamless and allow the user freedom of eyepoint and wide arcs of view.

Another essential requirement is to make the external scene replicate as closely as possible the shapes and colours and textures of the ground and any buildings and of military equipment. The simulated external scene must be more authentic, for example,

Although the least interesting view of a simulator, this serves to show how the vision system screen is wrapped for 200° around the front of the cockpit. *Thales*

The simulated flight deck of an Airbus A320 with wrap-round visual display. *Thales*

than the scenery usually provided with some computer games. The latter is obviously artificial and therefore destroys the viewer's illusion of flying in a real world, particularly as, unlike the professional flight simulator, the view of the outside world is not collimated so as to appear at infinity. The optical system and the methods used to generate the external scene have been the subject of considerable research ever since the first true moving-flight simulators were developed.

The view ahead and to the sides has to be of a quality that matches the realism of the cockpit environment and the movements of the simulator platform. If it fails in this important respect the illusion is broken. The image generator element of a modern simulator projects a collimated view of the outside world through the visual display system. The design target for image generation and projection is a realistic three-dimensionally variable, all-types-of-weather scene outside the cockpit; along with dynamic representations of other aircraft and ground vehicles. The simulated world in which the aircraft is supposed to be flying has to change its aspect in real time. The generated image is refreshed at a rate of 30 Hz for a civil aircraft simulator. The rate is increased to 50 or 60 Hz (the frequency respectively of British and USA domestic power) for a combat simulator used for low-level flight training, because the pilot needs enhanced detail from which to acquire accurate visual information when attacking a target.

A typical visual scene system is the cross-cockpit collimated display. Projectors above the simulator cockpit project images onto an intermediate screen. The pilot cannot directly see this back-projected screen, but views its image in a large curved mirror positioned ahead of the cockpit windscreen. The vertical curvature of the mirror provides the collimation of the image so that to the pilot it is focused at infinity. The horizontal curvature of the mirror provides a seamless wide-angle view of the environment in which the simulator is 'flying'. Some simulators have their image generating systems integral with the motion platform, others have the image projection system separate from the platform, which reduces the dynamic loads on the jack legs.

Feeling the G

Fighter/attack aircraft pilots are subjected to psychological and physical stresses as they experience the extreme effects of flight: high-

G manoeuvring, including 360° rolling, pitching up to 90° and looping. These need to be reproduced in a simulator. However, by the very nature of accelerative forces the effects of G cannot be reproduced completely, even in a six-degrees-of-freedom simulator platform. The moving platform mechanism has mechanical limitations that limit the extent to which a rotary or linear movement can be sustained.

A typical G-simulating fighter/attack seat is a modified standard ejection seat. The seat pan is mounted on a parallel-motion mechanism operated by a hydraulic servo-actuator, which moves the up or down pan to give a harder or softer feel in proportion to the G signal. Another mechanism tightens or loosens the seat harness shoulder-straps. Even the comparatively mundane research task of the optimum positioning of controls in a cockpit benefits by testing under extreme environmental conditions such as high G.

Combat simulation

The cost and complexity of providing a simulated cockpit environment that can replicate all the manoeuvres and attitudes achievable with a real aircraft have so far set limits to realism. However, at less cost a fixed-base flight simulator can be acceptable for combat training because the visual information is more important than the full range of acceleration and attitude sensations. Therefore fixed-base fighter cockpits at the centre of a dome onto which are projected one or more target aircraft may be acceptable for air-to-air combat training. In the 1970s air forces started to make increasing use of combat 'dome' simulators in which two pilots could intercept and attack each other's aircraft. Air-to-air fighting using guns or missiles can be practised at a fraction of the cost of the USN's Top Gun 'academy' at which real aircraft engage in combat.

A typical example used for combat simulation was the twin-dome system introduced by BAE, Warton. Initially this was developed in the 1970s for evaluating the characteristic of different types of fighter/attack aircraft. At the time of the 1982 Falklands War the RAF used BAE's twin-dome simulator so that pilots could 'engage' Argentinian Mirage IIIs and determine the best tactics to be used. The flight characteristics and the weapons eventually selected for the

The simulated cockpit of an F-15 during the interception of two 'enemy' fighters. *Boeing*

Eurofighter/Typhoon were the results of 'flying' the aircraft in one dome against known and potential opponents in the other dome.

In this type of simulator each dome houses a cockpit and image projection system. Seated in the cockpits the pilots see the terrain and sky in different visibility conditions. The spatial reference provided by the scene moves in response to the manouvres demanded by each pilot. A typical 'dome' simulator provides the pilot's visual senses with apparently large angles of movement about all three axes. The projection system provides one or more 'enemy' aircraft. The computer works out in microseconds the very complicated mathematics needed to position and move a target on the inside of the dome relative to the control actions of the two pilots. Each dome can also be used individually and its aircraft flown against a target aircraft, or more than one aircraft, 'flown' by the computer. The comprehensive record of every flight provides a means of assessing pilot ability as well as highlighting mistakes that in real combat might be fatal.

The twin-dome combat simulators might seem at first sight to be just a very clever way for pilots to engage in aircraft-to-aircraft combat without leaving the ground. They can be used for that, but they have an even more important role to play. This is as a research and development tool. Their cockpits can be equipped to represent a number of different aircraft types so that, for example, a MiG-29 can fight it out with an F-18 or with the JSF. Realism is enhanced by a wide range of noise effects, the application of vibration and buffeting, seat-pressure variation, and dimming and blacking out of the visual scene when pulling high G.

To provide a projected visual scene that is highly detailed over the entire surface of a dome-type simulator is very expensive when it comes to computer power. One solution is

F-16 simulator cockpit mounted at the centre of a dome onto which are projected images of other aircraft. *Thales*

to have two image-projection systems. One is used to project a low-detail scene over the complete surface of the dome. The other projects a circular highly detailed scene of about one metre that is merged into the low-detail scene. The high-detail projector is arranged to follow exactly the pilot's point of regard, so that he or she assumes that all the dome's surface outside the periphery of their vision is also a high-definition scene. This is yet another example of the cunning of those who design simulators.

Research pilots can evaluate DVI and HUD, HMD, and RIS graphics and alphanumerics in different simulated flight conditions as part of the development of new types of display hardware. Analogous to a chess master playing a computer is the software-generated opponent that can be programmed to be more agile and more aggressive than any known aircraft type.

A simulator can be used for research into all aspect of military aircraft operation; including determining the optimum design of head-up, head-down and helmet-mounted displays. Direct voice input research and evaluation can be undertaken in simulated extreme environments of noise, vibration, G effects and all the other distractions of combat.

Blame the simulator

A complex legal situation might arise when the simulated performance of an aircraft does not match that of the real aircraft. For example, the certificated, placarded and demonstrated stalling speed of a real aircraft must apply also to its flight simulator, otherwise pilots might be led into a false sense of security. To avoid the latter a flight simulator is subjected to 'flight' trials by experienced test and line pilots. These evaluation and proving 'flights' are as thorough as those to which the real aircraft is subjected. This aspect also brings in the important overall philosophy of flight simulators that emphasizes that a simulator must not just be an example of clever technology for the sake of clever technology.

Flight simulators that fly

To the basic fixed-platform and moving-platform simulator types can be added those simulators that actually fly. In 1932 the RAF's Central Flying School installed a pilot's seat, instruments and controls within the fuselage of a Vickers Victoria twin-engined bomber/transport biplane. There were no windows from which to determine aircraft attitude. The object of the exercise was to determine the effects of sensations of movement and acceleration on a pilot when attempting to maintain control in zero

Twin dome air combat simulator complex. *BAE*

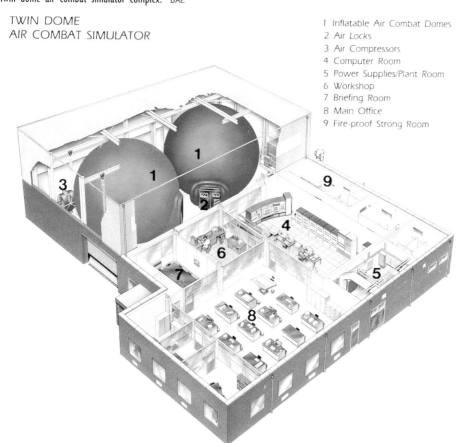

TWIN DOME
AIR COMBAT SIMULATOR

1 Inflatable Air Combat Domes
2 Air Locks
3 Air Compressors
4 Computer Room
5 Power Supplies/Plant Room
6 Workshop
7 Briefing Room
8 Main Office
9 Fire-proof Strong Room

visibility. It was also used to teach pupil pilots the effects and pitfalls of 'blind' flying. To add to the control problems of the pilot under test, the 'cockpit' faced aft. Because the sensations received were completely opposite to those usually experienced in flight, the importance of trusting the instruments and of ignoring what the aircraft seemed to be doing was emphasized.

There have been a number of aircraft types that have been modified so that the stability and response to the pilot's control inputs can be varied. The aircraft is thereby endowed with the flight characteristics of a completely different type. Using a real aircraft as the motion platform has many advantages, including a natural operating environment for the pilot, and there is no need for a simulated display of the real world. At the USAF Edwards Air Force Base in the USA a fully equipped cockpit simulator was added to a Convair C-131H to give the Avionic Systems Test Training Aircraft (ASTTA). The existing flight deck was retained for the use of the safety pilots, who at any time could 'pull the plug' on the test and experimental pilots. The windowless cabin housed the cockpit instruments and controls of an F-16, along with its side-stick controller for the fly-by-wire system. This allowed pilots to familiarize themselves with new, as yet unproved, avionics such as radar and infra-red target-acquisition and aiming systems. Another airborne flight simulator at Edwards was a modified Learjet whose flight characteristics could be changed by a variable-stability system. In 1966 the flight-control system of a Mirage III was modified so that test pilots could experience the handling characteristics of the supersonic Concorde.

In the 1970s Cranfield University in the UK operated a twin-engined Beagle Basset in this role. However, the Basset's performance and airframe limitations restricted the range of simulation. It was not possible to simulate

a high-performance agile jet fighter. Therefore Cranfield developed the Astra Hawk. This was a modified BAE Hawk high-performance trainer. Its flight-control system could be 'tuned' so that the aircraft's handling characteristics could be made to represent those of other aircraft types, ranging from a First World War biplane, through modern civil and military jets and on to variable geometry and modern super-agile fighters. The Astra Hawk provided a real pilot/aircraft environment that could be varied. It found a particular application at the Empire Test Pilots School (ETPS) at Boscombe Down. An ETPS student, of course already an experienced pilot, could fly a selected aircraft type, the control characteristics, feel and responses of which were very different from those of the standard Hawk. The ability to vary the control characteristics and response, as well as instrument display (ADI and HUD) dynamics, so as to mimic different types of aircraft, was one of the significant advantages over a ground-based simulator. A helicopter example of a 'flying simulator', whose control characteristics and performance can be changed, is a version of the Eurocopter EC 135. This is used to train pilots in flying a number of different helicopter types, including, for example, the twin-rotor Chinook.

Virtual reality

Present-day virtual reality systems require the user to wear sensors and effectors so that there is an interface with the computer-generated images, visual effects, sounds and other elements of the virtual environment. However, when we come to consider a virtual cockpit there are special problems. The virtual cockpit has to impart to the human body the effects of accelerations and G, and to achieve such perfection in simulation the body has to be able to receive signals that will affect the cardio-vascular system and other organs that provide the sensation of acceleration and G.

The virtual cockpit can provide images of the controls, and the pilot can 'see' images of his hands touching or holding the controls. It is important that each element of the virtual cockpit interface provides 'feel', particularly when this is essential for flying the real aircraft. The present technology available for the virtual cockpit requires equipment mounted on the pilot's body. This is contrary to the present concept of simulation – that attempts to 'deceive' the pilot into thinking that he or she is in the real thing. As a forceful advertisement for his invention, Link used to tell the story of the pilot who during a very stressful flight on instruments completely lost control, baled out and broke an ankle on the floor alongside the Link Trainer.

Simulating the Virtual

During the design and development of a new aircraft, a virtual version of the cockpit can be simulated by computer so that variations in detail can be assessed in relation to expected performance. Simulation includes computer-aided design, which enables design variations to be viewed at far less cost than building physical mock-ups. As the design process proceeds towards 'cutting metal', the cockpit or flight deck can be built as a simulator in which the test pilots can become familiar with the expected flight characteristics. The simulator cockpit also provides an essential tool in the total design process because the cockpit with its machine/human interface is a critical element. At one time in pre-computer design days the designers of the cockpit had to depend on wooden mock-ups in which to achieve the best positions for controls and instruments. They and the test pilots hoped that that they had got everything right before

the first flight took place. Today there is a near-seamless progress from CAD on to the completely simulated cockpit. Today both civil and military designers depend on simulators for achieving aircraft that will be operationally effective.

The future

In the future greater use will be made of the concept in which real aircraft and real sea and ground vehicles are linked to simulators. Integrating real elements of a tactical force with simulated elements can enhance training. Flight simulators integrated with real aircraft and with the real environment of a tactical situation provide the important familiarization of the way in which all tactical elements operate. By simulating all the elements of a sortie aircrews can be trained to react correctly to all the variations and complications of real warfare.

A similar integration can be used to familiarize pilots with operating civil aircraft within the air traffic control environment. It can also be used to verify in detail the operation of a projected new aircraft within both the airport and airways environments. Test pilots can operate the flight simulator of the proposed aircraft from start engines, through taxiing and take-off phases and on to climb-out, noise-abatement and ATC departure routeing, as was done during the development of Concorde. Flight simulators are proliferating to the mutual benefit of pilot training and research. By 2004 there were more than 900 in use by civil aviation alone, the majority of which had six axes of motion.

The future usually has one foot in the present. Today's computers, vastly larger in memory and speed than those of the twentieth century, along with virtual reality, head, body and seat effectors, presage a time when the massive 'six-legged' simulator might be consigned to a museum.

CHAPTER THIRTEEN

Cockpits of the Future

About every ten years there have been upward leaps on the curve of technical progress. Nevertheless, predicting the pace at which a particular technology will advance, such as the cockpit, is very difficult.

It is not easy to attempt to predict the extent to which the cockpit of the future will incorporate techniques that at present are only at the experimental stage. As it is, virtual reality and remote control in themselves are already two techniques that could directly affect the design of the future cockpit – the latter, of course, eliminating the need for a control and information interface. The extent to which automation, based on very intelligent computers, can simplify the interface is an important factor in the development of the cockpit of the future. We cannot try and predict an all-purpose cockpit for the future because there will be different specific operating environments and functions among future aircraft. The cockpit of a fighter/attack aircraft imposes a more extensive and demanding set of design problems than that of a civil aircraft.

The past has merged into the present and the future will emerge from the present. The boundaries are not sharply defined. The gestation period for new aircraft has increased every decade, from the time when a design went from drawing board to first flight within only a few weeks to our present five to ten years. Concorde, alas no longer with us, occupied about ten years of ideas, development and testing before it entered revenue service. The cockpit instruments were 1960s state of the technology. Despite the advances made in instrumentation, particularly the elimination of electro-mechanical types, Concorde retained much of its original set to the end. It was not possible for space, avionic and cost reasons to upgrade the flight deck by installing electronic displays.

Throughout any survey, such as this book, of the relationship between the human pilot and the aircraft, the contrasting abilities of the two form a background. In the future the interface between the human and the computer will become more 'transparent' to each other. At the beginning of this book human lateral influences were related to the design and operation of aircraft. Will those influences be relevant in the future cockpit interface? Many machines are controlled by touch and voice. However, although the modern keyboard or pad interface can be accessed by either hand, the majority are located to the right of the equipment on which they are mounted. Revolving doors and doors into rooms have their push-bar or handle on the right. The tools and appliances of the present world, requiring hand and arm movements, are still designed to suit the right-hand-preferring majority. As the cockpit of the future is likely to be a finger-touch, eye-movement and voice interface, large hand and arm movements may not be needed. Therefore human limb preferences may not be significant in the design of the cockpit. However, future pilots accustomed from birth to text and numerals arranged in order from left to right, may continue the trend to scan instruments and the real world from left to right. The present tendency to look first at the left field of view may be retained as a human preference.

The principal design target for the cockpit of the future is that of optimum interaction between pilot and aircraft. In other words, the aircraft's information systems must not only 'talk' to each other without ambiguity and loss of data, but must also clearly and precisely keep the human element of the cockpit aware fully of what is happening to the aircraft, both as a vehicle and as one element in a transport or military environment. There must be no opportunity for errors on the part of the pilot that are induced by the machine. In this respect the human pilot has to be considered in terms of bionics, and his or her mental and physical limitations and range of abilities must be matched to those of the aircraft.

At the beginning of this book reference was made to 'airmen' and 'chauffeurs'. For about the first sixty-five years of aviation the 'airmen' were in control. However, as automatic control systems and, later, computers became more reliable and effective, the 'airmen' qualities of the human component of the interface in high-performance aircraft tended to be neglected. Once it became possible to enter into the avionic systems the coordinates of a position in three-dimensional space along with time, by touching just a few keys, the very nature of the relationship between human and machine was set on the path towards the future. For the past forty years we have been able to make 'hands-off' approaches and landings and to navigate from waypoint to waypoint without touching the primary flight controls. This has encouraged a tendency toward the 'chauffeur', or manager, role of the human, with much of the airmanship devolved to intelligent automatic systems.

During the First World War and for the following six years, there was an upsurge in the number of instruments, equipment and weapon-aiming devices. But not much was done to improve instruments and provide pilots with guidance when attempting to navigate to a destination and effect a landing in fog or heavy rain. Between 1926 and 1936 increased aircraft performance, and attempts to make operations independent of the weather, forced the development of instruments for 'blind' flight. In this period the stepped-nose, side-by-side, partly or completely enclosed cockpit became the international standard for commercial aircraft.

Between 1955 and 1970, cockpits, both civil and military, started to include instruments and control panels that were no longer discrete or independent units but parts of systems. The successors to the electromechanical wartime air-and-ground-position indicators, the hyperbolic systems such as DECCA and the inertial navigation system (IN), gave the pilot an instantaneous position without the need for the time delay of pencil, chart and calculator. As for the number of seats on the flight decks of commercial aircraft, one by one the navigator, then the radio operator and finally the flight engineer were dispensed with as systems that could be directly accessed, selected and interpreted by two pilots increasingly became the standard. In fighter/attack aircraft the HUD not only introduced a 'pilot-friendly' means of aiming weapons but was essential for low-level strikes in poor visibility. HOTAS and later VTAS became important design principles for the fighter/attack cockpit.

After 1970, the microprocessor and the digital computer made even greater changes to the aircraft control interface. By 1985 avionic technology appeared to have reached a peak with AFMS, HMDs, voice-actuated systems, FLIR, LLTV and laser targeting. The number of acronyms now ran into thousands to match the proliferation of avionic systems directed at safety, efficiency and, for military aircraft, lethality.

Civil futures

The pace of future civil aircraft developments depends very much on the way in which electronic data and control systems develop over the next twenty years and on advances made in display technology. When Boeing studied its concept for a Mach 0.98 passenger aircraft, about the size of the 777, it had to decide between sticking with the familiar cockpit and taking a big leap forward in interface technology. The cockpits of the 747-400, 757, 767 and 777 have a 'common' set of instruments and controls. Boeing decided that with the 7E7 it would not perpetuate the 777 cockpit but advance to a new level by incorporating the most advanced fly-by-wire controls and display-screen technologies.

The rival to Boeing's bid to corner the civil aircraft market is Airbus, whose A380 gives us a look into the future. The cockpit has eight multi-function LCD screens. For the first time Airbus is providing the pilots with two interactive tracker balls as screen-pointing devices. These simplify the setting and selection of operating parameters. In addition Airbus aims to provide the crew with a 'paperless' cockpit by having a complete electronic library. The electronic displays can be accessed to show a vertical profile along the aircraft's track so as to give the pilots a pictorial representation of vertical hazards such as terrain above the current altitude. The A380 has a number of video cameras so that the crew can make external checks of the aircraft in flight and when taxiing assist in keeping to the optimum position relative to the dimensions of a taxiway. As with the Boeing future

aircraft, Airbus has opted for a number of individual multi-function AMLCDs, and has not decided on a 'big-picture' cockpit: possibly a question of 'safety in numbers'. The A380 cockpit is bigger than that of the A330 and the A340 but in general appearance is similar. Airbus is keeping to a 'common-cockpit' philosophy so that the instrumentation and the controls are nearly identical, except for the tracker balls, to those of the other aircraft in the Airbus family. This reduces the amount of type-specific training and helps with cross-crew qualification.

Situation Awareness

Enhancing situation awareness was an important requirement for the control interface in the cockpits of the twentieth century. In this new century it is of even greater importance because of the complexity and speed of a future flight. It will also be important because of the need to make the most effective use of what will be extremely costly aircraft. To lose an aircraft because the pilot was not fully aware of what was happening must be avoided. Together the cost of training the pilot and the cost of the aircraft are big items in any air force's budget. During the past seventy years the quantity and quality of information, in the form of instrument displays, has steadily improved. The improvements have been absolutely necessary in order that aircraft in general can achieve increased performance and versatility. In the last decade of the twentieth century the combination of the digital computer, data buses, electronic displays and electronic sensors gave us a virtually real view of the world outside the aircraft, irrespective of the quality of the visibility.

Workload and fatigue

The related subjects of workload and fatigue

have always occupied the attention of those concerned with safety. For the first forty years of aviation, research into pilot behaviour under stress was not given much priority. The endurance flights, such as the pioneering transatlantic and transpacific flights, were not scientifically analysed or reported on in relation to human behaviour or endurance. In the Second World War greater attention was paid to human performance under stress, and after the war air safety authorities started to impose flight-time-limitation regulations. Future air transport services are certain to include a large number of non-stop flights extending to more than 10,000 nautical miles; which at 500 knots cruising speed is twenty hours. In the last two decades of the twentieth century relief crews were being carried on some long-haul flights. For the future, proper rest compartments will be provided. They were already a feature of the long-range version of the Airbus 340.

Multi-vision

The future shape of the cockpit may depend on the extent to which direct vision of both the real world and of the aircraft itself is replaced by the indirect: by, for example, CCTV/FLIR. At extreme operating altitudes, such as those in which future aircraft may operate, cosmic radiation can be harmful to both crew and passengers and therefore will have to be closely monitored.

A multi-camera LLTV and FLIR system could, for example, provide omni-directional viewing when an aircraft is operating in proximity to the ground or other aircraft, friendly or otherwise. Aerodynamic considerations and protection against harmful radiation may mean that direct-vision transparencies for the human operator may not be practicable. A possible line of development is the variable-geometry cockpit, which can adapt to a particular

phase of flight. The civil Concorde was an early example of a 'two-phase' cockpit.

In 1995 NASA initiated a civil flight deck research programme, some of the results of which were also applicable to the military aircraft cockpit. A complete aircraft flight deck was enclosed within the fuselage of a Boeing 737. The test pilots controlled the aircraft in all phases of flight, including landing, using a closed circuit TV that provided a view ahead. A safety crew occupied the normal cockpit in the nose of the 737. The object of the test flights was to evaluate a cockpit having no direct external view of the real world outside the aircraft. Supersonic transports of the future are being developed with optimum nose shapes related to aerodynamic factors that may not permit the discontinuity of a windscreen

Pathway in the sky

Although the introduction of electronic displays in the 1970s and 1980s enabled a better integration on the part of the pilot of a number of discrete parameters, a mental image still had to be composed of the aircraft's position in three-dimensional space. One analogy of the problem is to imagine that the space volume around the aircraft is defined by a 3-D lattice. Each node of the lattice is defined by an alphanumeric symbol. The pilot has to assimilate a plethora of alphanumerics from the cockpit instruments and integrate them with the spatial coordinates along with the fourth dimension, time.

An important design target from the earliest years of flight instruments has been a pictorial representation of the earth's surface and the relevant position of the aircraft. An extension of this design target has been a 'highway in the sky' that indicates either the course to be flown or the instantaneous trajectory of the aircraft. Attempts to achieve such a system with electromechanical instrument technology were only partly successful. Attitude directors in the 1970s, for example, included symbols to indicate the control actions required to achieve a selected path, such as an approach to land using an ILS. With the advent of the digital computer and the all-electronic displays there was a significant step toward the 'highway in the sky'. However, even in its most advanced form the EADIs of the twentieth century did not give the pilot a bird's eye view of the terrain from which to determine instantaneously, and without recourse to other instruments, the aircraft's trajectory in relation to the optimum path in all three dimensions, and at the same time provide speed, height and attitude parameters at the sides of the display. The electronic HUD used in military aircraft from the mid-1960s went some way towards the 'highway in the sky' in that weapon-aiming information provided the pilot with weapon trajectory symbology.

In 1985 the cockpit of an F-14A was equipped with a three-dimensional graphic primary electronic flight display. This was an important step forward in improving the quality of the visual control interface. The primary design objective was to get away from the alphanumerics plus symbols of current instrumentation, particularly those of the primary flight displays.

During the 1980s new display technologies were developed. Some were derived from the work done by the simulator specialists. Representing the real world in a simulator by a gridded surface was one of the first steps toward simulated 'contact' flying. Eventually the grid became the 'wire frame' on to which were laid textures and features to present a simulated real world. This technology also embraced the 'highway in the sky' principle. A wire-frame 'tunnel' or a pathway could be presented as a guide to the simulator pilot when flying a selected track, approach or landing.

Both the electronic display designers and the simulator people came up with a similar idea. The former developed a display technology that made the pilot far less dependent on integrating the alphanumerics and symbols of the instrument displays with a mental image of where and what the aircraft was and what it was doing. The technology of the simulator world provided 3-D visualization of the world so that the pilot could manoeuvre the 'aircraft' so as to avoid hazardous terrain and obstacles. By integrating FLIR, LLTV and a photo-mapped terrain database the pilot was given a system from which could be selected a variable degree of the real and artificial view ahead on to which was overlaid a highway in the sky.

Fighting cockpits

The avionic and sensor systems of the future fighter/attack aircraft will provide 100 times, perhaps even more, information than those of the twentieth century. But the human element of the future is unlikely to have any increase in mental ability over that of today's aircrews. This fact introduces a particular key cockpit system requirement: namely, that any advances, such as computing power, in the information-control interface must recognize that the mental performance of the human component may not have increased to match the technology.

Therefore future fighter/attack cockpit design has to take account of the limited abilities, both physical and mental, of a human pilot. These abilities are limited and can vary in response to different levels of workload. When events occur at a rate greater than that to which the pilot can respond there is a serious problem. In practice the human mentally 'switches off' attention to some of the tasks. Then the performance of the overall control interface in the cockpit, of which the human is an integral part, will deteriorate.

To avoid overloading the pilot's abilities the interface has to be designed to present information to the pilot unambiguously and at the same time without cluttering up the visual task with 'not needed at the moment' information. The tactile elements in the cockpit must be designed for easy operation and accurate selection, even during extreme environmental conditions such as high-G. The loads imposed on the human pilot during combat in a high-agility fighter can preclude the use of the hands for tactile inputs, and therefore as many as possible of the aircraft's systems must have built-in intelligence so that they can operate for the greater part of the time automatically.

As with the cockpits of the twentieth century, the design of a future fighter/attack cockpit has to be based on the information and outputs of the control interface, of which the pilot is an integral part. The pilot can receive information from the real world seen through the transparent areas of the cockpit, from representation of the real world provided by instruments and display, and from aural signals and the physical sensations associated with aircraft movement and accelerations. The pilot's inputs to the aircraft as a weapon system include head and eye pointing, tactile selection and movements using hands and feet, as well as voice and, possibly, thoughts. The aerodynamic characteristics of future combat aircraft, particularly the agile high-performance types, may limit direct control by a human pilot even more than those of the twentieth century. The pilot, in the outer control loop, may be concerned only with simple commands such as 'start', 'go to', 'intercept X' and 'search for'.

Pilot's body equipment

Another important design factor, and one that came to prominence at the end of the twentieth century, is the proliferation of equipment 'mounted' on the pilot. Apart from helmet-mounted sights and communications equipment, the pilot is festooned with environmental protection and safety devices. Some of this equipment, of course, is there to provide protection in the event that the pilot has to eject. An important design target has to be a reduction in the amount and volume of equipment carried on the pilot's body. Although the comfort of flying in one's shirt-sleeves is not practicable, except in transport aircraft, nevertheless it provides a useful target at which to aim when designing flying-clothing, helmets and protection equipment.

Unusual cockpits

Both as a diversion and as part of serious studies, designers try out unusual aircraft configurations. Tailless, deltas, canards, lifting bodies, multi-bodies and other configurations form and merge on computer screens. It is predicted that engines will be developed able to produce many times their present thrust without an increase in size. These will provide enough thrust, without excessive fuel consumption, to raise or lower all types of aircraft vertically. Therefore, future manned aircraft will most likely include specialized types able to take off and land vertically, hover and move in any direction, not necessarily pointing in the same direction. This omni-directional ability is in conflict with the present convention that the pilot faces toward the front of an aircraft and is able to see directly over the generally forward arcs of vision. This suggests that all-round, including above and below, visual arcs will have to be provided using visual sensor electronics. These will present their visual information on the helmet visor or directly onto the pilot's retinas.

In 1966 the USAF changed its thinking from how many aircraft it would take to destroy one target, to how many targets could be destroyed by one aircraft. This philosophy affects directly the overall cockpit design requirements for the future fighter/attack aircraft. It emphasizes the required multi-role capability, which in turn leads to the complexity required for an aircraft able to take on, sometimes simultaneously, more than one target during a sortie. This complexity has a direct effect on the cockpit and its equipment. The air forces of the global powers are no longer interested in the unsophisticated aircraft. The present generation of fighter/attack aircraft is designed to participate in wars that are planned to be over within a few days – wars in which the maximum number of enemy targets are 'taken out' in the first day, and both airborne and ground resources of the enemy's air force are eliminated. Such a war scenario demands expensive and complex aircraft, which in turn demands the most efficient human-machine interface design possible in the cockpit.

Advanced visualization techniques based on virtual reality enable design progress to be monitored with fewer opportunities for mistakes. The cockpit, for example, can be visualized not just on a computer screen but through the visual input units worn by the designers. It can be viewed from any angle, and equipment can be moved around and conflicts instantly resolved. Using linked computer systems designers located remotely from each other can view and interact with a common visualization. They can individually move, insert or eliminate features. The ergonomists can virtually move the extremities and head of an anthropometric 'dummy' to check arcs of vision, reach and all aspects of the pilot's ergosphere. In fact, he or she can be the 'dummy'.

In the West the cockpits of the Eurofighter/Typhoon and the F-22 incorporate much of the thinking for the next two decades, and influence, therefore, the cockpit design of the Future Offensive Air System (FOAS) and the Joint Advanced Strike Technology (JAST) aircraft. The FOA is supposed to enter squadron service in about 2018. The RAF wants the FOA to retain its potential as a weapon system until at least 2050. Such a requirement places an onerous task on the designers. Systems and cockpit interface equipment will have to adapt easily to changes in the inevitable operational requirements. In the past, aircraft types that have started their service lives as, say, a high-altitude interceptor have had to be modified to take on the role of low-level attack. In the decades when such changes could be accommodated by a different version of the basic engine and a number of 'bolt-on' systems, an aircraft could be adapted comparatively easily to a new role. Even the cockpit and its interface usually needed only a few small changes, such as switches and weapon control and aiming systems to fit the new operational role. This often no longer applies because the systems of an aircraft form an integrated whole: change one thing and you change the lot.

HMD

There are many ways of presenting information to the pilot's eyes – HMDs, or retinal imaging systems (RISs), for example. Irrespective of the technology used, there are the overriding requirements of freedom of head movement and low weight. The conventional 'bone dome' is already an additional load on the pilot's neck muscles, particularly when subjected to high-G effects. Whatever form a helmet of the future takes it must help to maintain the wearer's consciousness, clarity of speech, and acuity of hearing and vision during the violent manoeuvres of an agile, 'point in any direction', fighter.

The HMD is likely to continue in the

COCKPITS OF THE FUTURE 303

future as the primary visual interface in the majority of fighter/attack cockpits. An HMD can present FLIR images and flight data and symbology similar to that of a HUD. The HMD can also be used with target designator and aiming. Such systems have to avoid overloading the pilot during critical phases of flight, such as when attacking a heavily defended ground target. It is also just as important to prevent a 'fixation' on the target display to the extent that the pilot is unaware that the aircraft is no longer keeping to the required trajectory or is too close to the ground. Once again, additional information has to be displayed, such as ground proximity warning. Because a target-designator system may not be pointing directly along the aircraft's flight path an additional display on the HUD or HMD is needed to show the pilot the relative bearing of the target.

As noted in an earlier chapter, HMD-pointing with DVI has been demonstrated as a non-tactile, i.e. without the use of the pilot's extremities, method of controlling an aircraft's weapon system. This has been achieved without the need for the pilot to keep the head in one position. The pilot looks at a position in three-dimensional space and confirms that what he or she is looking at is the desired position or target to which the aircraft must be directed. The key to all this is the computer, which is able to sense eye movements. Eventually, the present technologies will be advanced to a level at which the computer systems detect eye-pointing movements and smoothly control the aircraft without subjecting it to unacceptably excessive G loads. This is, after all, only an extension of the system whereby the pilot controls the aircraft using hands and feet in response to 'director' symbology on the HUD or HMD, or even on the RIS. However, it is a case of 'possible' rather then 'when' before direct control by eye-pointing is perfected, because the accurate measurement of eye position is a very difficult task compared with detecting head position.

Thrust integrated with flight control

The designs for agile, variable-geometry STOVL fighters, with dirigible nozzles, studied in the 1990s posed the question of how many primary flight and thrust control levers should be provided. For example, the Harrier AV-8B has three primary inceptors: longitudinal thrust (throttle), thrust vector (nozzle position lever) and the three-axis central control-stick. (An 'inceptor' is a term used for describing an input device, such as a lever, used by a pilot to control a system.) A UK research programme studied three different methods of controlling a STOVL. One was a two-inceptor system – one for longitudinal velocity and the other for flight path control. The left hand controlled longitudinal velocity. Although it acted like a throttle it did not directly control engine thrust because engine power needed to be high during hover as well as at wing-borne, high-speed flight. At the lower end of the speed range the left-hand inceptor controlled ground speed and then blended into acting as a conventional throttle as the aircraft accelerated away from the hover mode. Another system studied was a one-inceptor system that had a thumb-wheel at the top of the stick for longitudinal velocity.

Super-agility

Mention has been made of aircraft, such as the 'Cobra' with thrust vectoring that enables them to be flown at extreme angles of attack, at an angle to the horizontal flight path, and to perform super-agile manoeuvres. In 1994 a modified F-16D gave a window onto flight control in the twenty-first century. Thrust vectoring was simultaneously controlled by the digital engine-control system and the flight-control system. No longer were the primary flight controls of roll, yaw and pitch operated independently of thrust control. The F-16D took the 1960s-generation Harrier-type vectoring thrust control a significant way forward and showed the way in which fighter/attack controls will develop. The new concept required additional controls in the cockpit. Extra switches were added to the basic HOTAS layout. These enabled the pilot to vary the rate at which pitch, roll and yaw control was exercised. The angle-of-attack (Alpha) display on the HUD was expanded to match the aircraft's ability to achieve extreme angles.

Full-authority DVI?

DVI is already used for some commands and questions. It is envisaged that DVI could be used for aerodynamic/thrust control. Control about the three axes of roll, pitch and yaw as well as thrust vectoring requires coordination, whether by a computer or by a human pilot. It is a task in which information from a number of sensors, either artificial or human, is processed and acted upon simultaneously to provide the desired integrated control of the aircraft's movements. 'Simultaneously' is the key word. DVI has the disadvantage that commands, such as 'Roll 15 degrees left and dive 10 degrees' is a mouthful that takes far too long compared with the reaction times of the sensory and nervous systems of man or computer; even the former can react in hundredths of a second. The above voice command takes at least five seconds That may be acceptable for a slow-responding big transport aircraft, but not for an agile fighter/attack aircraft.

Voice commands are serial inputs of data. One word has to follow another, in the correct sequence and using an agreed syntax. This type of control input on the part of the pilot takes seconds for which there may be no

time in an air-fight because events occur and change in milliseconds.

Head control

Using head movement to control pitch, yaw and roll is a concept introduced in the 1960s by Melville Jones and others. Although there are few electromechanical or electronic problems in devising such a system, there may be limitations. One disadvantage would be the need to restrain the pilot's head in such a way that the only head movements allowed would be those for controlling the aircraft's trajectory. It would be most unwise to predict that 'head' control will never be used. However, the present trend is towards the development of combined head and eye movements for 'pointing' to desired ground features, targets and elements of the cockpit interface.

The 'big picture'

The modern man-machine interface in combat aircraft is an integration of touch-screen, DVI, VTAS and HMD. Depending on the current environmental conditions and operating mode, each technique contributes to good situation awareness, reduced workload and combat effectiveness. However, one cockpit technology developed in the 1970s has not so far proved popular. This is the 'big-picture' display that fills the front of the cockpit from just above the pilot's legs to the top of the windscreen. Information is presented in graphical format to give a 3-D view of the aircraft in its operating environment. Such a display combines a view of the real world with all the 'head-down' information and with HUD and HMD inputs to the pilot. Some would argue that for a military aircraft the 'big picture' could be vulnerable in combat and that the all-in-one concept could be compromised by the need to have standby controls and instruments. One answer to that might be found with the philosophy behind the single side-stick control available to only one of the pilot's hands. In the event of injury to the right hand the pilot would more than likely have to eject. The same might apply to the big picture. If it were damaged then the pilot might have to abandon the aircraft. It may be used in the future, but only when there is no longer a question about putting all the information eggs in one basket. However, technology and operational requirement changes can outpace the production of this book, and the 'big picture' may be in use next week.

Synthetic vision systems

Combining the HUD's view of the real world with that of a virtual world generated by external vision sensors is also applicable to civil aircraft. In the 1990s Martin Marietta developed its Autonomous Precision Approach and Landing System. This was radar based, and used a radar/terrain matching system, derived from the guidance system used in cruise missiles.

Technologies available for the future include terrain-matching radar and virtual approach and runway lighting systems from images pre-stored in the aircraft's database. These are projected in the right place on the HUD combiner glass. The aircraft's instantaneous position is continuously derived from IN/GPS. This technology is applicable to both military and civil aircraft. For the pilot of a transport aircraft making an approach to an airport surrounded by hazards and obscured by Cat III visibility conditions, such a system provides both safety and regularity of flight operations. During an approach the pilot will follow an electronically generated 'path-in-the-sky' image. This will lead to a virtual image of the approach lights. Closer to touch-down the artificial world will merge into that of the real world. This technology is particularly applicable to regional airlines and commuter operators using those airports that are not equipped with ILS or even with approach lighting.

A real or a virtual world?

Increasingly we are being faced with the possibility of abandoning our present convention that the pilot's vision, directly or indirectly, of the world outside is from an eyepoint within the aircraft. A remote eyepoint, or 'fly-on-the-wall', position may be preferable. The fighter/attack cockpit of the future, say for the year 2020, may be designed primarily around the concept of the virtual world. This is a cockpit in which all information is synthetic in origin and computer generated. The pilot will derive an entire view of the outside world from an image of database information and from electronic sensors such as radar, TV, and IR. The electronic sensors combined with powerful computers can provide the pilot with an enhanced view of what is going on both inside and outside the cockpit. The pilot's arcs of vision will no longer be limited; views directly astern or underneath the aircraft will be available.

A key feature of the virtual-world cockpit is the pilot's helmet visor. This becomes the primary visual-information display. Information gathered and processed from FLIR, LLTV, GPS, inertial navigation systems and the databases of the aircraft's computers will be projected onto the pilot's visor or, as mentioned, directly onto the retinas of the eyes, using RIS. It will need far more research before the answer is known. A virtual-world system eliminates the need for conventional fenestration. This has three major advantages: firstly, it simplifies the design of the cockpit; secondly, it protects the pilot against adverse radiation such as laser beams; and thirdly, it avoids the aerodynamic penalty of a cockpit whose shape usually interrupts the ideal aerodynamic lines of an aircraft and is a surface whose geometry may not be in accord with the requirements of stealth.

Future research

Those charged with thinking about future aircraft have to think as far ahead as they can. For example, the USAF has had a series of 'future' programmes projected thirty years ahead. In the USA there have always been a number of 'black' projects. Among the more important goals of the 'black' projects are the hypersonic (Mach 5 to 25) aircraft. Aircraft within this category have to perform both as present 'conventional' types and as spacecraft able to orbit the earth.

What can be predicted with some certainty, based on present technology, is the greater use of aircraft having no human crew, and therefore the cockpit, as we now know it for military aircraft, may be consigned to history. We already have pilotless aircraft and cruise missiles, whose computers are programmed and updated throughout their flight by electronic reference to topographical features. They are certain to be used in future wars so as to avoid the loss of human pilots, expensive to train and expensive to protect. Remotely controlled surveillance aircraft, drones, are increasingly in use. The design of a remote control position also requires attention to detail and to achieving an efficient and effective control interface. However, the absence of complex health and safety systems for the human operator significantly reduces the number of design problems. And the designer can programme the controlled vehicle to perform agile manoeuvres at 10 G or higher. The design of the control interface for an Unoccupied Aerial Vehicle (UAV) presents few problems compared with the physiological and psychological considerations of a manned aircraft cockpit.

Although a simplistic concept, a remote operator cannot endanger his or her life either by carelessness or a 'do or die' attitude when controlling a UAV that may be thousands of miles away. However, consideration has to be given to the way in which a human operator, i.e. 'pilot', at the control station reacts to events that involve real human beings on the ground or in the air. Obviously they must not treat it as if it were an arcade computer game.

Artificial intelligence

An embarrassment of information riches confronted aircrews in the past three decades. Too much information increased, instead of decreasing, workload – possibly a case of having more data but less knowledge. With so much information generated both by an aircraft's own systems and by sensors of information external to an aircraft, a pilot could be confused and unable to sort out the necessary from the unnecessary. The key factor, particularly in the military combat aircraft cockpit, is that of time. Given plenty of time and a pencil and paper the pilot can sort out and allocate priorities among many items of information.

The 'need to know' is one criterion for discriminating among different data. Another is 'knowing is not much good if nothing can be done about it'. The first encourages the design of the 'black' cockpit in which information is only displayed or announced for those systems which are relevant to a particular phase of flight and have failed or are about to fail. A mass of green lights and a string of verbal 'OK's do not enhance situation awareness. To compensate for the difference in performance between the system and the human, the latter can be helped by simplifying individual tasks and by providing unambiguous and easily assimilable information displays, by uncomplicated controls and by greater use of automatic systems and artificial intelligence (AI).

In the 1970s the 'pilot associate' concept was debated. At the time, it was seen as the answer to a number of interface problems, particularly those involving the different abilities of the human and the machine. Taken to the limit of programming and versatility, the pilot-associate computer becomes the 'pilot' of an unoccupied aerial vehicle.

AI is certain to find even greater application in the future for both civil and military cockpits. In its most advanced concept it is a computer that acts as an assistant pilot. The 'AI' pilot associate alerts and advises the human pilot about the best of a number of available options following aircraft problems or changes to the tactical situation. The AI system's software, the knowledge base, is constructed from many different people's experiences. As many as possible of the different aircraft operating situations are analysed. Each is subjected to the collective knowledge of pilots, engineers and tacticians. The knowledge base of the AI can be constantly updated. For example, during each aircraft sortie the AI system stores each of the pilot's decisions. The successful or most appropriate are used to reinforce the knowledge base. Any wrong decisions or actions are also noted.

Therefore the AI system figuratively sits beside the pilot and provides instant answers to complex problems as they arise. It works in parallel with other aircraft systems that have a degree of AI. For example, systems such as an electrical power-management system (EPMS) use a form of AI to react instantly to events, such as the loss of electrical power following damage, by switching electrical loads without the intervention of the human crew.

With AI as a foundation, mission management systems (MMSs) have been developed that focus the pilot's attention on what is essential to know about at any particular moment or phase of flight. The EPMS, referred to above, is an example of a system within a hierarchy of intelligent vehicle-management system (IVMS) elements. IVMS points the way towards many aircraft systems for the future, and particularly those that interface with a human crew. Another element is the central warning system (CWS), which sorts, weights and presents warnings and advice in such as way as to avoid increasing pilot workload.

The relationship between the human and the computer depends on two simple precepts: mankind is a thinking machine able to process a number of different situations virtually simultaneously, and to think about a number of possible courses of action at the same time. In contrast the computer, although it too can operate on millions of bits of information in microseconds, nevertheless has to be programmed to do so. The human pilot instinctively, and not necessarily trained to do so, can predict the likely outcome of a number of possible courses of action. Programming a computer to the same wide-ranging assessment of a situation will present a challenge. It is a big step from a computer that reads out a take-off check list and moves to the next item on receiving the correct vocal response, to one that can advise a course of action following a complicated set of events involving loss of thrust, fire, unexpected weather and visibility conditions and closure of airfields.

Together the human and the computer make up a formidable team. Individually and alone, they are two different types of thinking machine. The machine brains can already match that of a chess master. Introducing the chess-playing computer into the subject of the future cockpit leads to the subject of common sense for the pilot associate. Since the advent of the electronic computer, one of the benchmarks of its ability has been that of playing chess.

Unfortunately this could be a misleading goal or attribute. Particularly when we come to consider the pilot-associate concept using artificial intelligence and knowledge-based systems. The argument for this goes something like this: Surely, if an AI system can play at a high level of competence against a chess master then it must also be capable of assimilating and acting upon a knowledge base for managing the progress of an aircraft from take-off to touch-down? But this argument neglects the need for sense even if the system is intelligent. The difference between the attributes of intelligence and sense is significant; even in humans. However quickly, and by quickly we mean millions of operations per second (MIPS), a computer can absorb and process data, its ability to make reasoned judgements, choices or decisions are confined to its knowledge base. This base is, of course, completely dependent on the extent and accuracy of the data fed into it by a human operator. Once again 'rubbish in, rubbish out' applies. Thus, when playing chess there are a limited number of pieces, clearly defined rules relating to the movements of the pieces and a mathematically limited number of strategies. Above all, the goal, that of winning, is not necessarily unambiguously defined.

On the other hand, if we widen the operating envelope, for example, by programming the 'chess' computer to play backgammon simultaneously, then the software-writing task becomes more difficult. If we go further in pushing the original 'chess' computer to embrace perception of objects and their dynamics as well as verbal statements, then the operating 'world' is expanded vastly and in consequence the harder it is for the computer to make reasoned judgements, even if it is very intelligent. Unless we are able to endow a computer-based system, such as a pilot associate, with sufficient knowledge to deal with all the nuances, combinations of events and operating parameters, the system has to be limited in the extent to which it can intervene in the control process. Fortunately, we can get by with a pilot-associate system that is limited to a specific operating 'world' and one whose boundaries are clearly defined. Nevertheless, it is important to realize that sometime in the future such systems will benefit from computers that can exercise 'common sense' and a high level of intelligence. The relationship with the human pilot will be one that optimizes aircraft safety, navigation and economy. Safety as a goal is self-evident, and navigation is the efficient conduct of the aircraft about its ways, applicable to both civil and military aircraft.

To construct heuristic principles for problem solving to emulate the processes of the human brain assumes that we understand accurately the ways in which our brains process information and conceptualize. As we cannot be sure about this, computers comparable in ability to the human brain may still be some way off in the future.

Flocks of birds

An essential component of a future aircraft, civil or military, will be an AI system that prevents collisions by monitoring all hazards, be they airborne or on the ground. This will keep a grain or envelope of space around each aircraft. The model for such a system is a flock of birds that wheels, dives and soars; with each bird acting in concert with all the others and not colliding. Humans also exhibit a similar shared brain, as evidenced in a crowded city, when people move in potentially conflicting directions but rarely collide. This 'flock brain' concept will be an extension of current development towards an ATC system that allows aircraft to move freely in three-dimensional space and not necessarily have to keep to defined airways. An individual military aircraft's AI system will link with the AI systems of other aircraft in a formation so as to act in the same way as the shared 'brain' of a flock. The two-seater version of the JS-39 has been designed so that the pilot in the rear cockpit can act as the tactical commander of a formation of other Gripens, as well as UAVs. Controlling more than one UAV at a time can be simplified if the 'flock' control principle is available.

Thinking about control

Experiments have already been conducted that verify, albeit crudely, the basic principles. In 1996, for example, a severely paralysed man had electrodes implanted into the motor cortex of his brain. The detected brain signals were connected to a computer so that the patient could move the cursor and select functions. An alternative approach to thought control, investigated at the same time, used a finger-stall sensor of the wearer's thoughts. This detected brain signals transmitted through the skin.

By implanting hundreds of electrodes into the brain of a Macaque monkey, scientists have been able to 'pick off' the thought signals that control the animal's muscles. Each electrode is no thicker than a human hair. When the monkey thinks about certain arm movements the signals are transmitted to a robotic arm. This moves in accord with the movement of the monkey's arm and hand, which in turn moves a joystick. The monkey soon learnt that it did not have to move its arm to move the joystick. It only had to think about the way in which it wanted the joystick to move. This important research was directed primarily at providing mobility to people who suffer paralysis of the limbs. The basic aim of the research is to find out how the human brain controls movement, and to apply the results to controlling devices by thought alone.

When control of an aircraft by using the pilot's brain signals was first investigated in the early 1980s, the USAF was sceptical. It pointed out that a pilot could move a switch or press a button almost as quickly as thinking about the action. A few thousandths of a second might be saved, but was that worth the millions of dollars' research needed to perfect a safe and effective system? However, the Air Force did not give up, and fifteen years later it announced that it was still investigating the use of brain-actuated control technology as a possible way of controlling an aircraft. Test pilots at Wright Patterson made simple control inputs into a flight simulator using only the power of thought. An interesting outcome of the research programme was the realization that the pilots could not describe exactly what they were trying to do. They described their experiences as if they were learning to walk. After a time they no longer had to think about what they were doing.

The experiments at Wright Patterson are not being rushed towards the operating of the primary flight controls by thought. The first step is to limit such control to non-critical functions, and particularly for reducing workload. For example, when the pilot is busy moving, touching or pressing the controls and selector switches and keys, it would be useful just to have to think, 'I'd like to see the fuel status display on the primary display.'

From these research programmes will come thought-control technology for aircraft. The usual question is, of course, 'When?' But the drive towards enhancing human performance, particularly for the disabled and impaired, is a strong one, and therefore thought control in aircraft may come sooner than we might predict.

Possibly in two or three generations of aircraft ahead, i.e. about thirty years, thought control might be a fully fledged science. Even though the aircraft control computers can be programmed to reject all but the acceptable commands, so as to eliminate catastrophic thoughts, this still imposes a fearsome discipline on the part of the human pilot. If, as may happen, thought control is perfected, it may be so constrained in application that it will not be worth the effort. When and if it is adopted as the primary human contact with the machine, the cockpit, as we now know it, will no longer be the same. Thought control is a technique that is going to need a lot more development before we can be certain of the role it might perform in the control interface.

Future technologies

The cockpit of the future will certainly include a greater use of DVI. In combat aircraft, combined head and eye pointing, using HMD or RIS, will be used for controlling the aircraft as a weapon system and as a means of indicating to the computer systems the direction in which the weapon system is to be pointed. Again the computers will eliminate any ambiguous or dangerous inputs. Eye pointing is also important in those aircraft that are able to point the nose or weapon system at an angle to the aircraft's trajectory. For example, future attack aircraft will be able to 'crab' along a line that is at an angle to the direct line to the target. Sometime in the future an additional control panel may be installed through which the pilot can command the aircraft to change its body shape while in flight. Another control might allow the pilot to command a 'chameleon' change to the overall appearance of the aircraft so that it would be difficult to detect visually.

In the future, for both civil and military aircraft there will be a greater integration of the pilot into the total computer system. Scientists are continually trying to find new ways of merging man and machine using artificial intelligence systems. The future may include 'plug-in' pilots that act as another computer but have no tactile link with the aircraft. They will be required to think but not touch. Thought control is an attractive idea for the cockpit because it greatly simplifies the interface. It might even replace the need for DVI. A pilot will be that part of the aircraft that at the end of a flight unplugs itself and walks away. However, irrespective of the degree to which automatic 'intelligent' systems are applied to aircraft of the future, they are likely to remain very dependent on the human pilot. Human intelligence and the ability to decide on priorities and to cope with sudden emergencies are significant reasons for retaining the human pilot.

Left and right

What of the hand and side preferences and influences discussed in this book? Will they still be factors to be considered in the future? We have already entered an era in which we no longer look back at equestrian practices and agricultural machinery, and therefore hand and side preferences will no longer be of importance. However, alphanumerics will still be read from left to right, and pilots may still tend to scan the interface and the real world from left to right.

Postscript

1.04.2030 at 1030Z: the chief cabin attendant on Flight XA 100 is busy with hurrying along the rest of the cabin crew who are getting the food carts ready. She makes one of her frequent and virtually automatic glances at the aircraft-status display panel. Its alphanumerics confirm that they are on time and on track and that all systems are functioning. She moves forward between the rows of passengers and at the forward bulkhead turns to supervise the feeding of the three hundred.

The bulkhead is smooth. There is no door. Only five years earlier there had been a door. Even though it could only be opened from the other side, there were other members of the crew, the pilots, in the 'sharp end' of the aircraft. Now the once traditional two-pilot crew up front is a thousand miles away and 30,000 feet below. They are on the ground monitoring the computer that is 'flying' the aircraft. At the same time the computer is also 'flying' other aircraft.

Fully automatic flight with complete and only control from a ground station is a well-established technology for military aircraft. Not only can unmanned aircraft and missiles fly a complicated route, they have a 'brain' that enables them to follow ground features and identify a pre-programmed target.

Despite the undoubted advances in technology related to pilotless flying machines, when it comes to carrying passengers there was and is much argument against the idea. Essentially the obvious question is, 'What happens if something goes wrong?' The supporters of the pilotless machine base their arguments on the extremely low probability that something might go wrong. Civil aircraft have for many years been designed in such a way that they could survive quite serious failures. Everyone involved in the aircraft industry and the operation of aircraft applies standards and working practices aimed at avoiding more than one accident, for example, in a million landings. Therefore there is a body of statistical data derived from many years of aircraft operation and millions of flights arrayed against the very understandable human reluctance to trust a machine rather than a human being.

However, despite the multiple path systems intended to give a 99.99999 per cent level of reliability of an aircraft's structure and systems, the 'doubtful' link is the radio link between ground and aircraft. This has to be immune to sabotage, both physically and electronically, and above all it must not be affected by nature's own electrical and electronic phenomena. Security of a flight during, for example, a severe electrical storm must be assured by the ability of the aircraft's onboard computer systems to ignore corrupted and spurious signals. A train or ship or even a road vehicle having no human 'pilot' is in certain circumstances acceptable, because none of these can 'fall out of the sky'. In other words most of their failures can be survivable, 'soft' failures.

Therefore, irrespective of the merits or demerits of a passenger aircraft operated by a 'pilot' located somewhere on the ground, the vital question is to what extent control, and in particular remedial action, can be exercised in the event of a sudden emergency. For the first two decades of the twenty-first century designers and certificating authorities will wrestle with the conflicting demands of safety, human nature, public perception and the economics of aircraft operation. The last factor can have significant weight, because without a human crew there is no need for a cockpit along with its heavy structure and equipment, as well as its incursion into revenue space.

And, of course, the cockpitless transports will not be alone in the sky, because there will be utility helicopters as well as the remotely controlled flying machines of the air forces. All will be competing for space in the air. As already mentioned, it is envisaged that every aerial vehicle will have an envelope or grain of air space, generated electronically, which other craft cannot penetrate.

Chapter Notes

Chapter One
McFarland, M.W., The Papers of Orville and Wilbur Wright, McGraw Hill, 1953
Ibid.
Gibbs-Smith, C.H., The Aeroplane: An Historical Survey, HMSO, 1960

Chapter Two
Yeates, V.M., Winged Victory, Jonathan Cape, 1932
Williams, Neil, On Gossamer Wings, Flight International, 9 January 1975
Grinnell-Milne, D., Wind in the Wires, Hurst & Blackett, 1933
TNA, AIR 1/756/204/4/91
Haslam, Gp Capt Rev. J.A.G., RFC and RAF Cooperation With The Meteorological Service 1914-1939,
        Cambridge University Press

Chapter Three
Lindbergh, C., Spirit of St Louis
Flight, 8 July 1932
Ogilvy, D., DH 88, Airlife, 1984

Chapter Four
Templewood, Viscount, Empire of the Air, Collins, 1957
Correspondence with Gp Capt Rev. J.A.G. Haslam
Coombs, L.F.E., The Lion Has Wings, Airlife, 1997, p. 59

Chapter Five
Flight, 13 December 1945
Hendrie, A., Lockheed Hudson in the Second World War, Airlife, 1999
Price, A. (ed.), The Spitfire Story, Arms & Armour, 1995
Melville-Jones, RAeS Journal, Vol. 72, p. 835 et seq.
Currie, J., Mosquito Victory, Goodall Publications, 1983, and Rawnsley, C.F. & Wright, R., Night Fighter,
        Collins, 1957
Letter from Dr Norman Anderson
Flint, P., Dowding and HQ Fighter Command, Airlife, 1996, p. 142

Chapter Seven
O'Rourke, G.G., Proceedings US Navy Institute, June 1966, p. 23
Chapanis, A., Research Techniques in Human Engineering, Johns Hopkins ed., 1965, p. 61
Wooldridge, E.T., Into The Jet Age, Naval Institute Press, 1995, p. xix
Woolridge, p 51
Correspondence with Capt E.M. Brown, RN

Chapter Ten
Newman & Greeley, Cockpit Displays: Test and Evaluation, Ashgate (ISBN 0 7546 1549 9), 2001, p. 54

Chapter Twelve
Rolfe, J.M. & Staples, K.J., Flight Simulation, CUP, 1994
Rolfe, J.M. & Bolton, M., Flight Simulation in the Royal Air Force in the Second World War, RAeS, 1988
Rolfe, J.M., 'Training Effectiveness of Flight Simulators', Applied Ergonomics, December 1982
Newman & Greeley, Cockpit Displays: Test and Evaluation: 2001, Ashgate (ISBN 0 7546 1549 9)
Robson, D., Human Performance and Limitations for the Professional Pilot, Airlife, 2001
        (ISBN 1 84037 332 6)
Strachan, I.W., 'Simulation and Training Systems', Janes's Defence Weekly

Appendix

The rule of the road

From the procedure for mounting a horse governed by the sword and scabbard we can find a key point for the evolution of rules of the road for vehicles, and this can be extended to apply to the traditions and rules for the conduct of aircraft. The practice of mounting a horse on the left, 'nearside', may have been one of the origins of the keep-left rule of the highway. When grooms led a horse to the door or gate of a house, the tendency would have been to position the animal with its left (nearside) side to the side of the road. From this it follows that the rider, once mounted and intending to move off in the direction to which his horse is already facing, is on the left-hand side of the road and would tend to keep to that side. If the journey were to the right it is possible that in pulling the horse's head to the right and turning it to face the opposite direction the majority finished the turn on the other side of the road: in other words the left-hand side in the direction of travel.

This would be reinforced by the natural tendency to keep the sword-arm opposed to the sword-arms of travellers approaching from the opposite direction, so that, as with motorists in the UK, the British ex-colonies, Australasia and Japan today, they passed sword-arm to sword-arm. This practice was reinforced in mediaeval Europe by Papal ordinances requiring travellers to keep to the left of a path so as to be in the best position to defend themselves from travellers coming the other way.

Another possible influence comes from the practice of postilions riding the left-hand horse of a pair. As they were to the left they would tend to keep the equipage close to that side of the road when avoiding opposing traffic. Of most significance is the influence of the right-hand preference that required the driver of a team of horses to sit to the right of his vehicle so as to leave his whip-wielding arm free.

The earliest enactment concerning the side of the road on which traffic should move in Britain is an Act of Parliament of 1754, which ruled that traffic should keep to the left when crossing London Bridge. The earliest statute applying to all roads in England and Wales, but not Scotland, is the Highways Act of 1835. In Scotland there were earlier ordinances. All these rules referred to the keep-left requirement because in general wheeled traffic kept to the left for the reasons already outlined.

Before Napoleonic influences spread over the greater part of Europe at the end of the eighteenth century, a combination of tradition and Papal ordinances dictated a keep left-rule of the road. After 1800 the Napoleonic administration changed Europe over to the right. There are at least two possible reasons for this: Napoleon is said to have gained a tactical advantage by reversing the 'knightly' conduct of war that required opposing forces to lead with the left flank; and secondly, 'keep-to-the-right' may have simplified the passing of teams of horses drawing wagons and guns because their postilions would pass man to man.

The custom of leading a draught animal by walking at its left side carried over to North America in the second half of the eighteenth century. The teamster of a span of oxen hauling the giant Conestoga freight wagons sometimes had a 'lazy-board' on the left protruding outwards from the side of the wagon on which he could sit. On meeting a team coming towards him he kept over to the right of the trail as they passed. This practice was endorsed by successive state legislations of the nascent USA when forming rules of the road.

Rules at sea

The control practices of the sailing ship evolved for 3,000 years, and considering, by present-day standards, the crudity of this control, a considerable degree of skill was achieved. Right-side dominance governed the position of the steering-board, from which is derived the nautical terminology for left side and right side and, possibly, the rule of the road. The last, as will be discussed, can only be a possibility, and not a positive fact having any influence on subsequent practices, because from the fourteenth century onwards the steering-board was replaced progressively by a centrally positioned rudder. This removes a convenient line of reasoning, which could have taken us from the steering-board to the formulation of keep-to-the-right rules as sea traffic increased, particularly inshore and in estuaries. However, right-side preference, or preference of the right hand, appears to have influenced sea traditions and customs, though much of the evidence relating to this subject is not supported by conclusive facts. There are many interesting anecdotes and references to side precedence, but few people are able to state positively the reason why. All that can be discerned is a tendency, when there may have been an equal choice between left and right, to designate by habit, tradition, custom, or even regulation, the right-hand position as the superior.

At the time of the Dutch Wars, when many practices and traditions were established, it is possible that the military custom of the senior officer standing in command with his subordinates to his left might have been applied when commanding from the quarterdeck of a ship. This is just a conjecture, but it is significant that more than two hundred years later the vestigial quarterdeck of a British warship would be demarcated so that the senior officers had the starboard side reserved to their use. We can go on to look at the practice of the officer of the watch taking position to the right of the centre-line of the conning position. It has been suggested that the captain stood or sat in the right forward corner of the compass platform of a Royal Navy ship. Because there are always many exceptions to a rule, we cannot state positively that this was a standard practice, and one exception is on the bridge of an aircraft-carrier, where the captain's chair is usually to the left.

Furthermore, the practice has to be related to the international Rules of the Road at Sea; in particular the one that requires a ship to give way to another that is on its starboard side. Did the rule make the habit or the habit the rule? If there has always been a strong tradition that the senior officer at the conning position occupied the right-hand side, then it is logical to assume that the rule makers in the nineteenth century followed suit. However, if this right-side preference idea is not founded on fact then the introduction of the rule resulted in the practice of the officer of the watch keeping to the starboard side of the bridge, as this was the side from which conflicting vessels would appear to which he had to give way. The United States Navy provides us with an example of right-side precedence, as the starboard forward station of a group of symmetrically arranged stations is designated the 'lead' position. For example, the forward starboard engine-control platform would be designated the 'lead' and would be the station of the senior engineer officer of the watch.

Starting with the basic port, or 'dock', side and starboard, or 'operating', side, we can see how these basic definitions and uses of the two sides of a vessel influenced subsequent 'side' practices. For example, drifters and trawlers usually had their net-operating gear, such as the gallows, to starboard so that that became the 'working' side. A Venetian gondolier stands on the left side of his craft operating the single oar to the right, and this is an example of right-side dominance, or right-side preference, influencing the design of a vessel that has a 'working' side and a 'docking' side, the hull form of a gondola being asymmetrical to compensate for the use of an oar on one side.

We can go on further, and consider the disposition of the controls on the bridges of some merchant ships at the beginning of the twentieth century. For example, on the bridge of the RMS *Dufferin* (1909) the docking telegraph was on the port side and the anchor telegraph on the other side. It is unlikely that there were strong mechanical reasons for this choice, as the connections could have been on either side with equal facility. This suggests that when the bridge designer came to choose, either instinct or tradition governed his actions. In 1924 the TS. *Orama* had a similar arrangement of the docking and anchor telegraphs. If we go on to look at Royal Navy vessels, an additional anchor was put on the starboard bow because if an anchored vessel was caught by a veering wind in a squall it was easier to work an anchor on the starboard side. However, the nineteenth-century German navy preferred the port bow for the additional anchor.

It is not easy to find evidence from which to determine whether the keep-to-the-right rules, adopted in the first half of the nineteenth century, were based on commonly accepted practices arising as suggested, from convenience of operation, or were arbitrary decisions. The Rules for Navigation were established regularly by customs and prudence some four hundred years ago, but they were not presented in a codified form until 1863. In 1839 a UK Parliamentary Report on accidents to steam-powered vessels referred to the rule of the road. This report notes that although there was an agreed keep-right rule there were a number of local left-hand rules applied by different port authorities. In 1840 Trinity House promulgated regulations covering both sail and steam, although it was not until Acts of 1883 that the courts had to look into whether a collision was caused by infringement of the rules.

It would seem that the rule of the road arose from an increasing number of steamship accidents between 1830 and 1840. Admiralty courts gave rulings, and therefore precedents, which reinforced the keep-right rule. All this was happening at a time when the steamship started to share crowded waterways with sailing ships. At this point we should remember the rule for sailing vessels by which, in an idealized situation of two ships approaching bow on, the one with the wind on its port hand had to give way. The action of giving way was easier to do by bringing the helm up and allowing the ship to bear to starboard. This rule that the larboard (port) tack should give way to the starboard tack is attributed to Lord Howe in 1782. Previous sailing regulations for fleets, such as the Earl of Warwick's Sailing Directions 1645 and the Duke of York's Sailing Directions 1670,

did not mention the larboard tack rule.

The increase in collisions between steamship and sail in the nineteenth century arose in part from the ability with which a steamship's master could choose a heading unrestricted by wind and tide. When two sailing ships were on a collision course, their respective masters were limited to a common set of possible moves as dictated by wind and tide. In contrast, when a sailing ship met a steamship her master could not be sure which of a greater range of manoeuvres the steamship would exercise.

Bridge design in the second half of the twentieth century tended towards better all-round vision and the use of a flexible and unambiguous control and instrumentation, in which evidence of original side and hand preferences is non-existent and of little consequence. Only the rule of the road and terminology remain to remind us of the right-hand and side-preferences of earlier mariners.

Associated with aviation's left-hand circuit is the custom of placing the 'island' superstructure of an aircraft-carrier on the starboard side of the flight deck. This is done to give a better position from which to judge progress toward a berth on the starboard side; the side to which the bow tends to swing under the action of clockwise-turning screws. When moving in a buoy-marked channel, the officer conning the ship prefers to be to the right of the centre-line of the vessel so as to be in a better position to see and pass close to the starboard-hand buoys. With the island to starboard, a left-hand circuit keeps aircraft in full view. So one custom reinforces the other.

Aviation inherited some nautical jargon and practices, of which few now remain.

Select Bibliography

Beamont, Roland,   The Years Flew Past,   Airlife, 2001   (ISBN 1 84037 299 0)

Bragg, M.,   RDF 1: the location of aircraft by radio methods, 2002   (ISBN 0 9531 5440 8)

Brooks, A.,   Flights to Disaster,   Ian Allan, 1996   (ISBN 0 7110 2475 8)

Brown, D.,   View From The Cockpit,   Airlife, 1995   (ISBN 1-85310-302-0)

Coombs, L.F.E.,   The Aircraft Cockpit,   Haynes, 1990   (ISBN 1-85260-281-3)

Fighting Cockpits,   Airlife, 1999   (ISBN 1-85310 9150)

The Influence of Human Laterality on the Design of Vehicle Controls, University of Surrey Dept of Psychology, 1973

The Lion Has Wings,   Airlife, 1997   (ISBN 1 85310 805 7)

Gunston, Bill,   Back To The Drawing Board,   Airlife, 1996   (ISBN 1 85310 758 1)

Plane Speaking, Patrick Stephens Ltd, 1991   (ISBN1 852260 166 3)

Avionics,   Patrick Stephens, 1990   (ISBN 1 85260-133-7)

Hirst, M.,   'Anatomy of an Airliner',   Air International, Vol. 47, Nos 3-6, 1994

Hoffman, Paul,   Wings of Madness,   Fourth Estate   (ISBN 1-84115-368-0)

Hooks, M.,   Croydon Airport: the peaceful years, Tempus, 2002   (ISBN 0-7524-2758-X)

Jane's Simulation and Training Systems, Jane's Publishing, 2002   (ISBN 0 7106 20306)

Jane's Special Report: Virtual Reality and Simulation – technology trends and markets, Jane's Publishing, November 2000   (ISBN 97106 16643)

Jarrett, P. (ed.),   Pioneer Aircraft: Early Aviation to 1914, Putnam, 2002 (ISBN 0 85177 869 0)

(ed.), Aircraft of the Second World War, Putnam, 1997   (ISBN 0 85177 875 5)

(ed.), Further, Faster, Higher, Putnam, 2002   (ISBN 0 85177 876 3)

Marson, P.J.,   The Lockheed Twins, Air-Britain (Historians), 2001   (ISBN 0-85310-248-X)

Moir, I. & Seabridge, A., Aircraft Systems, Professional Engineering Publishing Ltd, 2001

Neillands, R.,   The Bomber War, John Murray, 2001   (ISBN 0-7195-5644-9)

Newman & Greeley,   Cockpit Displays: Test and Evaluation, Ashgate, 2001   (ISBN 0 7546 1549 9)

Pallett, E.H.J.,   Aircraft Instruments and Integrated Systems, Longman, 1992   (ISBN 0 582 08627 2)

Robson, D.,   Human Performance and Limitations for the Professional Pilot, Airlife, 2001   (ISBN 1 84037 332 6)

Robinson, D.H.,   The Dangerous Skies, Foulis, 1973

Rolfe, J.M.,   Keeping Up on the Ground, RaeS, 1977

'Training Effectiveness of Flight Simulators', Applied Ergonomics, December 1982

& Bolton, Light Simulation in the Royal Air Force in the Second World War, RAeS, 1988

& Staples, K.J., Flight Simulation, CUP, 1994   (ISBN 0 521 35751 9)

Ross, A.E.,   Through Eyes of Blue,   Airlife, 2002   (ISBN 1-84037-345-8)

Morrison,   The Quest for All Weather Flight: Airlife, 2002

Strachan, I.W.,   'Simulation and Training Systems', Janes's, Defence Weekly, No. 23

Index

Page numbers in *italics* refer to illustrations.